Let Your Light So Shine

A Special Update for Faithful Supporters • Published by The Navigators

How Your Generosity Touched Lives in 2022

Frontline Military Outreach

PICTURED At least 40,000 military personnel and dependents are helped by Navigators each year.

Navigator Larry Hutson could tell that U.S. Merchant Marine Matthew* was hungry for spiritual growth. The two started a Bible study together, and it wasn't long before other sailors were also growing in their faith. Matthew sees the armed forces as his mission field. "Anyone can go on a mission trip," he says. "But not just anyone can walk onto a U.S. warship." Friends like you keep Navigators like Larry and Matthew engaged in Life-to-Life® discipleship on 120 military installations. *NAME CHANGED

New Navigators, New Assignments

PICTURED Evert (left) met Scott (right) and soon found himself in deep conversations about faith.

Scott and Briana Trout serve as Navigators in Amsterdam, the Netherlands. Scott connected with a trainer named Evert at his gym, and Evert now joins Scott for small group spiritual discussions. Briana teaches cooking classes as a dietitian, and two women she disciples — one from Japan and the other from Curaçao — both have asked to be baptized! You enable families like the Trouts to embrace the challenge of living abroad and forming life-changing relationships with spiritually hungry internationals.

New College "Special Forces"

PICTURED (Left to right) Caroline, Hilda, and Rachel didn't only find friendship at college; they found relationships that deepened their faith.

Hilda Ng connected with The Navigators as a student at the University of Florida. During her time there, women named Courtney and Kat discipled Hilda. In turn, Hilda later discipled two younger students named Caroline and Rachel. "I get excited when someone I've discipled shares with me how they want to pour into someone else because of how I've poured into them," Hilda says. Your support results in spiritual generations like these on 136 college campuses in the U.S. — and abroad.

NL23

Let Your Light So Shine

A Special Update for Faithful Supporters · **Published by The Navigators**

How Your Help is Needed in 2023

Train New Navigators in the Military

PICTURED Tony Kollias (left) and Chris Green (right), serving in Navigators First Responders ministry, study the Bible in a SWAT team vehicle.

Brave men and women on the front lines protect our communities from threat — both foreign and domestic. That's why The Navigators' military ministry has expanded to include first responders. These families face unique spiritual, emotional, and physical needs, and Navigators are ready to help. New Navigators can reach seeking hearts in areas restricted to others. With your support, generations of believers will continue to share Jesus on military bases, warships, and battlefields, and faith will continue to deepen and grow in these hard-to-reach places.

Recruit New Collegiate Navigators

PICTURED Navigator Alice Matagora (left) prays with students on the campus of the University of California, Irvine.

Bold love is needed to share Jesus on a modern university campus. Students face unprecedented pressures from the culture and the enemy. But through weekly Bible studies, NavNights, and seasonal retreats, collegiate Navigators aren't shrinking back. Your partnership forms disciple-making communities with students right on campus. New Navigators help freshman and other young believers establish an enduring faith while living on their own for the first time. In 2023, with your help, they're expanding to 20 new campuses!

Devoted in Hard-to-Reach Nations

PICTURED Navigators pursue Life-to-Life® discipleship in Amsterdam, the Netherlands.

It's beautiful to share your faith and disciple others, but that doesn't mean it's not challenging. Now, imagine pursing that already-challenging mission in a different cultural context, or while speaking a new language! That's what Navigators do in over 50 countries, including some of the hardest, most spiritually dark places on the planet. Despite these obstacles, 70 new Navigators are preparing to make that commitment. Your generosity sends these brave "workers into His harvest field" (Matthew 9) and helps fulfill the Great Commission.

BLACKOUT WARFARE

Attacking The U.S. Electric Power Grid
A Revolution In Military Affairs

Dr. Peter Vincent Pry

With An Introduction By

Dr. William R. Graham and Ambassador R. James Woolsey

CONTRIBUTORS
Admiral William O. Studeman (Retired)

Ambassador Henry Cooper

Congressman Curt Weldon

Dr. William A. Radasky

Colonel Robert P.J. Lindseth (Retired)

Colonel Kevin Riedler (Retired)

Dr. Edward M. Roche

Michael Mabee, CSM USA (Retired)

Professor Zhanna Malekos Smith, Esq.

Professor Cynthia Ayers

David T. Pyne

Jeffrey R. Yago

Dr. John M. Poindexter

EMP Task Force on National and Homeland Security

Published by the EMP Task Force on National and Homeland Security.

ISBN: 9798462218309

Congress of the United States
Washington, DC 20515

August 27, 2019

Congressional Electromagnetic Pulse (EMP) Caucus:
Task Force on National and Homeland Security

We strongly endorse and approve the Task Force on National and Homeland Security as it pertains to Electromagnetic Pulse (EMP) applications. This reestablished task force will operate under the leadership of Dr. Peter Pry, as Executive Director, who long served on the Congressional Commission to Assess the Threat to the United States from Electromagnetic Pulse Attack.

We, as co-chairs of the Congressional EMP Caucus, support policies and legislation that will protect against nuclear and non-nuclear EMP, solar activity, and geomagnetic disturbances (GMD) threatening the critical infrastructure of the United States which sustains the U.S. economy and the lives of the American people.

Today, no credible official body such as the Congressional EMP Commission exists to inform and support the Congress on issues of national and homeland security related to grid security.

Accordingly, a Task Force on National and Homeland Security may serve, to the extent possible, as a surrogate for the Congressional EMP Commission, by providing expert views and advice on any and all technical, operation, and policy matters of relevance to EMP. Protection of the critical infrastructure—including electric power, communications, transportation, energy, banking and finance, food and water—is a very broad challenge. Issues for the Task Force on National and Homeland Security include: EMP, proliferation, energy security, missile defense intelligence, and other issues of relevance to grid threats posed by EMP, GMD, and solar activity.

It is understood that, as there are no congressional funds available for the support of the Task Force on National and Homeland Security, the Task Force must be self-sustaining by means of private contributions of funding, labor, and other support.

Sincerely,

Doug Lamborn
Member of Congress

Yvette D. Clarke
Member of Congress

This book is dedicated to
Dr. William R. Graham
Ambassador R. James Woolsey
Ambassador Henry Cooper
Senator Ron Johnson
Rep. Roscoe Bartlett
Rep. Curt Weldon
and
Rep. Trent Franks
Who strived so long and so valiantly to protect our nation.

EMP TASK FORCE ON NATIONAL AND HOMELAND SECURITY
www.emptaskforce.us

BLACKOUT WARFARE
IS AVAILABLE FROM
AMAZON.COM
AS ARE OTHER BOOKS BY THE
TASK FORCE ON NATIONAL AND HOMELAND SECURITY:

THE POWER AND THE LIGHT:
The Congressional EMP Commission's War To Save America

WILL AMERICA BE PROTECTED?

EMP MANHATTAN PROJECT

APOCALYPSE UNKNOWN:
The Struggle To Protect America From An Electromagnetic Pulse Catastrophe

BLACKOUT WARS

ELECTRIC ARMAGEDDON

POSEIDON:
Russia's New Doomsday Machine

ALL THE UNCLASSIFIED EMP COMMISSION REPORTS ARE AT:

www.firstempcommission.org

ACKNOWLEDGEMENTS

Writing on the 76th anniversary of the atomic bombing of Hiroshima, China has threatened to make nuclear strikes on Japan, jointly with its partners Russia and North Korea, should Tokyo support the U.S. in defending Taiwan. The year has witnessed increasingly aggressive cyber-attacks on U.S. critical infrastructures from Russia, including threats to defeat the U.S. by blacking-out the national electric grid in a Cyber War. Wondering with me whether deterrence is breaking down, and we are near the edge of witnessing outbreak of the first Blackout World War, are the contributors to this book, to whom I am very grateful:

Admiral William O. Studeman: Former Director of the National Security Agency, Acting Director of Central Intelligence and the CIA, and Director of U.S. Navy Intelligence.

Ambassador Henry Cooper: Former Director of the Strategic Defense Initiative and Chief Negotiator at the U.S.-USSR Space Talks.

Congressman Curt Weldon: Former Vice Chairman of the House Armed Services Committee and Vice Chairman House Homeland Security Committee.

Dr. John Poindexter: Former National Security Advisor to President Ronald Reagan.

Dr. William Radasky: Senior scientific and technical EMP expert for the Congressional EMP Commission, U.S. Airforce Weapons Lab, and Defense Nuclear Agency.

Colonel Robert P.J. Lindseth: Former faculty National Intelligence University.

Colonel Kevin Riedler: Formerly with the office of the Joint Chiefs of Staff.

Dr. Edward M. Roche: Cyber Warfare and Security expert for the United Nations and Columbia University.

Professor Zhanna Malekos Smith, Esquire: Faculty West Point and former faculty USAF Air War College.

Professor Cynthia Ayers: Former 40-year veteran of the National Security Agency and Cyber Warfare and Security professor at the U.S. Army War College.

Mr. David T. Pyne: Deputy National Director, EMP Task Force.

Mr. Michael Mabee: Former Command Sergeant Major and veteran of the Iraq War, one of the nation's foremost experts on U.S. electric grid vulnerability to special forces attack.

Mr. Jeffrey Yago: Physical Engineer with more than 50 years of experience working on energy and emergency electric power systems, including for U.S. Government facilities.

Special thanks to **Mr. Glenn Rhoades**, National Director of the EMP Task Force, who manages our nationwide army of volunteers and special projects seeking to advance national preparedness against Blackout Warfare from "the bottom up" in states and localities.

Dr. Peter Vincent Pry
Executive Director
EMP Task Force on National and Homeland Security
Former Chief of Staff
Congressional EMP Commission
August 6, 2021

Who is in charge of the clattering train?
For the pace is hot, and the points are near,
And sleep hath deadened the driver's ear;
And signals flash through the night in vain.
Death *is in charge of the clattering train!*

TABLE OF CONTENTS

INTRODUCTION

"Blackout Warfare" is the term used in this report to describe a revolutionary new way of warfare planned by Russia, China, North Korea, and Iran that is still little understood in the United States, but poses an imminent and existential threat to Western Civilization. These potential adversaries describe their new way of warfare as "Non-Contact Wars," "Total Information War," "Cyber Warfare" or "Electronic Warfare" but the focus is all the same—using cyber-attacks, sabotage, and electromagnetic pulse (EMP) weapons in combination to blackout national electric grids to achieve quick and decisive victory.[1]

The Congressional EMP Commission describes this unprecedented new threat well:

"Combined-arms cyber warfare, as described in the military doctrines of Russia, China, North Korea, and Iran, may use combinations of cyber-, sabotage-, and ultimately nuclear EMP-attack to impair the United States quickly and decisively by blacking-out large portions of its electric grid and other critical infrastructures. Foreign adversaries may aptly consider nuclear EMP attack a weapon that can gravely damage the U.S. by striking at its technological Achilles Heel, without having to confront the U.S. military."[2]

"The synergism of such combined arms is described in the military doctrines of all these potential adversaries as the greatest revolution in military affairs in history—one which projects rendering obsolete many, if not all, traditional instruments of military power," warns the EMP Commission.[3]

Blackout Warfare that paralyzes the U.S. electric grid and other life-sustaining critical infrastructures—communications, transportation, natural gas and petroleum, business and finance, food and water infrastructures, and the military—could kill most Americans. EMP Commission:

"A long-term outage owing to EMP could disable most critical supply chains, leaving the U.S. population living in conditions similar to centuries past, prior to the advent of electric power. In the 1800s, the U.S. population was less than 60 million, and those people had many skills and assets necessary for survival without today's infrastructure. An extended blackout today could result in the death of a large fraction of the American people through the effects of societal collapse, disease, and starvation."[4]

---

[1] Dr. Peter Vincent Pry, *Blackout Wars* (EMP Task Force: 2012) Chapter II "The Blackout War."

[2] EMP Commission, *Assessing the Threat from EMP Attack* (July 2017) p. 5.

[3] Ibid. See also: General Vladimir Slipchenko, *Non-Contact Wars* (Moscow: 2000); Shen Weiguang, *World War, the Third World War—Total Information Warfare* (Beijing). Army of the Islamic Republic of Iran, *Passive Defense—Approach to the Threat Center* (Tehran: Martyr Lt. General Sayad Shiraz Center for Education and Research, Spring 2010). EMP Commission, *Nuclear EMP Attack Scenarios and Combined-Arms Cyber Warfare* (July 2017). All unclassified EMP Commission reports are at www.firstempcommission.org.

[4] Ibid, p. 4.

The EMP Commission estimates up to 90% of the U.S. population could die from a nationwide blackout lasting one year.[5] The military would be paralyzed by a nationwide blackout, as CONUS military bases depend for 99% of their electricity upon the civilian electric grid.[6]

Yet Washington does not understand the threat from Blackout Warfare, focusing almost entirely on cybersecurity, largely ignoring the other major threat vectors against electric grids—sabotage and EMP. Although there is a White House "Executive Order on Coordinating National Resilience to Electromagnetic Pulses" that is supposed to make national EMP preparedness a high priority, very little progress is being made protecting electric grids and other critical infrastructures from EMP.[7]

In contrast, the White House and Congress regard cybersecurity for the U.S. Government and private sector critical infrastructures as a national security highest priority. The White House now has a newly established "Cybersecurity Czar." Congress established new committees to advance national cybersecurity. A new U.S. Government agency, the Cybersecurity and Infrastructure Security Agency (CISA) has been established. The United States Government and private sector are expected to spend over $100 billion for cybersecurity.[8]

Washington's tunnel vision, seeing only cyber threats, is in response to a series of escalating and increasingly dangerous cyber-attacks by Russia, China, and North Korea on the U.S. Government and private sector over the past decade.[9] In October 2020, China's apparent cyber-blackout of Mumbai, and potential threat to blackout all India, as part of China's aggression against India's borders in the Himalayas, will no doubt reinforce the myopic U.S. focus on cybersecurity.[10]

Thus, U.S. strategic thinking and planning for Cyber Warfare in 2021 is analogous to thinking and planning about future warfare by the Allies in 1939, before nearly losing World War II to Nazi Germany's revolutionary Blitzkrieg and Imperial Japan's revolutionary use of carrier aviation.

In 1939, most Allied political and military leaders thought World War II would be like World War I trench warfare. So few thought war was likely, and France poured its resources into the fortified "super-trench" called the Maginot Line. Field Marshal Douglas Haig, Britain's victorious military leader in World War I, once a cavalry officer, thought that in the next war the decisive role would be

---

[5] Dr. William Graham, Ambassador R. James Woolsey, Dr. Peter Vincent Pry, "Prepare For The Worst" Real Clear Defense (21 October 2019). "Threat Posed By Electromagnetic Pulse Attack" Hearing before the House Armed Services Committee (10 July 2008) pp. 8-9. "The Report of the Commission to Assess the Threat to the U.S. from Electromagnetic Pulse Attack" Hearing before the House Armed Services Committee (22 July 2004).

[6] "Critical U.S. Military Sites Can't Cope With A Prolonged Power Outage" www.forbes.com (18 May 2018). "Fact Sheet: DOD Installation Energy" www.americansecurityproject.org (25 July 2013).

[7] Dr. Peter Vincent Pry, *Will America Be Protected?: Implementation of the White House "Executive Order on Coordinating National Resilience to Electromagnetic Pulses"* Volumes I and II (EMP Task Force: March 2021).

[8] "Cybersecurity Spending To Reach $123B In 2020" www.forbes.com (9 August 2020).

[9] "Scope of Russian Hacking Becomes Clear: Multiple U.S. Agencies Were Hit" New York Times (14 December 2020). "China-Backed Hackers Broke Into 100 Firms and Agencies, U.S. Says" New York Times (16 September 2020). "Hacking Linked To China Exposes Millions Of U.S. Workers" New York Times (5 June 2015). "North Korean Military Hackers Indicted In Cyber Plot To Rob Banks, Attack Companies" Los Angeles Times (21 February 2021). North Korean Hackers Behind Global Cyber Attack?" cbsnews.com (16 May 2017).

[10] "China Appears To Warn India: Push Too Hard and the Lights Could Go Out" New York Times (28 February 2021). "Lessons of the China-India Blackout War" Washington Times (16 March 2021).

played by cavalry: "I believe that the value of the horse and the opportunity of the horse in the future is likely to be as great as ever. Aeroplanes and tanks are only accessories to the men and the horse…" (June 4, 1925).[11]

In 1939, on the side that would become the Allies, a few visionaries thought the next war would be dominated by air power. A few thought that the future battlefield would be dominated by tanks. Fewer still understood that air power, tanks, motorized infantry and artillery would be coordinated to overwhelming decisive effect, as actually planned and successfully executed overrunning Europe, by Nazi Germany's General Staff. U.S. Captain Billy Mitchell was court-martialed for insisting that battleships would be made obsolete by carrier aviation, as proved by Imperial Japan in 1941 at Pearl Harbor.

Today, the Pentagon thinks World War III will be fought much like World War II, a clash between air, naval, and land power; takes cybersecurity seriously, but not seriously enough; and is totally blind to the larger threat, the real threat, from combined-arms Blackout Warfare.

Today, U.S. experts on cybersecurity, sabotage, and EMP do not cooperate, do not talk to each other, see each other as irrelevant, or worse as undeserving competitors for resources. Cottage industries of mostly non-expert academics assert that both cyber and EMP threats are overblown. Hardly anyone thinks about physical sabotage of electric grids as a potentially nationwide threat. Electric power industry lobbyists claim the utilities are prepared or preparing for all these threats—many without making the effort to understand the threat, learn the science, and apply the technology that has been developed by the United States military for protecting U.S. strategic systems over the last five decades.[12]

Almost no one "connects the dots" that adversary cyber aggressions are the tip of the spear, often coordinated with missile or satellite launches and strategic forces exercises, practicing combined-arms Blackout Warfare.[13]

The stage is set for the U.S. and its allies to be surprised in a way far worse than 1939-1941, surprised technologically, tactically, operationally, and strategically, in a war that might be won and lost at the speed of light.

Washington and the general public mostly think there can be "no more Pearl Harbors" because of the U.S. nuclear deterrent. But the nuclear deterrent can also be paralyzed in a Blackout War.[14]

Washington might not even know who launched the Blackout War, since cyber, sabotage, and EMP attacks can all be made anonymously. Would an American President respond to a nationwide blackout by launching a nuclear attack on a suspected adversary's cities? Once the Great American Black-

---

[11] Quoteinvestigator.com/2012/11/30/horse-in-war/

[12] Dr. Peter Vincent Pry, *The Power And The Light: The Congressional EMP Commission's War To Save America 2001-2020* (EMP Task Force: 2020) Chapter 12 "EMP Disinformation: Losing the Next War."

[13] "Russia's Cyberattacks Must Be Viewed With Nuclear Exercises" www.centerforsecuritypolicy.org (22 December 2020). "Cybergeddon" theconservativepundit.com (23 December 2020).

[14] Dr. Peter Vincent Pry, *Surprise Attack: ICBMs and the Real Nuclear Threat* (EMP Task Force: 31 October 2020) pp. 16-19. "Threat Posed By Electromagnetic Pulse Attack" Hearing before the House Armed Services Committee (10 July 2008).

out happens, and the clock starts ticking toward mass starvation, Washington may well decide that all still operating assets, including the military, need to focus on national recovery.

For the first time in the West, this report fights back against looming catastrophe by thinking about and planning for Blackout Warfare the way our potential adversaries do.

For the first time, subject matter experts in all relevant disciplines will think about attacks against the U.S. electric power grid, first individually, and then collectively, learning from each other and pooling their talents to outline against the U.S. a coordinated combined-arms Blackout War:

—Chapter I "Weaponizing the Weather": Potential adversaries would likely exploit severe weather in making an attack on the national electric grid, circumstances permitting.

—Chapter II "Cyber-Attacking Electric Power Grids": Hacking, worms, logic bombs, and other cyber-weapons are deployed to attack the national electric grid.

—Chapter III "Physical Security": Small teams of highly trained commandoes can attack a surprisingly small number of electric power substations to achieve a national blackout.

—Chapter IV "Non-Nuclear EMP (NNEMP) Attack": NNEMP warheads delivered by sophisticated stealthy cruise missiles, unsophisticated drones, or man-carried can blackout the grid.

—Chapter V "Nuclear High-Altitude EMP (HEMP) Attack": The ultimate "cyber-weapon" attacks not only the national electric grid, but all the other critical infrastructures at the speed of light.

—Chapter VI "Advancing National Preparedness Against Blackout Warfare": Makes recommendations to protect electric grids and other critical national infrastructures from EMP/Cyber/Sabotage.

—Chapter VII "Conclusions And Commentary": What have the experts learned from thinking about Blackout Warfare?

Dr. William R. Graham was Chairman of the Commission to Assess the Threat to the United States from Electromagnetic Pulse (EMP) Attack, served as White House Science Advisor and Director of the Office of Science and Technology under President Ronald Reagan, ran NASA, and has been contributing to the defense of the United States from EMP since 1963.

Ambassador R. James Woolsey was a Senior Advisor to the EMP Commission, is a national security and energy specialist, formerly Director of Central Intelligence and the CIA, Under Secretary of the Navy, and Chief Negotiator of the Conventional Forces in Europe Treaty.

KEY JUDGMENTS

Potential adversaries including Russia, China, North Korea, Iran and international terrorists have the capability to inflict a protracted nationwide electric power blackout on the United States—causing the collapse of such life-sustaining critical infrastructures as electric grids, communications, transportation, business and finance, food and water—and severely crippling U.S. capabilities to project military power.

Blackout Warfare can be waged with cyber-attacks, physical sabotage, Non-Nuclear Electromagnetic Pulse (NNEMP) weapons, and/or nuclear High-altitude Electromagnetic Pulse (HEMP) attack. Any one of these means could inflict a protracted nationwide blackout. But a conservative military planner is likely to use all his capabilities in combinations calculated to achieve the greatest damage and the most decisive results.

Weather may be exploited in Blackout Warfare, as electric grids are most vulnerable in severe weather, including extremes of hot and cold weather.

Russia and/or China is likely to make a massive cyber-attack against the entire U.S. electric grid prior to the outbreak of conventional or nuclear war, or during an extreme international crisis, to deter or defeat the U.S. with "gray-zone aggression" instead of or prior to outbreak of a "real shooting war": consistent with their military doctrine that Cyber Warfare is an unprecedented and decisive Revolution in Military Affairs.

For U.S. relations with both Russia and China, the emergence of viable paths to cyber-attacks against critical infrastructure as a new strategic weapon has lowered the barriers to conflict, and presents a heightened danger with the potential to disrupt the long-standing balancing calculus dependent upon nuclear deterrence.

North Korea, Iran, and non-state actors probably cannot inflict a protracted nationwide blackout on the U.S. by cyber-attack, but could do so with small numbers of special forces using small arms, explosives and/or NNEMP weapons to attack electric grid substations and control centers.

Russia, China, and North Korea presently have the capability to make a HEMP attack that would blackout the U.S. electric power grid and other life-sustaining critical infrastructures. Iran may have clandestinely developed capabilities to make a HEMP attack against the U.S. or may soon be able to do so.

Russia, China, and North Korea have developed "Super-EMP" nuclear weapons that can generate extraordinarily powerful HEMP, exceeding hardening standards for U.S. military forces.

The HEMP threat is not merely theoretical, but well-established empirically, including by real world blackouts: *"With few exceptions, the U.S. national electric grid is unhardened and untested against nuclear EMP attack. In the event of a nuclear EMP attack on the United States, a widespread protracted blackout is inevitable."* (EMP Commission Chairman, Dr. William R. Graham)

I

WEAPONIZING THE WEATHER

by Dr. Peter Vincent Pry

An attack on the U.S. electric power grid, with the objective of causing a regional or nationwide protracted blackout, is likely to exploit severe weather as a weapon. Hurricanes, heat waves, ice storms, tornadoes, summer temperature highs and winter lows, and other weather extremes, can stress electric grids and tax emergency resources, facilitating attacks by cyber, sabotage, and EMP to orchestrate a protracted blackout.

Severe weather may not cooperate with an aggressor's plans to wage a "blackout war" against the U.S. during a fast-breaking international crisis, and is not a necessary condition for attacking electric grids. Indeed, cyber-attacks, sabotage, or EMP attack alone are each potentially capable of inflicting a nationwide blackout. Nonetheless, a conservative military planner is likely to exploit the synergistic effects of all these threat vectors in a combined-arms operation to maximize damage and prospects for paralyzing the U.S. through "blackout warfare"—including by exploiting severe weather.

Military history abounds with examples of "weaponizing" weather to prevail in war:

—480 BC the Battle of Salamis, ranked as one of the most important battles in world history, Athenian naval commander Themistocles used superior knowledge of local winds to defeat the Persian navy and thwart King Xerxes' attempt to conquer the free Greek city-states.
—1274 and 1284 AD typhoons, called Kamikaze "divine winds" by Japan, sank and scattered huge invasion fleets from Mongol Emperor Kublai Khan's China, enabling badly outnumbered samurai to defend Japan's independence.
—1588 the Spanish Armada's planned conquest of England is thwarted by superior British seamanship exploiting a "Protestant wind" that scatters Spain's fleet and makes invasion impossible.
—1776 after losing the Battle of Long Island, General George Washington saves his Continental Army and the American Revolution from annihilation by evacuating across the East River under cover of night and fog in "America's Dunkirk."
—1709, 1812, 1941 Russia exploits "general winter" to defeat invasions by Sweden's Charles XII, Napoleon, and Hitler.
—1945 cloudy skies over Kokura, Japan, spared the city from atomic bombing, but sealed the fate of secondary target, clear-skied Nagasaki.[15]

Today, exploiting severe weather to wage a "blackout war" offers numerous strategic, tactical, and operational advantages supporting a combined-arms cyber, sabotage, and EMP attack:

Strategic Surprise: Political and military leaders in peacetime would be distracted, and might be distracted even if in the midst of an international crisis, by a hurricane or other severe weather that becomes a natural disaster and domestic crisis. Strategic surprise attack against the national electric grid would be easier to achieve.

---

[15] Laura Lee, "10 Surprising Ways Weather Has Changed History" www.livescience.com (4 October 2006).

Strategic Surprise: During extreme severe weather that becomes a natural disaster, electric utilities are usually overwhelmed and must be helped by emergency crews and resources from utilities located in neighboring States, sometimes nationwide. Consequently, other States are stripped of emergency resources to cope with an attack against their electric grids.

Strategic Surprise: During extreme weather that becomes a natural disaster, electric utilities are often overwhelmed and must be helped by U.S. Government emergency resources, including from the Federal Emergency Management Agency, Department of Homeland Security, and Department of Defense. Consequently, Federal emergency resources would be less available or unavailable to cope with an attack on the electric grids of other States.

Operational Surprise: During severe weather electric utilities typically lower or drop cybersecurity safeguards to facilitate remote access to control systems in order to increase system nimbleness responding to the stresses of severe weather. Cyber-blackout becomes easier to achieve: *"Recent Texas power outages and the loss of both electricity and water across Texas demonstrate how vulnerable ERCOT and Texas are to natural disasters such as snowstorms and hurricanes but also manmade and malicious activities...it also demonstrates the vulnerability of the entire U.S. energy grid...Closer analysis shows the same effects created by natural disasters can also be triggered by adversaries able to create the same disruptions and cascading effects by exploiting control systems (e.g., SCADA systems, plant distributed control systems, controllers, relays, process instrumentation, etc.). Cyber vulnerabilities are often more exposed during natural disasters when the focus is elsewhere, while at the same time many security procedures and practices are suspended to be able to expeditiously restore operations and connectivity...Hurricanes Katrina and Harvey are earlier examples where cyber security considerations were intentionally 'bypassed' to expeditiously bring facilities back online...From a cyber security perspective what has changed over the years is the cyber capability of nation-state actors such as China and Russia to not only monitor but also affect the magnitude and recovery of events such as what happened in Texas. Think of what additional impacts could have occurred if there were hardware backdoors in Chinese-made transformers that were manipulated or if the SolarWinds cyber compromise were used to manipulate the Operational Technology (OT) networks and building control systems in power grid and natural gas control centers and plant control rooms."* [16]

Operational Surprise: Severe weather, particularly cold weather, can improve the effectiveness of non-nuclear and nuclear EMP attack, according to an assessment done by Metatech for Oak Ridge National Laboratory, the Department of Defense, and the U.S. Federal Energy Regulatory Commission: *"...if it is an intentional attack and the enemy is sophisticated enough to develop a high capacity EMP device, then they would also be sophisticated enough to subscribe to 'The Weather Channel' and launch their attack under conditions which would greatly magnify the debilitating impacts of their assault on critical infrastructures. For example under very cold-weather conditions, breakers and equipment at substations and power plants can be enormously more difficult to re-energize when they become cold. This can translate into the possibility of significantly delayed restorations...Unfavorable weather conditions (particularly cold weather) should be assumed as an important compli-*

---

[16] Joe Weiss, "Texas Power Outages Demonstrate Grid Cyber Vulnerability And Inadequacy Of Existing Regulations" www.controlglobal.com (28 February 2021).

cating factor that would have potential to make restoration of all facilities and infrastructures more problematic."[17]

Tactical Surprise: Severe weather stresses electric grids, that are usually operating near full capacity, on the verge of failure normally, facilitating grid collapse by cyber, sabotage, and EMP attack. Severe weather makes it easier to down the "first domino" causing a chain of cascading failures that can blackout electric grids regionally and nationally.

Tactical Surprise: During severe weather, a cyber-attack, Non-Nuclear EMP (NNEMP) attack, or even nuclear EMP attack might be mistaken, at least initially, as damage inflicted due to severe weather inducing system generated overvoltages or causing aged equipment to fail or other failures mistakenly attributed to weather. Damage inflicted by cyber-attacks and NNEMP weapons can look like and easily be confused with system generated overvoltages or routine equipment failures. Surprise becomes easier to achieve and may be achieved longer during severe weather, so electric grid operators may not even know they are under attack, until too late.

The above assessments are supported by a survey and analysis of historical severe weather events. History of severe weather is also strongly indicative of vulnerabilities of all critical infrastructures to electric power grid blackout and its larger societal consequences.

Lessons from the Weather and the Weathermen

Storm-induced blackouts of the electric power grid are suggestive of the possible consequences of a "blackout war" such as could be waged against the United States by Russia, China, North Korea, Iran and/or international terrorists. Electric power grid failure caused by storms cascade through other critical infrastructures—such as communications, transportation, emergency medical services, food and water supply systems. Storm-induced blackouts provide an objective basis for extrapolating judgments about the threat posed by "blackout warfare" to the civilian infrastructures that sustain economic, political, and social life.

The vulnerability of critical infrastructures to various forms of attack has been a growing concern over many years. Presidential attention perhaps began with President Bill Clinton's Marsh Commission, receiving additional impetus after the terrorist attacks of September 11, 2001, that moved President George W. Bush to establish the Department of Homeland Security.

However, the science of analyzing critical infrastructures, their interdependencies, and their possible vulnerabilities is relatively new. Much effort and significant resources have been invested in an inductive approach to understanding the potential for cascading failures through the critical infrastructures that may result from failure of the power grid. The prevailing approach relies heavily on complex mathematical calculations, theoretical models, and computer simulations.

Analysis of storm-induced blackouts and their consequences offers an empirical approach that complements the predominant inductive approach to understanding infrastructure interdependence and

---

[17] James Gilbert, John Kappenman, William Radasky, Edward Savage, *The Late-Time (E3) High-Altitude Electromagnetic Pulse (HEMP) and Its Impact on the U.S. Power Grid*, Meta-R-321 (January 2010) p. 5-2.

vulnerability. Moreover, beyond the interdependence and potential vulnerability of critical infrastructures, analysis of storm-induced blackouts provides some empirical basis for estimating the effects of infrastructure failure on social order.

Storm-induced blackouts are an imperfect analogy to cyber, sabotage, and EMP attacks. Taken at face value, storm-induced blackouts and their consequences grossly understate the threat posed by "blackout warfare."

Storms are much more limited in geographic scope compared to cyber-attack and EMP, and even potentially compared to sabotage, which can also be geographically widespread. So power grid recovery from storms, compared to recovery from "blackout warfare" is likely to be much faster because of the "edge effect"—the capability of neighboring localities and States to provide recovery assistance.

Because "blackout warfare" is likely to damage or disrupt electronics over a much wider geographic area than storm-induced blackouts, rescuers from neighboring States and localities would face a much bigger job, and recovery would take a much longer time.

Nor do storm-induced blackouts replicate the damage from a nuclear EMP attack that may occur in small-scale electronic systems such as computers, aircraft, and automobiles. Compared to the worst storms, a nuclear EMP attack is likely to inflict, not only much more widespread damage geographically, but deeper damage, affecting a much broader spectrum of electronic equipment.

Storms are merely suggestive of, and provide some basis for extrapolating, the greater destructive effects on critical infrastructures and social order by a "blackout war" employing cyber-attack, sabotage, and EMP.

The worst and most severe hurricanes, like Katrina, Sandy and Harvey, their storm-induced blackouts and consequent physical damage to other critical infrastructures, may be equivalent to a small-scale cyber-attack, kinetic-attack, or EMP attack by non-nuclear weapons such as terrorists might be able to build. Storm-induced blackouts and their cascading physical effects on other critical infrastructures may be taken as representative of the lowest, and most benign, level of the "blackout warfare" threat spectrum.

However, although the most severe weather may approximate lowest-level "blackout warfare" in physical damage to the power grid and other critical infrastructures, the most severe storms, like the worst hurricanes, almost certainly fail to approximate even low-level "blackout warfare" in its psychological effects.

Unlike "blackout warfare" hurricanes and other storms are familiar to the public and understood to be acts of nature, not the destructive agents of a foreign enemy. Public perceptions of and reactions to mass destruction differ markedly when the agent of destruction is a familiar natural event or accident, versus destruction by unfamiliar means inflicted deliberately by malignant actors.

For example, the American people endure tornadoes and hurricanes without mass panic, and accept with equanimity 50,000 deaths yearly from automobile accidents. But the same number of deaths inflicted over a decade by a foreign enemy was enough to cause a political and cultural revolution in the United States, and broke the will of the people and political elites who accepted defeat in the Vietnam War.

3,000 deaths and other destruction inflicted by the terrorist attacks of September 11, 2001, moved the United States, initially with wide popular support, to prosecute unsuccessful wars in Afghanistan and Iraq as part of a broader ongoing War on Terrorism. The United States Government and people supported this effort because, although U.S. society can survive the worst hurricane, the September 11 events forged a decade-long consensus that U.S. society, and civilization itself, may not be able to survive future terrorist attacks.

The Vietnam War and War on Terrorism were waged overseas, the latter from fear of mass destruction terror attacks on the U.S. homeland. The magnitude of the U.S. investment of military and economic resources waging the long War on Terrorism reflects the magnitude of American's fear of terror attacks on their homeland.

The Vietnam War and War on Terrorism were both lost at home, a fact surely not lost on potential adversaries planning for war against the United States.

Activism against the Vietnam War, that included a cultural revolution and domestic terrorism by such groups as the Weathermen, indicate that U.S. elites will surrender to levels of social chaos inflicted on the homeland far below the violence inflicted on U.S. troops serving overseas in Vietnam. Americans lost their enthusiasm for the War on Terrorism because of seemingly unwinnable "forever wars" and, after a decade, the apparent security of their homeland.

More recently, violent activism by Black Lives Matter and Antifa, indicate that U.S. elites will surrender to levels of social chaos inflicted on the homeland far below the violence inflicted on U.S. troops serving overseas in Vietnam or the War on Terrorism.

Thus, "blackout warfare" against U.S. electric grids and other life-sustaining critical infrastructures would attack not only the U.S. technological Achilles heel, but by sowing protracted chaos in the homeland, attacks America's psychological Achilles heel.

Life Without Electricity

Psychologically benign though storms may be, compared to terrorist attacks that inflict lesser or greater physical destruction, even storms challenge social order. This survey has found that some storm-induced blackouts have caused crime waves and disintegrated organized communities into disorganized refugees.

Significantly, some observers of storm-induced blackouts—even when blackouts lasted only a day or two, as is commonly the case—were struck by the potential fragility of modern society and its near total dependence upon electricity.

For example, a January 1999 ice storm that blacked-out electricity in the Washington, D.C. area moved the Washington Post to note that "daily life was crippled, if not halted—dramatically illustrating the fragile dependence of modern times on the flip of a switch."[18] The Washington Post continued:

"Automated teller machines were out, as were gasoline pumps at many service stations. WETA-TV (Channel 26) went black for more than 10 hours until employees found a diesel generator to put that station back on the air. The Montgomery County jail conducted bond hearings by flashlight. Families seeking refuge at Tysons Corner Center were booted out at 6 p.m. because of water problems at the mall...Up and down Metro's Red Line, riders confronted with stalled elevators, inoperable farecard machines and even closed stations. Negotiating roads...was often no easier. Of more than 700 traffic signals in Montgomery, 430 were dead. Across the area, but especially in Montgomery, hotels filled to capacity with customers fleeing cold, dark homes. The 365-room Double Tree hotel on Rockville Pike was sold out by 8 a.m...Other residents, with pioneering spirit, decided to ride out the outage. More than two dozen people were waiting when the Home Depot in Germantown opened at 6 a.m. By 10 a.m. the store had sold every generator, log of firewood, candle, kerosene heater and any other supply that could warm hands and feet."[19]

Another dramatic example of the dependency of social order upon electricity occurred in October 2002, during the aftermath of Hurricane Lili that blacked-out much of coastal Louisiana. In some areas, the absence of street lights caused "looting and vandalism bad enough to require enforcement of a dusk-to-dawn curfew."[20] Local police had to be reinforced by police from neighboring localities in order to cope with the crime wave. "The looting," remarked Abbeville Mayor Mark Piazza, "Is not expected to go away until the lights come on."[21]

Experts claim an EMP attack that collapses the national power grid would, in effect, return society to a pre-industrial condition. A February 1987 snowstorm that blacked-out the Washington, D.C. area suggested exactly this to many of its victims. According to press reports, people were reduced to using open fires for heat, cooking and, in some areas, melting snow for water. Homes with fireplaces became havens for multiple families seeking refuge from houses heated by electric, gas, or oil that no longer worked. As she "stoked a fire and began sterilizing water for her baby's formula," one woman told reporters, "It's like the Colonial days."[22]

Storm-induced blackouts are localized and last usually no more than a day or two. Yet they can momentarily return part of our society to technological primitivism and begin cracks in the social order.

Compared to storms, the consequences of a "blackout war" would be far graver. Compared to the worst storms, a "blackout war" would destroy critical infrastructures more completely within a region and over a much larger region—perhaps over the entire continental United States. "Blackout warfare" compared to the worst storms would certainly inflict more lasting damage—requiring months or years to repair, if repair is possible.

---

[18] Susan Levine and Tom Jackman, "Region Iced Over and Blacked Out" Washington Post (16 January 1999) p. A1.

[19] Ibid.

[20] Leslie Williams, "One Town's Battle" Times-Picayune (9 October 2002) p. 1.

[21] Ibid.

[22] John Lancaster and Chris Spolar, "Washington's Wet Blanket" Washington Post (24 February 1987) p. 1.

Therefore, we can reasonably infer from the data on storm-induced blackouts and the known greater severity of cyber-attacks, sabotage, and EMP that the consequences of a "blackout war" on the United States' critical infrastructures and society would be an unprecedented and first order catastrophe.

Some of the salient critical infrastructure and social consequences of storm-induced blackouts are listed below. Not all of the failures and effects described occurred during all storms. This survey was careful to select only failures and effects traceable to power grid failure. Failures and effects resulting from phenomenon other than electric power grid blackout (downed trees, flooding and etc.) are not assessed here. Storm- and weather-related blackouts examined in this survey include Hurricane Andrew (1992), Western Heat Wave (1996), the Great Ice Storm (1998), Washington Ice Storm (1999), Hurricane Floyd (1999), Hurricane Lili (2002), Hurricane Katrina (2005), Hurricane Sandy (2012), Hurricane Harvey (2017), California Wildfires (2019) and Texas Ice Storm (2021):

- **Social Order:** Looting requires dusk to dawn curfew. People become refugees as they flee powerless homes. Work force becomes differently employed at scavenging for basics, including water, food, and shelter.
- **Communications:** No TV, radio, or phone service.
- **Transportation:** Gas pumps inoperable. Failure of signal lights and street lights impedes traffic, stops traffic after dark. No mass transit metro service. Airlines stopped.
- **Water and Food:** No running water. Stoves and refrigerators inoperable. People melt snow, boil water, and cook over open fires. Local food supplies exhausted. Most stores close due to blackout.
- **Energy:** Oil and natural gas flows stop.
- **Emergency Medical:** Hospitals operate in dark. Patients on dialysis and other life support threatened. Medications administered and babies born by flashlight.
- **Death and Injury:** Casualties from exposure, carbon dioxide poisoning and house fires soar.
- **Edge Effect:** Recovery depends heavily on neighboring regions unaffected by blackout. For example, Louisiana rescued from Hurricane Lili blackout by 14,000 workers from 24 states.

Hurricane Andrew (August 1992)

Hurricane Andrew struck southern Florida on August 24, 1992, and reached the coast of Louisiana on August 26, two days later. At the time, Andrew was described by some experts as the worst natural disaster in U.S. history.[23] Andrew laid waste to 165 square miles in South Florida, destroying some 100,000 homes in Florida and Louisiana, and leaving more than 3.3 million homes and businesses without electricity.[24]

Federal and state officials were at first unaware of the magnitude of the disaster and slow to react.

Three days into the crisis, Kate Hale, the Director of Dade County's Office of Emergency Management called a press conference to demand of State and Federal authorities, "Where the hell is the cavalry on this one? We need food. We need water. We need people. For God's sake, where are they?"[25]

---

[23] "Mother Nature's Angriest Child" Time (7 September 1992) p. 15.
[24] Tom Mathews, Peter Katel, Todd Barrett, Douglas Waller, Clara Bingham, Melinda Liu, Steven Waldman, and Ginny Carrol, "What Went Wrong" Newsweek (7 September 1992) p. 23.
[25] Ibid.

By the end of the first week, President George Bush had ordered 14,400 troops into the Florida disaster area "with mobile kitchens, tents, electrical generators, water and blankets….Even those lucky enough to have homes may not have electricity for more than a month."[26]

Andrew's aftermath posed an immediate threat to life in South Florida because of damage to the infrastructures for water and food.

A widespread electrical blackout prevented pumps from working, so there was no running water.[27] Most grocery stores had been destroyed. Massive traffic jams, caused in part by non-functioning signal and street lights, prevented the surviving supermarkets from being re-supplied. To meet the crisis, the Army Corps of Engineers distributed more than 200,000 gallons of water and the Department of Agriculture gave out tons of surplus food.[28]

Nonetheless, two weeks after the hurricane, food was still not reaching many victims. On September 7, fifteen days after Andrew struck, reporters witnessed the following scene: "In the ruins, Charlie Myers, 65, stood holding a peach and a loaf of bread. "This is all I have left, he said. What plans did he have? 'Survive buddy.'"[29]

Andrew's blackout of the power grid made the crisis over water, food, and shelter worse by severing communications between relief workers and victims.

Without power, there was an almost complete collapse of communications—no phones, radio or television.[30] "Without electricity to power radio and television sets, mass communication remains difficult or impossible," according to authorities and press reports.[31] Consequently, people were unaware of relief efforts or of where to go for help.

For example, although the U.S. Marines erected "tent cities" able to accommodate thousands of homeless hurricane victims, many did not know of this refuge: "Many people in the vast storm-stricken area, even those who live within easy walking distance of the sprawling encampment, said they were not aware of the tents' existence."[32] Unable to communicate where victims could get water, relief workers stacked "pyramids of bottled water…on street corners, free for the taking."[33]

The blackout of power and communications, according to press reports, imbued "South Florida with an end-of-the world aura":

---

[26] "Mother Nature's Angriest Child" Time (7 September 1992) p. 16.

[27] William Booth and Mary Jordan, "Hurricane Rips Miami Area, Aims at Gulf States" Washington Post (25 August 1992) p. A7.

[28] Tom Mathews et al., "What Went Wrong" Newsweek (7 September 1992) p. 27.

[29] Ibid.

[30] One report indicates the phone system continued to operate or experienced only partial failure. See John Mintz, "Phones Withstand Hurricane's Fury" Washington Post (26 August 1992) p. F1. For a different view see William Booth and Mary Jordan, "Hurricane Rips Miami Area, Aims at Gulf States" Washington Post (25 August 1992) p. A7.

[31] Laurie Goodstein and William Booth, "Marines Ready Tent Cities in South Florida" Washington Post (1 September 1992) p. A1.

[32] Ibid.

[33] Ibid.

"Hundreds of thousands of people found themselves in a Stone Age existence, left to pursue hunting and gathering, forced to forage for food and water. Because many people in the devastated areas had no radios or batteries, the location of food distribution sites has been a mystery....Each time word spread about establishment of a new relief outlet, people suddenly would swarm forward on foot, and National Guard troops often had to be summoned to keep order. The hurricane robbed steamy South Florida of the two amenities deemed essential to life here: air conditioning and ice cubes. 'We can't stand this heat any longer,' said Rita Larraz, whose house in South Dade County was spared but who, like 750,000 customers here, still had no electricity, and therefore no air conditioning in the 90-plus degree heat and humidity...'The heat is killing us.'"[34]

The blackout crippled the transportation infrastructure, further impeding relief efforts. "More than 5,000 traffic lights are on the blink...," according to press reports. Consequently, "Traffic was snarled for miles. The simplest chore, indeed almost everything, seemed to take forever."[35]

Andrew's blackout of the power grid contributed significantly to societal anarchy in South Florida. With the blackout-induced collapse of communications there was no way for survivors of Andrew to report crimes in progress. An orgy of looting provoked vigilantism. Unable to rely on the police, individuals armed themselves to protect their homes and remaining possessions.

"Andrew had made one zone of society come unglued," according to Newsweek, "Disasters penetrate like lasers, revealing weaknesses beneath the smooth surfaces of a community."[36] Lack of streetlights encouraged "thieves...to take advantage of a general feeling of lawlessness, particularly before federal troops began arriving":

"At night, in darkened streets cordoned by National Guard troops enforcing a curfew, machine-gun fire has been heard. Spray-painted on the side of a house in Perrine was: 'I'm armed and dangerous! Looters shot on sight!' 'Everyone is armed, everyone is walking around with guns,' said Navy physician Sharon Wood, who worked at a mobile hospital in Homestead, where workers refused to dispense calming drugs such as valium for fear that word might get out and the hospital might be robbed. In Kendall, senior citizens sleep at night with revolvers by their sides....Miami and its surrounding municipalities, which have a long history of racial and ethnic tension, were considered a tinderbox."[37]

Some 3,300 National Guard troops enforced a dusk-to-dawn curfew, when looting was worst, under cover of darkness. More than 200 people were arrested for looting or violating the curfew.[38] However, some efforts to restore law and order impeded relief efforts:

"Roadblocks set up to stop looters continued to hamper delivery of emergency food supplies. Truckers with emergency food aid were forced to wait for police escorts after reports that some drivers

---

[34] William Booth, "Hurricane's Fury Left 165 Square Miles Pounded Into the Ground" Washington Post (30 August 1992) p. A1.

[35] Laurie Goodstein and William Booth, "Marines Ready Tent Cities in South Florida" Washington Post (1 September 1992) p. A1.

[36] Tom Mathews et al., "What Went Wrong" Newsweek (7 September 1992) p. 24.

[37] William Booth, "Hurricane's Fury Left 165 Square Miles Pounded Into the Ground" Washington Post (30 August 1992) p. A18.

[38] William Booth and Mary Jordan, "Painful Awakening in South Florida" Washington Post (26 August 1992) p. A27.

had been shot and beaten by thugs. State troopers thwarted the progress of some private help when they began stopping all trucks entering the state, demanding that the drivers show that they and their cargo had been officially requested and that they were from a recognizable organization."[39]

Ultimately, some 16,000 federal troops from every branch of the armed forces turned the lights back on and restored order to South Florida.[40]

Western Heat Wave (10 August 1996)

A heat wave, with near record high temperatures, blacked out large parts of nine western states on a torrid Saturday afternoon, August 10th, 1996. Near-record high temperatures covered most of the West at the time: for example, over 100 degrees in eastern Oregon and the San Joaquin Valley, 113 degrees in Red Bluff, and 104 degrees in Boise, Idaho.[41]

Initial speculation that the blackout was sparked by a brushfire near Oregon was later discounted. According to Dulcy Mahar, spokeswoman for the Bonneville Power Administration, the blackout was caused by the heat wave:

"Some of the lines sagged because of the heat. Some of those lines sagged down onto trees and then tripped off for safety reasons. The power that those lines were carrying was moved off to other lines and overloaded those, and then the safety devices tripped those lines off and you had the outages."[42]

Although the blackout lasted less than 24 hours, it was "one of the largest power outages on record."[43] The blackout effected "an estimated 4 million people in nine states, trapping people in elevators, snarling traffic and generally causing widespread chaos."[44]

The blackout caused problems that could have become a significant threat to life and society, had they been more protracted.

Water supplies were interrupted in some regions because electric pumps would not work. Arizona, New Mexico, Oregon, Nevada, Texas, and Idaho experienced blackout-induced disruption in water service during the heat wave. For example:

"In Fresno, where most of the city receives water from wells powered by electric pumps, the city manager declared a local emergency. Only two of the city's 16 fire stations had water sources and most of the fire hydrants were out. The county and Air National Guard rushed in tankers to boost the Fire Department's capacity."[45]

---

[39] Mary Jordan, "President Orders Military to Aid Florida" Washington Post (28 August 1992) p. A14.

[40] Rick Gore, "Andrew Aftermath" National Geographic (April 1993) p. 20.

[41] Rich Connell, "Massive Power Outage Hits Seven Western States" Los Angeles Times (11 August 1996) p. 1.

[42] Tim Golden, "2nd Power Failure in 6 Weeks Creates Havoc for the West" New York Times (12 August 1996) p. 13. See also Tina Griego, "Regulators Will Take Up Western Power Failures" Albuquerque Tribune (12 August 1996) p. A1.

[43] Rich Connell, "Massive Power Outage Hits Seven Western States" Los Angeles Times (11 August 1996) p. 1.

[44] Robert Dintleman, "Western Power Failures Traced To Soaring Temperatures" All Things Considered, National Public Radio (11 August 1996) Transcript #2302-5.

[45] Rich Connell, "Massive Power Outage Hits Seven Western States" Los Angeles Times (11 August 1996) p. 1.

Air and ground transportation systems experienced significant disruptions because of the blackout.

For example, at San Francisco International Airport, although an emergency generator powered the control tower; security systems, computers, elevators, and luggage carousels would not work. Jetways could not be positioned at airplane doors. An estimated 6,000 passengers were stranded.[46] Incoming flights had to be diverted to San Jose and Oakland. Airport Spokesman Bob Schneider announced, "We are pretty much out of business."[47]

Signal lights failed, causing massive traffic jams in San Francisco and San Diego. "Traffic is a nightmare," declared San Francisco Police Department spokesman Bruce Metdors, "They're just backed up everywhere. It's gridlock."[48]

San Francisco mass transit—electric trollies and BART metro trains—were stalled by the blackout.[49] "We're responding in what amounts to our earthquake mode," said Orange County Fire Captain Dan Young, "We certainly had an increase in traffic collisions, since you've got thousands of signals with no control on them."[50]

Gas pumps were out of order, stranding motorists who needed to refuel. "All the pumps run on electricity," explained one station attendant, "When you think about it, everything runs on electricity."[51]

"Even a few hours without electricity caused chaos," according to press reports:

"Los Angeles police went on a citywide tactical alert as supervisors ordered some day shift officers to stay on duty into the night. Firefighters patrolled the city, responding to dozens of reports of stuck elevators. Department of Transportation crews checked on 4,000 intersections where the outage could have put traffic lights on the fritz. Blaring fire alarms and broken water lines added to the havoc."[52]

Communications were disrupted by the blackout.

"Radio stations reported power outages at locations throughout the midsection of California," according to press reports, "In San Francisco, TV stations KPIX and KQED were off-line for some time due to the outage."[53] Radio Station KNBR and the Canadian Broadcast Corporation went off the air.[54] Cable television networks crashed.[55]

Emergency medical services were disrupted by the blackout because "trauma rooms across the state [California] were cut off for hours from the radio that tells them an emergency is heading their

---

[46] Ray Delgado, "Huge Blackout Hits West Coast" San Francisco Examiner (11 August 1996) p. A1.

[47] Rich Connell, "Massive Power Outage Hits Seven Western States" Los Angeles Times (11 August 1996) p. 1.

[48] Ibid.

[49] Ray Delgado, "Huge Blackout Hits West Coast" San Francisco Examiner (11 August 1996) p. A1.

[50] Kim Boatman and Lori Aratani, "Millions Lose Power" San Jose Mercury News (11 August 1996) p. 1A.

[51] Marilyn Kalfus, Ana Menendez, and Julio Laboy, "Blackout Brings Much Of O.C. To A Halt" Orange County Register (11 August 1996) p. A1.

[52] Rich Connell, "Massive Power Outage Hits Seven Western States" Los Angeles Times (11 August 1996) p. 1.

[53] Ray Delgado, "Huge Blackout Hits West Coast" San Francisco Examiner (11 August 1996) p. A1.

[54] Kim Boatman and Lori Aratani, "Millions Lose Power" San Jose Mercury News (11 August 1996) p. 1A.

[55] Marilyn Kalfus et al., "Blackout Brings Much Of O.C. To A Halt" Orange County Register (11 August 1996) p. A1.

way."[56] Fire crews equipped with portable power generators were sent to doctors' offices so the physicians could complete surgeries.[57] In Orange County, 200 fire units were dedicated to providing power to hospitals with emergency vehicles.[58]

The blackout disrupted control systems in some major industrial facilities.

For example, the Chevron refinery in Richmond, California, "was unable to control flues due to the outage," releasing "huge clouds of black smoke."[59] The blackout caused power plants throughout the west—"including nuclear plants near Central California's Morro Bay and west of Phoenix"—to shut down.[60] The Diablo Canyon nuclear power plant, near San Luis Obispo, shut down, and required several days for technicians to complete safety checks before it could be started again.[61] The Bonneville Power Administration told the press, "All of the utilities are relying on each other, and it has a cascading effect when one part experiences a major failure."[62]

The Great Ice Storm (January 1998)

Starting on January 4th and for six days, until January 10, 1998, freezing rain fell across a 600-mile weather front that included parts of Ontario and Quebec in Canada and Maine and upstate New York in the United States. Electric outages in the affected areas of Canada deprived 4.7 million people, or 16 percent of the Canadian population, of power, according to Emergency Preparedness Canada. In the United States, 546,000 people were without power (deprived of heat, light, and in many instances water) in the cold of mid-winter.[63]

Some of the 5.2 million people affected by the Great Ice Storm of 1998 went without power for five weeks. It was the greatest natural disaster in Canadian history, and generated more insurance claims than Hurricane Andrew, the costliest natural disaster in U.S. history.[64]

One historian of the Great Ice Storm notes that "the storm's biggest impact was, in a sense, not weather-related: It was the loss of electricity":

"Ice accumulations caused the collapse of more than a thousand...transmission towers...More than 7,500 transformers stopped working....Some parts of Monteregie, a region of 1.3 million people southeast of Montreal, went without power for so long that the area became known as 'the Dark Triangle.'"[65]

---

[56] Ibid.

[57] Douglas E. Beeman, "Hot West Goes Dim" The Press Enterprise (11 August 1996) p. A1.

[58] Jim Hill, "West Coast Power Outage Easing In Some Locations" CNN (10 August 1996) Transcript #1600-4.

[59] Ray Delgado, "Huge Blackout Hits West Coast" San Francisco Examiner (11 August 1996) p. A1.

[60] Douglas E. Beeman, "Hot West Goes Dim" The Press Enterprise (11 August 1996) p. A1.

[61] Tim Golden, "2nd Power Failure in 6 Weeks Creates Havoc for the West" New York Times (12 August 1996) p. 13.

[62] Ray Delgado, "Huge Blackout Hits West Coast" San Francisco Examiner (11 August 1996) p. A1.

[63] Eugene L. Lecomte, Alan W. Pang, and James W. Russell, Ice Storm '98 (Institute for Business and Home Safety: December 1998) pp. 1-2.

[64] Jacques Leslie, "Powerless" Wired (April 1999) p. 120.

[65] Ibid.

The blackout caused an immediate and life-threatening emergency in Montreal's water supply, that depended upon electricity for filtration and pumping. At 12:20 P.M. on January 9th, the two water filtration plants that served 1.5 million people in the Montreal region went down, leaving the area with only enough water to last 4 to 8 hours. Government officials kept the water crisis secret, fearing public knowledge would exacerbate the crisis by water hoarding. However:

"Even as officials deliberated, water pipes in some households were already dry. As reports and rumors of a water shortage spread, consumption jumped by 10 percent anyway, and bottled water disappeared from stores."[66]

The Toronto Star, in an article entitled "Millions Shiver In Dark: How A Major City Is Being Crippled By Deadly Ice Storm," reported that parts of Montreal had run out of water, "and those who still had it were warned not to drink tap water without boiling it first."[67] But most people had no way of boiling water.

Officials feared not only a shortage of drinking water, but an inadequate supply of water for fighting fires. So desperate was the situation that Alain Michaud, Fire Chief of Montreal, prepared to fight fires with a demolition crane instead of water, hoping that "if a building caught fire, it might burn to the ground, but the crane would demolish neighboring structures to prevent the fire's spread."[68]

By 9:30 P.M. on January 9th, one of Montreal's major reservoirs was nearly empty. Provincial officials considered evacuating the city. However, Hydro-Quebec, the government electric utility, managed to restore power to the filtration plants and restore water service.[69]

The blackout also threatened the food supply.

"Food poisoning has become a real threat as embattled Montrealers, unable to get to stores, eat food that has been kept too long in refrigerators that don't work."[70] In upstate New York, the electric utility Niagra Mohawk announced that it was focusing restoration of electric power on more populated areas "so that supermarkets, gasoline stations and hotels could reopen, and people in the more rural areas could find food and shelter."[71] New York State Electric and Gas helped customers get to shelters and distributed 200,000 pounds of dry ice for storing food."[72] One typical resident of Canada's "Dark Triangle" complained, "I've lost all my food…I melt ice for water. It's no way for a family to live."[73]

---

[66] Ibid, p. 176.

[67] Sandro Contenta, "Millions Shiver In Dark: How A Major City Is Being Crippled By Deadly Ice Storm" Toronto Star (10 January 1998) p. A1.

[68] Jacques Leslie, "Powerless" Wired (April 1999) p. 176.

[69] Ibid.

[70] Sandro Contenta, "Millions Shiver In Dark: How A Major City Is Being Crippled By Deadly Ice Storm" Toronto Star (10 January 1998) p. A1.

[71] "Monster Ice Storm Slays Transmission Facilities In Quebec, Upstate New York" Northeast Power Report (McGraw-Hill: 16 January 1998) p. 1.

[72] "Canada And New England Still Reeling" Electric Utility Week (19 January 1998) p. 1.

[73] Jack Beaudoin, "Quebec In Crisis" Portland Press Herald (8 February 1998) p. 45.

Shelter, another basic necessity for survival, was also threatened by the mid-winter blackout.

"People without power discovered just how many facets of their lives depended on electricity. Their stoves, appliances, and heating didn't work."[74] Many of Canada's newer, well-insulated homes relied on inexpensive electric heat.[75] Thousands of people fled their cold, dark homes to seek refuge in government and charitable shelters. The situation in Saint-Jean-sur-Richelieu, a working-class town of 36,000 was typical, where 3,600 people became shelter refugees, one-tenth of the population.[76] St. Hyacinthe in the "Dark Triangle" lost nearly half its residents, who mostly fled the city.[77] About 100,000 people took refuge in shelters.[78]

Communications, financial, and transportation infrastructures failed massively during the blackout.

In upstate New York, only French Canadian radio stations were still on the air. In Ontario, 50,000 telephones went dead, frustrating the electric utility from restoring power service, since it relied on customer phone calls to locate power failures. Credit cards and ATM machines became useless, so all financial transactions had to be in cash.[79] The blackout shut down Montreal's four subway lines for the first time in the system's 30-year history.[80]

Underscoring that the blackout, not the ice storm, was the real crisis, the Canadian Premier Lucien Bouchard declared that "the most urgent need" was for generators, and appealed to anyone in Canada with a generator to help.[81] Bouchard also appealed to the U.S. Federal Emergency Management Agency, "asking for beds and generators to provide shelters with heat and light."[82]

Hospitals in Canada and the United States were nearly overwhelmed with blackout victims. In Maine, where six out of ten residents lost power, a single hospital, in Lewiston, reported treating for carbon monoxide poisoning 120 people "who ran generators, kerosene heaters and even charcoal grills in their homes to keep warm."[83]

Hospital medical services underwent a crisis during the protracted blackout when their emergency generators failed. For example, at Montreal's LeMoyne Hospital:

"The generators broke down on the sixth day, and the staff instantly switched to flashlights. For two hours until the generators were repaired, the hospital lost the use of its life-support and monitoring equipment: Nurses pumped air by hand into the lungs of patients on respirators and manually took

---

[74] Jacques Leslie, "Powerless" Wired (April 1999) p. 176.

[75] Jack Beaudoin, "Quebec In Crisis" Portland Press Herald (8 February 1998) p. 45.

[76] Jacques Leslie, "Powerless" Wired (April 1999) p. 178.

[77] Jack Beaudoin, "Quebec In Crisis" Portland Press Herald (8 February 1998) p. 45.

[78] Jacques Leslie, "Powerless" Wired (April 1999) p. 122.

[79] Ibid, p. 176.

[80] Sandro Contenta, "Millions Shiver In Dark: How A Major City Is Being Crippled By Deadly Ice Storm" Toronto Star (10 January 1998) p. A1.

[81] Mark Dunn, "Ice Storm Holds Eastern Ontario In Its Beautiful But Deadly Grip" The Record (9 January 1998) p. A1.

[82] Sandro Contenta, "Millions Shiver In Dark: How A Major City Is Being Crippled By Deadly Ice Storm" Toronto Star (10 January 1998) p. A1.

[83] Peter Pochna and Abby Zimet, "Facing Down An Ice Storm" Portland Press Herald (18 January 1998), p. 1A.

each patient's pulse and blood pressure every 15 minutes. Instead of one nurse for each six patients, a ratio of at least one-to-one was needed."[84]

The blackout indirectly caused hundreds of deaths in Canada and the U.S., according to Great Ice Storm historian Jacques Leslie. Leslie criticizes the official death toll figures as too low:

"The official death toll was 45-28 fatalities in Canada, 17 in the U.S.—but those numbers understate the ice storm's effects. Hundreds of ill and elderly people, weakened by extended stays in shelters where flu became epidemic, died weeks or months later, succumbing to ailments they might otherwise have overcome."[85]

Over a year after the Great Ice Storm ended, according to Jaques Leslie, "The people who experienced it remain aware of one overriding lesson: Their dependence on electricity makes them more vulnerable than they'd ever imagined."[86] Mark Abley, author of *The Ice Storm*, makes a similar observation:

"Huddling in school gyms, church halls, shopping malls, and other shelters, the evacuees didn't pray for a return of fine weather. They prayed for a return of power. The ice storm demonstrated not that we are prisoners of brutal weather, but that we are all now hostages to electricity."[87]

Ice Storm Washington, D.C. (14 January 1999)

On January 14, 1999, an ice storm downed 250 high-voltage power lines in Washington D.C. and the neighboring suburbs in Maryland and Northern Virginia, causing what the Potomac Electric Power Company (PEPCO) described as "the worst power outage in the utility's 102-year history."[88] The blackout left 435,000 homes and businesses without power. Recovery took six days.[89]

Warm food, potentially a survival issue in the freezing winter conditions, was not available in most people's homes because electric ovens and microwaves no longer worked. Most gas-powered ovens also would not work because those built since the mid-1980s have electronic ignition and cannot be lit with a match.[90] Some resorted to cooking on camp stoves. Preserving refrigerated foods was also a concern that PEPCO tried to help address by giving away 120,000 pounds of dry ice, all it had.[91] Dry ice became a precious commodity.[92]

The blackout crippled ground and rail transportation.

---

[84] Jacques Leslie, "Powerless" Wired (April 1999) pp. 178, 180.

[85] Ibid, pp. 122-123.

[86] Ibid, p. 123.

[87] Ibid.

[88] Scott Wilson, "From Ice Storm To Firestorm" Washington Post (31 January 1999) p. A1. Manuel Perez-Rivas, "Six-Day Power Outage Is Over" Washington Post (21 January 1999) p. B1.

[89] Ibid.

[90] Phillip P. Pan and Spencer S. Hsu, "Without Power, Thousands Wait In Hotels, Malls And Cold Homes" Washington Post (17 January 1999) p. A1.

[91] Manuel Perez-Rivas, "Six-Day Power Outage Is Over" Washington Post (21 January 1999) p. B1.

[92] Scott Wilson, "From Ice Storm To Firestorm" Washington Post (31 January 1999) p. A1.

Gasoline pumps were rendered inoperable. Non-functioning traffic lights snarled traffic. Washington, D.C.'s Metro subway system was largely inoperable from stalled escalators and elevators, inoperable farecard machines, and closed subway stations. Arlington County motorcycle officers proved especially resourceful, borrowing portable generators from the public library system to help run traffic lights at four major intersections.[93]

A local television station, WETA-TV, went off the air for more than 10 hours because of the blackout.[94]

At least one hospital was blacked-out. Babies were born by flashlight.[95] Emergency medical services suffered to such an extent that patients requiring life support were put at risk, PEPCO admitted:

"The extent of damage caused by last week's ice storm prevented PEPCO and other area utilities from giving priority to customers with serious medical conditions, including those on life-support systems or dialysis machines, company executives said yesterday."[96]

Ice storm-induced blackout in freezing conditions posed a threat to life. Hypothermia surged among the elderly, trapped in their unheated homes. People tried to stay warm by burning charcoal indoors, causing an increase in carbon monoxide poisoning and house fires:

"At least a dozen houses…in Montgomery were damaged by fires caused by residents efforts to stay warm or cook…after burning charcoal indoors. More than a hundred people spent Friday night in emergency shelters…Hospitals reported an influx of elderly in their emergency rooms."[97]

In Maryland, the blackout moved Governor Parris Glendening to declare a state of emergency in six counties. The Governor activated the National Guard to assist firehouses.[98]

The power outage created a refugee population "of entire neighborhoods…searching for warmth and diversion at hotels, theaters, malls and even office towers."[99] Thousands were "fleeing cold, dark homes," according to press reports:

"Across the area, but especially in Montgomery, hotels filled to capacity with customers fleeing cold, dark homes. The 365-room Doubletree Hotel on Rockville Pike was sold out by 8 a.m.. Residence Inn by Marriott, on Wisconsin Avenue in Bethesda, with 187 rooms, was sold out by noon."[100]

The blackout moved the Washington Post to observe that "daily life was crippled, if not halted—dramatically illustrating the fragile dependence of modern times on the flip of a switch."[101]

---

[93] Susan Levine and Tom Jackman, "Region Iced Over and Blacked Out" Washington Post (16 January 1999) p. A1.

[94] Ibid.

[95] Scott Wilson, "From Ice Storm To Firestorm" Washington Post (31 January 1999) p. A1.

[96] Scott Wilson, "Utilities Say Blackout Overwhelmed Medical Priorities" Washington Post (22 January 1999) p. B3.

[97] Phillip P. Pan and Spencer S. Hsu, "Without Power, Thousands Wait In Hotels, Malls And Cold Homes" Washington Post (17 January 1999) p. A1.

[98] Ibid

[99] Ibid.

[100] Ibid. Susan Levine and Tom Jackman, "Region Iced Over and Blacked Out" Washington Post (16 January 1999) p. A1.

[101] Ibid, Levine and Jackman.

Hurricane Floyd (September 1999)

Expected to be a "killer storm" of rare power and destruction, when Hurricane Floyd made landfall near Cape Fear, North Carolina, on September 16, 1999, it had subsided into a tropical storm that inundated much of the east coast with heavy rainfall and flooding. But there was little of the destruction anticipated by Federal and State authorities that had prompted them to evacuate over 3 million people from the hurricane's path.[102]

Floyd blacked-out electrical grids in many areas. However, the consequences of those blackouts for other infrastructures and for society are difficult to evaluate since blackouts tended to occur in areas where the population had already evacuated.

Blackouts interrupted phone service in North Carolina.[103] In Salisbury, North Carolina, more than 200 of 1,200 supermarkets were put out of operation by protracted blackouts, causing substantial food spoilage despite emergency efforts undertaken before the storm to preserve perishable goods in freezers.[104]

Most cable TV customers lost service in Baltimore due to blackout.

Floyd blackouts are notable for causing water treatment and sewage plants to fail in some Virginia localities and, most notably, in Baltimore. Blackout induced failure of Baltimore's Hampden sewage facility for several days raised concerns about a threat to public health. With its three pumps inoperable, Hampden spilled 24 million gallons of waste into Baltimore's Jones Falls waterway and the Inner Harbor.[105]

Perhaps Floyd's blackouts are most significant for complicating the largest evacuation and return of civilians in United States history. Electrical outages apparently prevented many from finding shelter—some traveled over 500 miles seeking accommodations, and found none. Blackout- induced failure of traffic signals contributed to some of the largest traffic jams in the nation's history as evacuees tried to return home. For example, one traffic jam on Interstate 10 from the Carolinas to Florida stretched 200 miles.[106]

Hurricane Lili (October 2002)

Hurricane Lili struck the coast of Louisiana on October 3, 2002, coming ashore at Vermillion Bay, the eye of the storm centered on Abbeville about 90 minutes after landfall.[107] Lili knocked down 35

---

[102] Brad Liston, Melissa August, Delphine Matthieussent, and Timothy Roche, "A Very Close Call" Time (27 September 1999) p. 34.

[103] Amanda Milligan Hoffman and Sally Roberts, *Business Insurance* (Crain Communications: 1999).

[104] Ibid.

[105] Governors James Hunt and James Gilomore interviewed, "Hurricane Floyd Leaves Lingering Questions About Public Policy" CNN Crossfire (16 September 1999). Del Quentin Wilber, "Jones Falls Sewage Spill Lasts 2 Days" Baltimore Sun (19 September 1999) p. 1A.

[106] Brad Liston et al., "A Very Close Call" Time (27 September 1999) p. 34. Aaron Steckelberg, "Scenes From The Coast" Atlanta Constitution (16 September 1999) p. 10A.

[107] "Hurricane Lili" en.wikipedia.org.

transmission lines and destroyed 53 electric power substations.[108] More than 500,000 people were without electric power at the height of the blackout, immediately after the storm.[109]

Three days later, on October 6, over 100,000 homes and businesses were still without power in coastal Louisiana, according to the state Office of Emergency Preparedness.[110] Six days after Lili, on October 9, in Abbeville and surrounding Vermillion Parish, an estimated 80 percent of the 20,000 homes and 50 percent of businesses were still without electricity.[111]

As a consequence of the blackout, water and food were unavailable through the normal means to thousands. With no electricity, water pumping stations no longer worked. In south Louisiana, 30 supermarkets would not open because the blackout prevented their cash registers from operating. Those grocery stores that did open were stripped of food within hours.

In Abbeville, the parking lots of shopping centers became watering and feeding stations run by churches and the state Office of Emergency Preparedness. Associated Grocers, that supplies food to supermarkets in Louisiana, Texas, and Mississippi, sent food and refrigerated trucks to the stricken area. The food emergency was reflected in a skyrocketing demand for dry ice to preserve food stuffs during the hot weather and to preserve refrigerated foods. Local supplies of dry ice were exhausted—one store selling 20,000 pounds of dry ice to hundreds of customers in two hours—and had to be supplemented with supplies from the Red Cross.[112]

The electrical outage deprived thousands of phone service for days after the Hurricane.[113] Television service was also blacked-out.[114]

Blackout interfered with transportation by rendering signal lights inoperable.[115] Street lights were also inoperable, making driving at night difficult even for long-time local residents, who could not see landmarks and became disoriented in the dark.[116]

Power grid collapse caused failure in other energy infrastructures. Without electricity, natural gas service could not be restored for several days after Lili.[117]

Hospitals were plunged into darkness during the blackout because they had no emergency generators or emergency power systems failed to work. There was no hot water for bathing patients or steriliza-

[108] Angela Simoneaux, "Flooded, Battered La. Gets Busy Cleaning Up" Morning Advocate (5 October 2002) p. 1A.

[109] Angela Simoneaux, "Acadiana's Recovery" The Advocate (8 October 2002) p. 5B.

[110] Kevin McGill, "Rise Seen In Carbon Monoxide Poisoning Cases" The Advocate (7 October 2002) p. 2B.

[111] "Hurricane Lili" en.wikipedia.org. Leslie Williams, "One Town's Battle" Times-Picayune (9 October 2002) p. 1.

[112] Angela Simoneaux, "Flooded, Battered La. Gets Busy Cleaning Up" Morning Advocate (5 October 2002) p. 1A. Angela Simoneaux, "Acadiana's Recovery" The Advocate (8 October 2002) p. 5B. Suzan Manuel, "Lili Leaves Residents Powerless" Daily Town Talk (5 October 2002) p. 1A. Suzan Manuel, "Thousands Still Without Electricity Across Central La." Daily Town Talk (6 October 2002) p. 8A.

[113] Kevin McGill, "Rise Seen In Carbon Monoxide Poisoning Cases" The Advocate (7 October 2002) p. 2B.

[114] Angela Simoneaux, "Acadiana's Recovery" The Advocate (8 October 2002) p. 5B.

[115] Suzan Manuel, "Lili Leaves Residents Powerless" Daily Town Talk (5 October 2002) p. 1A.

[116] Leslie Williams, "One Town's Battle" Times-Picayune (9 October 2002) p. 1.

[117] Kevin McGill, "Rise Seen In Carbon Monoxide Poisoning Cases" The Advocate (7 October 2002) p. 2B.

tion. "We have to give them medicines in the dark," said one nurse, "We use a flashlight to make sure we don't give them the wrong one."[118]

Blackout caused indirectly some injuries and at least one death. Home generators used by people who lost power after Hurricane Lili led to more than 60 cases of carbon monoxide poisoning, including one fatality, according to Louisiana health officials.[119]

Officials and citizens considered the blackout the worst part of Hurricane Lili.

According to Mayor Chuck Butterfield, "We've taken electricity for granted and living without it for three or four days is devastating."[120] Law enforcement officers blamed a surge of looting and vandalism on the blackout. The crime wave became bad enough to require the imposition of a dusk-to-dawn curfew and police reinforcements from neighboring areas unaffected by the storm. "The looting," according to the Abbeville Sherriff's Office, "Is not expected to go away until the lights come back on."[121]

Recovery from the blackout, described by a CLECO electric utility spokesman as "the biggest customer outage event in our history," depended heavily on outside assistance.[122] Some 14,000 electric utility workers from 24 states and the District of Colombia joined CLECO's 3,000 workers to make recovery possible in about one week.[123]

Hurricane Katrina (August 2005)

Hurricane Katrina was one of the deadliest hurricanes in U.S. history, causing over 1,800 deaths, and at the time was the costliest, inflicting $125 billion in damages in August 2005, now tied in costly damage with Hurricane Harvey (2017). Katrina began as a tropical storm, strengthened into a hurricane when it impacted Florida on August 25, strengthened over the Gulf of Mexico into a Category 5, the most powerful class of hurricane, weakening to Category 3 when on August 29 it hit New Orleans and southeast Louisiana, Mississippi, and Alabama, turning these Gulf states into disaster areas.

Most of the deaths and damage from Hurricane Katrina resulted from immediate and protracted flooding:

"Flooding, caused largely as a result of fatal engineering flaws in the flood protection system known as levees around the city of New Orleans, precipitated most of the loss of lives. Eventually, 80% of the city, as well as large tracts of neighboring parishes, were inundated for weeks. The flooding also destroyed most of New Orleans' transportation and communication facilities, leaving tens of thousands of people who had not evacuated the city prior to landfall stranded with little access to food, shelter, or other basic necessities."[124]

---

[118] Suzan Manuel, "Lili Leaves Residents Powerless" Daily Town Talk (5 October 2002) p. 1A.

[119] Kevin McGill, "Rise Seen In Carbon Monoxide Poisoning Cases" The Advocate (7 October 2002) p. 2B.

[120] Suzan Manuel, "Lili Leaves Residents Powerless" Daily Town Talk (5 October 2002) p. 8A.

[121] Leslie Williams, "One Town's Battle" Times-Picayune (9 October 2002) p. 1.

[122] Angela Simoneaux, "Flooded, Battered La. Gets Busy Cleaning Up" Morning Advocate (5 October 2002) p. 1A.

[123] Keith Darce, "Lights Blink Out All Over Louisiana," Times-Picayune (4 October 2002), p. 1. "Lili Left Half A Million Without Power," Associated Press (4 October 2002).

[124] "Hurricane Katrina" en.wikipedia.org.

Because flooding played such a dominant role inflicting deaths and damage on New Orleans and the Gulf States afflicted by Katrina, it is more difficult to assess the consequences of Katrina's protracted blackout of electric power. However, since an EMP and cyber-attacks that collapse the electric grid would also blackout other life-sustaining critical infrastructures—including communications, transportation, and supply-chains for food and water—Katrina's drowning of critical infrastructures still exemplifies the consequences to victim populations of critical infrastructure destruction, regardless of cause.

Katrina blacked-out electric grids in Alabama, Florida, Louisiana, Mississippi, and Texas. Two weeks were required to restore electric power in Alabama and Florida. Much longer was required to restore electric power everywhere in Louisiana and Mississippi. Some localities remained in blackout for months.[125]

"By Sunday August 28, most of the infrastructure along the Gulf Coast had been shut down, including all freight and Amtrack rail service as well as the Waterford Nuclear Generating Station."[126] After Katrina, restoration of electric power depended upon restoration of other critical infrastructures, such as communications, transportation, and emergency crew availability.[127] This would also be the case after an EMP or cyber-attack that blacks-out other critical infrastructures.[128]

The Katrina blackout was a major factor disrupting communications that had a debilitating effect on emergency rescue and recovery operations. Because of loss of electric power, according to a White House after-action report:

"The storm debilitated 911 emergency call centers, disrupting local emergency services....Nearly 3 million customers lost telephone service. Broadcast communications, including 50 percent of area radio stations and 44 percent of area television stations, similarly were affected."[129]

"The complete devastation of the communications infrastructure left emergency responders and citizens without a reliable network across which they could coordinate," according to the White House report.[130]

Katrina flooding in New Orleans drove thousands out of their homes, 12,000 initially seeking refuge in the Superdome and other Red Cross shelters, joined later by an additional 18,000 fleeing to the Superdome and 20,000 to the New Orleans Convention Center. None of these facilities had resources to support such numbers.[131] Likewise, an EMP or cyber-attack that blacks-out electric power to households would stop running water, appliances, heating and air conditioning, making homes unin-

---

[125] Department of Homeland Security, *Power Outage Incident Annex to the Response and Recovery Federal Interagency Operational Plans: Managing Cascading Impacts for a Long-Term Power Outage* (June 2017).

[126] "Hurricane Katrina" en.wikipedia.org.

[127] Ibid. Dorothy Reed, Mark Powell, and Julie Westerman, "Energy Supply System Performance for Hurricane Katrina" Journal of Energy Engineering (December 2010).

[128] EMP Commission, *Critical National Infrastructures* (2008).

[129] President George W. Bush, *Katrina Lessons Learned* (The White House) www.georgewbush-whitehousearchives.gov.

[130] Ibid.

[131] "Hurricane Katrina" en.wikipedia.org.

habitable, causing a refugee problem, as has been seen in other storm-induced blackouts.

The Katrina blackout certainly contributed to breakdown of law and order.

As soon as the lights went out, looting, robberies, rapes, and general anarchy engulfed New Orleans, even perhaps provoking lawless excessive violence by police. New Orleans Mayor, Ray Nagin, ordered police: "Let's stop the looting, let's stop the lawlessness and let's put our police officers on the streets so that our citizens are protected."[132]

According to New Orleans Police Lieutenant David Benelli, the aftermath of Katrina was an unreal living nightmare: "We weren't living in the real world, we were living in a holocaust. We were living in a situation that no other police department ever had to endure."[133]

"They weren't shooting looters. They were shooting at people who they thought were shooting at them…That is part of the information they had with respect to lawlessness in the city. People being shot and raped…The streets had been taken away by armed gangs," according to Attorney Frank DeSalvo.[134]

Mass lawlessness continued in New Orleans after Katrina for about one month, until subdued by thousands of National Guard and Federal troops:

"Some residents of New Orleans who remained in the city began looting stores. Many were in search of food and water that were not available to them through other means, as well as non-essential items. Additionally, there were reports of carjacking, murders, thefts, and rapes in New Orleans… Thousands of National Guard and federal troops were mobilized and sent to Louisiana, with 7,841 in the area on August 29, to a maximum of 46,838 on September 10."[135]

Louisiana Governor Kathleen Blanco warned criminals: "They have M16s and are locked and loaded. These troops know how to shoot and kill and I expect they will." According to Congressman Bill Jefferson: "There was shooting going on. There was sniping going on. Over the first week of September, law and order were gradually restored to the city."[136]

Lawlessness in New Orleans after Katrina was so widespread and extreme that controversy still rages today, including what may be "denial behavior" by some academics who blame police violence and justify law-breaking. Five years after Katrina, legal scholar Casey Faucon described one local example of anarchy in New Orleans that she attempts through complex legal and philosophical reasoning to justify:

---

[132] Sabrina Shankman et al., "After Katrina, New Orleans Cops Were Told They Could Shoot Looters" Propublica (July 24, 2012).

[133] Ibid.

[134] Ibid.

[135] "Hurricane Katrina" en.wikipedia.org.

[136] Ibid.

"New Orleans was in chaos. Media reports of people vandalizing and looting stores portrayed the image that the city had disintegrated into a state of anarchy. Looters ransacked the shops at Canal Place, burned parts of Saks Fifth Avenue, and took roughly $250,000 of liquor, cigarettes and candy from three convenience stores."[137]

Recovery of New Orleans and the Gulf States took many months, significantly slowed by disruption of critical infrastructures including electric power. Ten years after Katrina, by August 2015, parts of the city were still unrecovered, and may never recover because of a massive refugee exodus to other States affecting "not only New Orleans but the entire country, rivaled only by the Great Migration of African Americans in the first half of the 20th Century and the mass migration of the 1930s as a result of the Great Depression...The effects of this migration are likely to endure for decades."[138]

Despite massive aid from the U.S. Government and emergency workers from all 50 States to rescue and recover New Orleans and the Gulf region from Katrina, President George W. Bush, Louisiana Governor Kathleen Blanco, New Orleans Mayor Ray Nagin and others came under media and public criticism. FEMA Director Michael Brown was forced to resign.

Consequently, President Bush and the Congress enacted "Katrina Reforms" that recognized the centrality to disaster preparedness of protecting and recovering critical infrastructures. According to the White House report *Katrina Lessons Learned*:

"The Department of Homeland Security, working collaboratively with the private sector, should revise the National Response Plan and finalize the Interim National Infrastructure Protection Plan to be able to rapidly assess the impact of a disaster on critical infrastructure. We must use this knowledge to inform Federal response and prioritization decisions and to support infrastructure restoration in order to save lives and mitigate the impact of the disaster on the Nation."[139]

But subsequent natural disasters from severe weather indicate that the lessons of Hurricane Katrina have not been learned, especially regarding protection and recovery of the electric power grid.

Hurricane Sandy (October 2012)

Hurricane Sandy was the strongest, most destructive, and deadliest storm of 2012. Sandy wreaked $70 billion in damage across eight countries from the Caribbean to Canada and killed 233 people in eight countries.[140] This analysis shall focus on the consequences of the storm-induced electric power blackout by Hurricane Sandy in the United States.

Sandy peaked as a Category 3 hurricane when it made landfall in Cuba, weakened to Category 2 when it arrived off the northeastern coast of the United States, weakening further to Category 1, the weakest class of hurricane, when on October 29 it hit New Jersey and New York. 24 States were im-

---

[137] Casey Faucon, "The Suspense Theory: Hurricane Katrina Looting, Property Rights, and Personhood" Louisiana Law Review (Summer 2010).

[138] "Hurricane Katrina" en.wikipedia.org.

[139] President George W. Bush, *Katrina Lessons Learned* (The White House) www.georgewbush-whitehousearchives.gov.

[140] "Hurricane Sandy" en.wikipedia.org. M. Diakakis et al., "Hurricane Sandy Mortality in the Caribbean and Continental North America" Disaster Prevention and Management (2015).

pacted by Sandy, which destroyed thousands of homes, mostly in New York and New Jersey, killed 160 people in the U.S., and left over 6 million without electric power.[141]

As a result of the Katrina reforms in emergency preparedness, Federal and State emergency services and the electric utilities "attempted to head off long-term power failures Sandy might cause":

"Utilities and governments along the East Coast attempted to head off the long-term power failures Sandy might cause. Power companies from the Southeast to New England alerted independent contractors to be ready to help repair storm damaged equipment quickly and asked employees to cancel vacations and work longer hours….Through regional offices in Atlanta, Philadelphia, New York City, and Boston, the Federal Emergency Management Agency (FEMA) monitored Sandy… President Obama signed emergency declarations on October 28 for several states expected to be impacted by Sandy, allowing them to request federal aid and make additional preparations in advance of the storm…In addition, the National Guard and U.S. Air Force put as many as 45,000 personnel in at least seven states on alert for possible duty in response to the preparations and aftermath of Sandy."[142]

Moreover:

"More than 1,500 FEMA personnel were along the East Coast working to support disaster preparedness and response operations, including search and rescue, situational awareness, communications and logistical support. In addition, 28 teams containing 294 FEMA Corps members were pre-staged to support Sandy responders. Three federal urban search and rescue task forces were positioned in the mid-Atlantic and ready to deploy as needed. Direct Relief provided medical supplies to community clinics, non-profit health centers, and other groups in areas affected by Hurricane Sandy, and mapped pharmacies, gas stations, and other facilities that remained in the New York City area despite power outages…the American Red Cross announced they had 4,000 disaster workers across storm-damaged areas."[143]

Emergency preparedness reforms enacted in response to Katrina, a Category 3 hurricane, do not appear to have made much difference in preventing and recovering from protracted blackout of electric power during and after Sandy, a much less powerful Category 1 hurricane. Unlike Katrina, where flooding was the chief destructive factor, while there was partial flooding of New York City subways and other flood damage, the most disruptive consequences of Sandy to critical infrastructures and social order can be directly attributed to protracted electric power blackout.

---

[141] Ibid.

[142] "Hurricane Sandy" en.wikipedia.org. Jason Samenow, "Cause for Concern: The 7 Most Alarming Hurricane Sandy Images" Washington Post (28 October 2012). Lars Anderson, "Closely Monitoring Hurricane Sandy" Federal Emergency Management Agency (25 October 2012). "It's Watch and Wait as Hurricane Sandy Approaches" News.Blog.CNN.Com (28 October 2012). Brian Sullivan and Dan Hart, "Hurricane Sandy Barrels Northward, May Hit New Jersey" Bloomberg (28 October 2012).

[143] "Hurricane Sandy" en.wikipedia.org. "Vicious Superstorm Sandy Smashes Northeast Cities" Newswire.com (30 October 2012). "Storm Aftermath: Live Updates" New York Times (2 November 2012). "Hurricane Sandy Relief" Direct Relief (5 April 2018).

The Sandy electric power blackout affected 15 States and Washington, D.C.. States blacked-out worst were New Jersey (2,040,195), New York (1,933,147), Pennsylvania (852,458), and Connecticut (486,927).[144] System-generated overvoltages from downed powerlines destroyed some transformers, their spectacular electric explosions, visible for miles, recorded by frightened Sandy victims in New Jersey.[145] Blackouts were most protracted in New Jersey and New York, the power outages disrupting critical infrastructures and slowing recovery so that, months later, thousands were still refugees in homeless shelters.[146]

Sandy's cost in lost economic activity is estimated at $30-50 billion due to "massive power outages, liquid fuel shortages, and a near shutdown of transportation" the latter two factors also attributable to "massive power outages":

"The destruction of physical infrastructure as a result of Sandy cost impacted states, including New York and New Jersey, tens of billions of dollars. EQECAT, a risk-modeling company that focuses on catastrophes, approximated that impacted regions lost between $30 billion to $50 billion in economic activity. The economic loss was attributed to the massive power outages, liquid fuel shortages, and a near shutdown of the region's transportation system."[147]

Hurricane Sandy's disruption of key critical infrastructures is briefly summarized below:

—*"Energy: Roughly 8.5 million customers were impacted due to power outages, including many businesses that were hard pressed to deliver products and services in a timely manner. Breaks in gas lines also caused fires in many locations, prompting explosions...Locating gas and diesel fuel proved difficult...which harmed transportation...The shortage of fuel held up first responders as well as other response and recovery officials. Therefore, portable generators remained unutilized, resulting in long lines at fueling stations while individuals were unable to differentiate between stations that did not [have] power from the gas stations that were operational."*

—*"Communications: Telecommunications infrastructure was heavily disrupted, impacting millions of people and thousands of businesses, destabilizing the economy of one of the biggest cities in the world. The Federal Communications Commission (FCC) found that roughly 25% of cell towers across 10 states were out of service at the height of the storm."*

—*"Transportation: Throughout the history of the country, the nation had not witnessed a worst disaster for public transit systems, including buses, subway, and commuter rail..."*

—*"Stormwater Management and Wastewater Treatment Systems: There was a massive failure in wastewater treatment facilities all around the mid-Atlantic coast due to floodwaters, large storm runoff, wind damage, and electricity loss. The region's waterways were hit with billions of gallons of raw and partially treated sewage, adversely affecting the health of the public...There was also a public health concern about the threat of contaminated water filling the pipes and wells that supplied*

---

[144] "Hurricane Sandy" en.wikipedia.org.

[145] For example "Hurricane Sandy Jersey City Transformer Explosion" www.youtube.com.

[146] "Tens Of Thousands Still Homeless Six Months After Hurricane Sandy As Some Areas Will Take Years To Fully Recover" U.K. Daily Mail (27 April 2013).

[147] "Hurricane Sandy" en.wikipedia.org. EQECAT, "Post-Landfall Loss Estimates—Hurricane Sandy" (1 November 2012).

potable water to large parts of the region. Large water utility companies experienced power outages, disrupting their ability to provide safe drinking water."[148]

The aftermath of Hurricane Sandy resembles Hurricane Katrina in the breakdown of social order, struggle to find food and water, and lawlessness in many localities due to collapse of critical infrastructures caused chiefly by protracted blackout of electric power. Vignettes below from Long Island describe the crisis one week after Sandy:

—Headline: *"Residents say...lack of power and law enforcement means more looting and violent crime."*

—Headline: *"Those in stricken areas stockpiling weapons like kitchen knives, machetes, and bats to protect themselves."*

—Headline: *"Coney Island residents say they are forced to 'scavenge for food like animals.'"*

—*"It is chaos, it is pandemonium out here. It seems like nobody has any answers. I feel like a victim of Hurricane Katrina. I never thought it could happen here in New York, but it's happened."*

—*"With little police presence on the storm-ravaged streets, many residents...have been forced to take protection in their own hands with guns, baseball bats and even bows and arrows to ward off thugs seeking to loot their homes."*

—*"It's like the Wild West."*

—*"Along with mounting safety concerns, homeowners...face hunger, complaining that federal officials have left them to fend for themselves."*

—There is *"anger and resentment over continued lack of power and gas...Crooks have been disguising themselves as Long Island Power Authority workers and coming by homes...in the middle of the night while real utility workers are nowhere to be found."*[149]

City Councilman James Sanders warned that lawlessness and anarchy would worsen because of the failure of the Long Island Power Authority (LIPA) to recover from the blackout and restore electric power: "We have an explosive mix here. People will take matters into their own hands...LIPA has failed the people."[150]

---

[148] "Hurricane Sandy" en.wikipedia.org. *Tropical Cyclone Report: Hurricane Sandy* National Hurricane Center (12 February 2013). David Turetsky, "NENA 2013 Conference & Expo Charlotte" Federal Communications Commission (18 June 2013). Peter Rogoff, "Testimony before the Senate Banking, Housing, and Urban Affairs Committee, Subcommittee on Housing, Transportation, and Community Development" Federal Transit Association (20 December 2012). "Sewage Oveflows From Hurricane Sandy" Climate Central (1 April 2018). "Christie Administration Advises Residents To Be Alert For Local Boil Water Advisories" State of New Jersey Environmental Protection Agency (31 October 2012).
[149] Rachel Rickard Straus and Snejana Faberov, "Misery For 2.5 Million Still Without Power After Six Days As Lawlessness And Fear Take Over New York's Outer Boroughs" U.K. Daily Mail (3 November 2012).
[150] Ibid.

New York State Governor, Andrew Cuomo, on November 28, about one month after Sandy, called the storm "more impactful" than Hurricane Katrina.[151]

Hurricane Harvey (August 2017)

Hurricane Harvey allegedly ties with Katrina as the most damaging hurricane measured in cost ($125 billion), although expert opinion differs, some arguing that the estimated cost of Harvey is overstated relative to Katrina because of inflation. Harvey caused catastrophic flooding and 106 deaths in the United States.[152]

Hurricane Harvey hit Texas on August 25, 2017, at San Jose Island as a Category 4, weakening to a Category 3 after making a second landfall in Texas at Holiday Beach, then rapidly weakening to a tropical storm, stalling near the coast to dump record amounts of rain, before making a final landfall on August 29 in Louisiana. Harvey broke the record for the most rainfall of any tropical system to make landfall in the U.S. and was the deadliest storm to hit Texas since 1919.[153]

According to the U.S. Energy Information Administration:

"Hurricane Harvey caused substantial electricity outages, as power plants and transmission infra-structures—particularly in south Texas and along the Gulf Coast—were affected by high winds and significant flooding. At its peak, more than 10,000 megawatts (MW) of electricity generating capacity in the Electric Reliability Council of Texas (ERCOT) grid and a substantial number of transmission and distribution lines experienced forced outages. At the same time, relatively cool temperatures across much of Texas also reduced electricity demand."[154]

Moreover:

"Power plant outages were largely caused by rain or flooding affecting generator fuel supplies, out-ages of transmission infrastructure connecting generators to the grid, and personnel not being able to reach generating facilities. Hundreds of high-voltage transmission lines, including six 345 kilovolt (kV) lines and more than two hundred 69 (kV)-138 (kV) lines experienced storm-related forced out-ages. Most of these transmission facilities were located in the immediate area along the Gulf Coast of Texas where the hurricane made landfall, but some were in the Houston area, where transmission facilities were damaged by flooding."[155]

---

[151] "Hurricane Sandy" en.wikipedia.org. Thomas Kaplan and Raymond Hernandez, "Cuomo, In Aid Appeal, Cites Broad Reach Of Storm" New York Times (2 December 2012).

[152] "Hurricane Harvey" en.wikipedia.org.

[153] Ibid. National Hurricane Center, *Tropical Cyclone Report—Hurricane Harvey* (National Oceanic and Atmospheric Administration and National Weather Service, 9 May 2018). "!2 Exceptional Facts From Official Hurricane Harvey Report" www.theweathernetwork.com.

[154] U.S. Energy Information Administration, "Hurricane Harvey Caused Electric System Outages and Affected Wind Generation in Texas" Today In Energy (13 September 2017).

[155] Ibid.

336,000 people in Texas had no electricity and many thousands were left homeless by storm damage, flooding, and the blackout, requiring rescue. Some 32,000 refugees from Harvey were relocated to emergency shelters. Over 210,000 victims registered with FEMA for disaster assistance.[156]

Texas Governor Greg Abbott declared a state of emergency for 50 counties. Governor Abbott mobilized the entire 12,000 troops of the Texas National Guard, which was joined by National Guard units from many other States, including: Alaska, California, Connecticut, Florida, Kentucky, New York, Oregon, Utah, Nebraska, and North Carolina.[157]

Louisiana Governor John Bel Edwards declared a state-wide emergency, ordered mandatory evacuations, and mobilized the National Guard for rescue and recovery made necessary by flooding. By far the locus of Harvey's damage was in Texas.

In Texas, Houston Mayor, Sylvester Turner, ordered a curfew to prevent looting.[158]

Lawlessness and looting happened in the aftermath of Hurricane Harvey, as after other hurricanes and natural disasters. But Harvey may be notable as the first case where "political correctness" within the national press corps imposed a "news blackout" or had a chilling effect on reporting looting and lawlessness.

For example, an ABC News reporter was widely condemned, who accurately reported acts of looting and notified police, for allegedly promoting "racism." TV commentator Tucker Carlson was falsely accused of "racism" for accurately reporting on looting in the aftermath of Hurricane Harvey. The Washington Post ran a story claiming that looting and lawlessness are often exaggerated after natural disasters because of racial stereotypes. A "cottage industry" appears to have grown-up dedicated to denying acts of looting and lawlessness or justifying such behavior.[159]

According to the usually accurate Houston Press, Houston police arrested 200 for looting and arrested or cited 338 others for illegal behavior in the immediate aftermath of Hurricane Harvey.[160]

Perhaps the greatest significance of Hurricane Harvey from a national security perspective are the many examples of how a protracted electric power outage can cripple other critical infrastructures and threaten mass destruction. For example, as a consequence of the Texas blackout, drinking water was widely unavailable, oil refinery production was so reduced that fuel shortages arose and national gas prices spiked, and enormous chemical plant explosions threatened residents within a radius of 1.5 miles necessitating evacuations:

---

[156] "Hurricane Harvey" en.wikipedia.org.

[157] Ibid. Steve Marshall, "Guard Units From Other States Join Harvey Response in Texas" www.defense.gov (Department of Defense: 29 August 2017).

[158] "Hurricane Harvey" en.wikipedia.org.

[159] Maxwell Tani, "ABC News Reporter Covering Hurricane Harvey Gets Slammed Online After Reporting Alleged Looters To Police" www.businessinsider.com (29 August 2017). Melanie Schmitz, "The History Behind the Racist 'Looting' Narrative" archive.thinkprogress.org. W. Joseph Campbell, "How the Media Got Hurricane Harvey Right" www.poynter.org. "Looting Rumors and Fear of Crime Often Exaggerated After Natural Disasters" Washington Post (2 September 2017).

[160] Stephen Paulson, "A Look At The Looting of Hurricane Harvey" www.houstonpress.org (23 October 2017).

—*"Energy production in the Gulf of Mexico declined in the wake of Harvey by approximately 21%... Many energy-related ports and terminals closed...About 2.25 million bpd of refining capacity was offline for several days; that is about 12% of total U.S. capacity...Due to the shutdown in refineries, gas prices did see an increase nationwide...the spike brought the highest gas prices in two years."*

—In Texas, *"Hurricane Harvey created a fuel shortage. Panicked motorists waited in long lines. Consequently, gas stations through[out] the state were forced to close due to the rush."*

—*"On August 30, the CEO of Arkema warned one of its chemical plants in Crosby, Texas, could explode or be subject to intense fire due to the loss of 'critical refrigeration' of materials. All workers at the facility and residents within 1.5 mi (2.4 km) were evacuated. Eight of the plant's nine refrigeration units failed without power, enabling the stored chemicals to decompose and become combustible. Two explosions occurred around 2:00 AM on August 31; 21 emergency personnel were briefly hospitalized."*[161]

"During and after Hurricane Harvey, a chemical plant suffered repeated explosions. Because the power went out. Beaumont, Texas was without drinking water. Because the power went out. Gasoline prices across the nation have spiked, thanks to oil refineries going off line. Because the power went out...North Korea's dictator Kim Jong Un, has explicitly threatened to destroy the rest of the U.S. electricity infrastructure with an electromagnetic pulse (EMP) attack...The conclusion made plain by such developments from the recent past and immediate future is that the most critical of all critical infrastructures—the nation's bulk power distribution system, better known as the grid—is not resilient. Indeed, it is dangerously vulnerable to both naturally occurring disasters and deliberate enemy action."—Secure the Grid Coalition.[162]

California Wildfires (2019) and Texas Ice Storm (2021)

Severe weather in 2019 and 2021 spotlighted that major electric utilities are so neglectful of electric grid security and public safety that the nation's electric utilities cannot be trusted to protect the American people from far more sophisticated and dangerous threats from foreign adversaries—like EMP and Cyber Warfare. Hundreds died in California wildfires and a Texas ice storm because of negligence by electric utilities and their Federal and State "regulators."

California Wildfires

California's chief electric utilities— Pacific Gas and Electric (PG&E), Southern California Edison (SCE), and San Diego Gas and Electric SDG&E)—failed to make basic commonsense upgrades to infrastructure, like replacing aged powerline towers that could collapse and cause fires. They failed to undertake obvious commonsense "vegetation management" safety precautions, like removing trees that could down powerlines and start fires.[163]

---

[161] "Hurricane Harvey" en.wikipedia.org. "Harvey Aftershock: Chemical Plant Near Houston Could Explode, CEO Says" Fox News (30 August 2017). "Harvey Live Updates: In Crosby, Texas, Blasts at a Chemical Plant and More Are Feared" New York Times (31 August 2017).

[162] "The Blackout Next Time" securethegrid.com (12 September 2017).

[163] "2019 California Power Shutoffs" en.wikipedia.org.

Regulators, including the U.S. Federal Energy Regulatory Commission (FERC), the North American Electric Reliability Corporation (NERC), and the California Public Utilities Commission, are complicit in this lethal negligence.[164]

Consequently, when high-winds hit California, downing powerlines, electric arcing ignited massive forest fires (7,860 fires), burning 259,823 acres, destroying thousands of homes. California electric utilities deliberately engineered rolling blackouts as a "strategy" to reduce likelihood that powerlines downed by high winds would cause more fires, seeking to contain the wildfire crisis.[165]

During October-November 2019, California's rolling blackouts affected 3 million, contributing to chaos caused by deadly wildfires consuming entire forests and neighborhoods. While millions of Californians endured periodic rolling blackouts, sometimes lasting days—inflicted on purpose by electric utilities—over 25 million were in "red flag" areas endangered by wildfires.[166]

The deliberately engineered rolling blackouts impeded first responders, and civilians trying to survive or escape, by stopping running water, degrading communications and fuel availability for vehicles, and causing other significant problems.

California Governor Gavin Newsom condemned PG&E for "greed and neglect." People "can't even access water or medical supplies."[167]

But Newsom compelled utilities to invest billions in "green energy" to combat climate change—short-changing public safety. Nor did Newsom's California Public Utilities Commission require electric utilities to protect the grid from high-winds and tree falls.

A San Jose Mercury News editorial rightly protested: "Northern California is not a third world country. It's unacceptable that the region is being forced to endure this level of disruption as the long-term strategy for dealing with the threat of wildfires."[168]

PG&E barricaded its San Francisco headquarters against angry customers.[169]

California electric utilities deserve condemnation, not only for the wildfire crisis, but for a long history of neglecting basic public safety before 2019. Six years earlier, a 2013 report to the California Public Utilities Commission warned: "Several aspects of the PG&E distribution system present significant safety issues."[170]

In 2015, powerlines caused a fire in Butte that killed two.[171]

---

[164] "The Lesson of California's Wildfires" Washington Times (2 November 2019).

[165] Ibid.

[166] Ibid. CNN Wire, "Over 25 Million People Are Under Red Flag Warnings in California as Fires Burn Across State" pix11.com (29 October 2019).

[167] Julie Makinen and Gabrielle Canon, "California Governor Slams PG&E, Saying 'Greed,' 'Mismanagement' Led To Widespread Power Cuts" USA Today (10 October 2019).

[168] "California Wildfire Spreads As Fears Mount Over Further Power Shutoffs" www.theguardian.com (11 October 2019).

[169] Ibid.

[170] "California Power Company Caused Wildfire That Killed 85, Investigation Finds" www.theguardian.com (15 May 2019).

[171] Ibid.

In 2017, a powerline tower built in the 1920s, long past safe service life, collapsed causing a wildfire that destroyed 5,000 homes in Santa Rosa and killed two dozen.[172]

In 2018, powerlines started a huge wildfire that consumed the town of Paradise and killed 85.[173]

PG&E's response to its worsening record of public safety was typical of the other utilities. Instead of stopping mismanagement and launching a crash program to fix grid infrastructure, PG&E filed for bankruptcy to escape liability for billions of dollars in damages inflicted on Californians.[174]

Texas Ice Storm

In February 2021, Winter Storm Uri swept across the Midwest, causing an ice storm over most of Texas, dumping 3-6 inches of snow on San Antonio on February 15, and plunging the State into unusually low temperatures. Electricity demand for heating soared, while about 25% of the State's electric power from windmills and solar went offline, crippled by the ice storm, as were some other sources of electric power unprepared for freezing weather.[175]

The Electric Reliability Council Of Texas (ERCOT) authorized rolling blackouts by utilities to prevent a disaster from becoming a prolonged catastrophic blackout, admitting: "Texas was seconds and minutes away from catastrophic months long blackout."[176]

Over one hundred froze to death and massive property damage resulted because FERC, NERC, and ERCOT failed to require electric utilities to take simple commonsense precautions, like insulation and heating of key grid equipment, to sustain operations during severe cold and winter conditions.

The Biden Administration claims the ice storm that crippled the Texas electric grid, causing state-wide rolling blackouts, depriving water and heat to millions, inflicting property damage and deaths, is a harbinger of catastrophic climate change.[177] If true, so-called "green energy" windmills and solar panels, alleged solutions to climate change, proved most vulnerable to the challenge of an unusual, but not unprecedented, Texas ice storm. Nuclear and coal-fired power plants were least affected.[178]

Climate change is not the cause of what may be remembered as the "great Texas blackout of 2021" which is really the result of politics.

---

172 Ibid.

173 Ibid.

174 "PG&E, Facing Massive Wildfire Liabilities, Seeks Bankruptcy Protection" www.cbsnews.com (14 January 2019).

175 U.S. Energy Information Administration, "Texas (TEX) Region Electricity Generation By Energy Source (2/12/2021-2/19/2021). Bryan Preston, "Did Wind Power Fall Hard During the Great Texas Storm?" pjmedia.com (19 February 2021).

176 Erin Douglas, "Texas Was 'Seconds and Minutes' Away From Catastrophic Months Long Blackouts, Officials Say" Texas Tribune (18 February 2021).

177 Joey Garrison, "'Climate Change Is Real': Biden Administration Says Texas Crisis Shows U.S. Unprepared for Extreme Weather" azcentral.com (18 February 2021).

178 U.S. Energy Information Administration, "Texas (TEX) Region Electricity Generation By Energy Source (2/12/2021-2/19/2021). Bryan Preston, "Did Wind Power Fall Hard During the Great Texas Storm?" pjmedia.com (19 February 2021).

In 2017 the EMP Commission warned: "Current institutional arrangements for protecting and improving the reliability of the electric grids…has proven to be ineffectual" because the "power industry is largely self-regulated."[179]

An excellent study by Jeffrey Ball concludes: "Those in charge of Texas's deregulated power sector were warned again and again that the electric grid was vulnerable."[180] Moreover, while ERCOT and Texas utilities tried to blame their self-inflicted disaster on unusually severe winter weather, while unusual, the ice storm was not unprecedented. Ball notes that almost exactly 10 years earlier: "In February 2011, an ice storm struck the State, crippling power plants and forcing rolling blackouts."[181]

On February 16, 2021, more than 4.5 million in Texas were without power, amidst freezing temperatures.[182]

Nationwide, Winter Storm Uri's blackout of Texas and other States inflicted damage estimated at $200 billion or higher, costing more than Hurricanes Harvey and Ike:

"As winter storms swept across much of the country last week, they shuttered oil and gas production, food processing facilities and manufacturing plants while plunging millions of people into darkness for days on end. Now many homeowners are dealing with burst pipes and other property damage… The Perryman Group, a Texas-based economic research firm, projected that Winter Storm Uri could end up costing a total of $195 billion on the low end and as much as $295 billion. Those figures include lost income as well as long-term reduction in economic output."[183]

Intelligence Treasure Trove

The history of storm-induced electric power blackouts that collapse other critical infrastructures and sow societal chaos, and the long record of inadequate preparation and response by Federal and State governments and electric utilities, is for potential adversaries planning EMP and Cyber Warfare an intelligence treasure trove:

—The record confirms that severe weather can cause disastrous blackouts of electric power grids that can be widened and worsened by EMP and Cyber Warfare.

—The record confirms that electric grid blackouts collapse other critical infrastructures and can cause societal breakdown, which can be widened and worsened by EMP and Cyber Warfare.

—Particulars of failures, mistakes, and systemic weaknesses in emergency planning and response by Federal and State governments and electric utilities (which faults never seem to get corrected) are

---

[179] EMP Commission, *Chairman's Report* (2017).
[180] Jeffrey Ball, "The Texas Blackout Is The Story Of A Disaster Foretold" www.texasmonthly.com (19 February 2021).
[181] Ibid.
[182] Ibid.
[183] Irina Ivanova, "Texas Winter Storm Costs Could Top $200 Billion—More Than Hurricanes Harvey And Ike" www.cbsnews.com (25 February 2021).

detailed after every major hurricane in unclassified reports by the U.S. Government Accountability Office.[184]

—The record proves that the U.S. Government strategy relying on the electric utilities to protect themselves from EMP and Cyber Warfare is doomed to fail.

This history of neglected public safety happened despite electric utilities being regulated by the U.S. Federal Energy Regulatory Commission (FERC) and North American Electric Reliability Corporation (NERC), the latter basically an industry lobby funded by utilities. Most recently, as described earlier, Federal and State "regulators" allowed electric utilities to cause deadly California wildfires in 2019 and an ice age in Texas in 2021, getting away with murder.

The EMP Commission *Chairman's Report* warns:

"The current largely self-regulatory structure of the U.S. Federal Energy Regulatory Commission (FERC), the North American Electric Reliability Corporation (NERC), and the electric power industry was not designed to address U.S. survival under nuclear EMP or other hostile attack. The Commission assesses that the existing regulatory framework for safeguarding the security and reliability of the electric power grid, which is based upon a partnership between the U.S. FERC and the private NERC representing the utilities, is not able to protect the U.S. from hostile attack."[185]

Unwisely, the strategy concocted by the Department of Homeland Security (DHS) and the Department of Energy (DOE) to protect electric grids and other life-sustaining critical infrastructures from the existential threats posed by EMP and Cyber Warfare relies on "public-private partnerships" where the U.S. Government is the junior partner, essentially trusting the expertise and competence of the utilities.

The EMP Commission *Chairman's Report* warns against this "doomed to fail" strategy:

"Regulatory inadequacy over the electric power industry for national security is demonstrated, not only in the failure of industry to protect the grid, but in lobbying by NERC, EPRI, EEI and other industry groups to oppose initiatives by federal and state officials and private citizens to protect the grid from EMP..."[186]

Russia, China, North Korea, and Iran surely find aid and comfort from activities by electric power industry lobbyists opposing protection for U.S. electric grids from EMP and Cyber Warfare. Texas State Senator Bob Hall speaks for many Americans frustrated by the electric power lobby's frequently dishonest opposition:

"As a Texas State Senator who tried in the 2015 legislative session to get a bill passed to harden the Texas grid against an EMP attack or nature's GMD, I learned first-hand the strong control the electric power company lobby has on elected officials. We did manage to get a weak bill passed in the Senate but the power companies had it killed in the House. A very deceitful document which was

---

[184] See for example: Dr. Peter Vincent Pry, *Electric Armageddon* (EMP Task Force: 2012) Chapter V "Design For Failure" and Chapter VI "The Hurricanes" passim.

[185] EMP Commission, *Chairman's Report* (2017) p. 39.

[186] Ibid, p. 40.

carefully designed to mislead legislators was provided by the power company lobbyist at a critical moment in the process. The document was not just misleading, it actually contained false statements. The EMP/GMD threat is real and it is not 'if' but WHEN it will happen. The responsibility for the catastrophic destruction and widespread death of Americans which will occur will be on the hands of the executives of the power companies because they know what needs to be done and are refusing to do it. In my opinion power company executives, by refusing to work with the legislature to protect the electrical grid infrastructure are committing an egregious act that is equivalent to treason. I know and understand what I am saying. As a young U.S. Air Force Captain, with a degree in electrical engineering from The Citadel, I was the project officer who led the Air Force/contractor team which designed, developed, and installed the modification to 'harden' the Minuteman strategic missile to protect it from an EMP attack. The American people must demand that the power company executives that are hiding the truth stop deceiving the people and immediately begin protecting our electrical grid so that life as we know it today will not end when the terrorist EMP attack comes."[187]

Electric utilities and their lobbies—NERC, the Electric Power Research Institute (EPRI), and Edison Electric Institute (EEI)—lack expertise on EMP and Cyber Warfare and are not competent to protect the national grid from either threat.[188]

Despite wildfires and rolling blackouts roiling California, despite over one hundred dead in Texas, DHS and DOE are out-sourcing national security to the electric power industry, trusting proven negligent utilities like PG&E and ERCOT and their NERC and EPRI lobbyists, to safeguard electric grids and the American people from EMP and Cyber Warfare.

If the largest electric utilities in the United States cannot be trusted competently to perform such basic and simple public safety precautions as vegetation management and powerline protection from high-winds and ice storms—as in California (2019) and Texas (2021)—clearly they are incompetent to protect the grid from more complex and much bigger threats, like EMP and Cyber Warfare, that could kill millions.

---

[187] Ibid, pp. 40-41.
[188] Ibid, pp. 39-42.

II

CYBER-ATTACKING ELECTRIC POWER GRIDS: A NEW STRATEGIC WEAPON

by Dr. Edward M. Roche

The United States faces imminent danger from a devastating cyber-attack against its electrical grid. This attack is more probable because a Revolution in Military Affairs has weakened the deterrence traditionally associated with conventional and nuclear weapons, changed the escalation ladder, and consequently lowered the barrier to intensive conflict between the superpowers.

In April 2021, Russia massed troops on Ukraine's border apparently threatening an invasion, raising alarms in the U.S. and NATO. Ventriloquizing for the Kremlin, Putin intimate and director of Russia's state-run international media giants, RT and Sputnik, Margarita Simonyan, in a TV interview declared:

"Russia will invade Ukraine, sparking a conflict with the U.S. that will force entire cities into black-outs…All-out cyber warfare, nation-wide forced blackouts."[189]

"War is inevitable," according to Russia's Simonyan, "I do not believe that this will be a large-scale hot war, like World War II, and I do not believe there will be a long Cold War. It will be a war of the third type: the cyber war."[190]

Russia's Simonyan:

—"In conventional war, we could defeat Ukraine in two days. But it will be another kind of war. We'll do it, and then [the U.S.] will respond by turning off power to [a major Russian city like] Voronezh."
—"Russia needs to be ready for this war, which is unavoidable, and of course it will start in Ukraine."
—Russia is "invincible where conventional war is concerned, but forget about conventional war…it will be a war of infrastructures, and here we have many vulnerabilities."
—"I've been agitating and even demanding that we take Donbas [eastern Ukraine]. We need to patch up our vulnerabilities as fast as we can, and then we can do whatever we want."
—"We only lose if we do nothing," agreed Russian TV interviewer Vladimir Soloviev. "He argued that by absorbing parts of Ukraine—or the entire country—Russia would be able to remove the zone of American influence further from its borders," reports Julia Davis.[191]

Russian TV described cyber-attack options ranging from small-scale to existential threats, including: blacking-out part of New York City (Harlem was mentioned), or blacking-out the state of Florida, or blacking-out the entire continental United States. To defeat the U.S., according to Russia's Simonyan: "We don't even need the nukes."[192]

---

[189] Julia Davis, "Top Kremlin Mouthpiece Warns of 'Inevitable' War with U.S. Over Another Ukraine Land Grab" www.thedailybeast.com (13 April 2021).
[190] Ibid.
[191] Ibid.
[192] Ibid.

Just weeks after the above Russian cyber-threats, in May 2021, the U.S. Colonial Pipeline was hacked, shutdown temporarily. Cyber-attacks can destroy pipelines, causing them to explode. Colonial Pipeline is crucial to fueling U.S. military power projection capabilities from the east coast to protect NATO, or to help Ukraine, during a Russian invasion.[193] That is why the Colonial Pipeline was really targeted, not for the millions paid in ransom, but as a demonstration of Russia's cyber-power.

The Colonial Pipeline cyber-attack proves Russia is not bluffing.

Moscow's Cyber War knockout blow—blacking-out U.S. electric grids and other critical infrastructures, has been planned for years:

—March 2016, U.S. Government Joint Technical Alert warned Russia's cyber-attack Dragonfly: "Targeted government entities and multiple U.S. critical infrastructure centers, including the energy, nuclear, commercial facilities, water, aviation, and critical manufacturing sectors."[194]
—2017, the Department of Homeland Security (DHS) disclosed, as headlined by Wall Street Journal and Newsweek: "Russian Hackers Could Have Caused Electricity Blackouts In The U.S."[195]
—March 2018, Reuters reported: "Senior U.S. intelligence officials said…the Kremlin believes it can launch hacking operations against the West with impunity." Russia "staged malware…and gained remote access into energy sector networks."[196]
—July 2018, DHS warned of Russian cyber-penetrations into hundreds of U.S. electric utilities. These cyber-attacks were probably the simulated "tip of the spear" for VOSTOK-18, a major joint Russia-China strategic exercise held in September 2018, practicing World War III.[197]
—December 2020, DHS disclosed Russia's Solar Winds cyber-attack penetrated 18,000 U.S. Government and private sector agencies and corporations, including the Defense Department and U.S. Cybersecurity and Infrastructure Security Agency. Damage is still being evaluated.[198]

On Sunday, April 11, 2021, the world woke up to alarmist complaints by Iran without proof blaming Israel for an attack on its electrical grid. Power supplying its Natanz nuclear processing facility disappeared. At the same time, newspapers in Israel were boasting that a cyber-attack engineered by its scientists and secret service had been responsible for this disaster.[199] Of the three parts to the electricity grid –a) Generation; b) Transmission; and c) Distribution – here the attack had been on

---

[193] "When Will America Protect Itself Against EMP, Cyber and Ransomware Attacks?" The Hill (21 May 2021).

[194] Dustin Volz and Timothy Gardner, "In A First, U.S. Blames Russia For Cyber Attacks On Energy Grid" Reuters (15 March 2018). CISA, Alert TA18-074A (15 March 2018) us-cert.cisa.gov/ncas/alerts/TA18-074A

[195] Jason Murdock, "Russian Hackers 'Could Have Caused Electricity Blackouts' in the U.S." Newsweek (24 July 2018).

[196] Dustin Volz and Timothy Gardner, "In A First, U.S. Blames Russia For Cyber Attacks On Energy Grid" Reuters (15 March 2018).

[197] Dr. Peter Vincent Pry "Understanding VOSTOK-18" originally published as "The Danger of Russia's Largest Military Exercise" Newsmax Platinum (8 October 2018) danhappel.com.

[198] Terry Thompson, "The Colonial Pipeline Ransomware Attack and the SolarWinds Hack Were All But Inevitable" news.yahoo.com (10 May 2021).

[199] Subsequent analysis showed that the disruption to the power supply in Natanz was caused not by cyber, but by setting off an explosion underground to destroy a transformer. This was done by somehow recruiting an individual to carry out this attack. Nevertheless, the world's press continued to circulate the story, shifting to more general arguments about the vulnerability of the grid. See Yonah Jeremy Bob, Lahav Harkov, Tzvi Joffre "Mossad behind attack on Iran's Natanz nuclear facility" The Jerusalem Post online (13 April 2021 10:12): "Western sources said the facility was hit by a cyberattack, but The Jerusalem Post learned that it was a confirmed physical attack."

the distribution side. An "electrical substation located 40 to 50 meters underground" was destroyed. "[T]housands of centrifuges" used to separate Uranium-235 from Uranium-238 had been put out of service, at least temporarily.[200] The strategic implications were grave. An electrical grid was being used as a strategic weapon to impede Iran's path in violation of its obligations under the Nuclear Non-Proliferation Treaty towards creation of an atomic bomb.[201] Here, interference with the electrical grid was used not to disrupt Iran's economy and society, but instead to injure a strategic military facility with pinpoint accuracy. As the press continued to reverberate the story, discussion widened to consider cyber-attacks as a means of war.

According to the Office of the Director of National Intelligence:

"Cyber threats from nation states ... will remain acute. Foreign states use cyber operations to ... damage ... physical ... critical infrastructure. ... [W]e remain most concerned about Russia, China, Iran, and North Korea."[202]

From 1965—2020 there were 68 blackouts in the United States affecting 100,000 or more persons for at least 1 hour and comprising at least 1,000,000 person-hours of disruption. Can a cyber-attack be used to turn an electrical grid into a strategic weapon? If so, then what type of planning would need be done by a rival effectively to harm the United States?

Attacking Electric Grids—A Tool Of Strategic Conflict

The United States is a superpower. Even its enemies know it should not be attacked lightly. There must be a reason, and that reason must fit into the grand strategy of the attacker. At the heart of the matter is "why?". What is the strategic logic? What type of international crisis would be severe enough to drive a rival Nation State to launch a major cyber-attack against America's electrical grid? We know that motivations vary, and so do the capabilities and boldness of attackers. For the time being, however, let's assume the reason is there. If this is the case, then the question becomes "What *type* of cyber-attack?"

Of course there are different levels of attack, ranging from small irritating skirmishing actions to a major attack aimed at taking out electrical power for a region of America or a single large metropolitan area. At the top extreme is an all-out attempt to disable the nation's entire electrical grid aiming to plunge the country into a chaotic and horrifying darkness. For a small Nation State, it is doubtful they could assemble enough capability successfully to launch a cyber-attack nationwide against such a giant electrical grid in its entirety. One of America's rival superpowers could.

---

[200] Tzvi Joffre, Yonah Jeremy Bob, "Natanz nuclear site blast: Iranian State TV identifies man behind attack" The Jerusalem Post (17 April 2021 13:44) *quoting* Iranian officials. The bomber was identified as Mr. Reza Karimi. What is surprising is that the Iranian government presented an "Interpol Wanted" card on the bomber, meaning that he had been able to carry out the bombing and get out of Iran. *It is likely the cyber-attack story had been a smoke screen to allow the bomber to escape from Iran.* Note in particular there are not "thousands" of centrifuges in that facility.

[201] Iran still was learning that no Nation State has a "right" to build this type of weapon.

[202] Office of the Director of National Intelligence, *Annual Threat Assessment of the US Intelligence Community*, p. 20 (9 April 2021 *hereinafter* "ODNI 2021 Rpt").

Cyber-attacks by tradition are broken down into two classes. One type is the "supplementary" variety, the other is "stand-alone". In the supplementary form, cyber-attacks are used to assist projection of military force. Cyber becomes one of many tools in a military confrontation. The highest priority targets usually are the command and control systems of the enemy's military. Only if the conflict reaches a higher level of intensity does it become a possibility to engage civil society targets. If there were cyber-attacks on both military and civilian targets, and these were being deployed as a supplement to national military force, then this would mean the parties were engaged in a "Total War."[203] This is the highest and most unfortunate level of conflict, but if we follow the traditional and accepted concepts regarding nuclear deterrence this scenario is unlikely between the superpowers. Under traditional strategic defense theory, all-out cyber conflict would take place only as an adjunct to either conventional or nuclear war.

Does this logic still hold? What about other types of attack? In the stand-alone form, cyber-attacks are launched from one Nation State to another *without* being a supplement to ongoing use of conventional or nuclear military force. These are "cyber-only" attacks. Not associated with a declared war, they often are anonymous. After all, a weaker attacker does not wish for a stronger power to know they are the source of the problem, because this would expose them to retaliation. To avoid a such a response, the smaller fry tend to "fly under the radar" in an effort to hide in the dimly lit vastness of cyberspace.

A new form of cyber-attack against the electrical grid has emerged in the form of a "non-shooting" war between Nation States. This type of attack might take place between superpowers as something that is short of use of conventional or nuclear force. Some argue that "non-kinetic" cyber-attacks are not an "armed attack" under international law and thus there is no right given to a Nation State for self-defense under Article 51 of the United Nations Charter.[204] Consequently, they argue, this lowers the chance of kinetic retaliation. With less to worry about, the result has been a perceived relaxation of inhibitions governing the use of cyber-attacks by Nation States. For example, one observer has stated that under some circumstances, Russia might take steps to injure the American electrical grid in response to a move by the United States in support of the Government of Ukraine. Such a scenario might happen in this sequence:[205] a) The separatist areas of Eastern Ukraine become involved in an internal fight with their Government; b) When violence escalates, Russia moves in to protect the majority Russian-nationality population, which perhaps is demanding a plebiscite on breaking away from the Ukraine and becoming an independent state or joining Russia; c) The United States makes the mistake of intervening in this civil war and launches a cyber-attack against the electrical grid *of Russia* or parts of it, such as a city; d) Having been attacked, Russia *always* responds, so it launches a counter cyber-attack against the mainland of the United States and takes out an equivalent part of the American Electrical Grid.

According to a commentator on Russian state television:

---

[203] *See* Erich Ludendorff, *Der Totale Krieg* (München: Ludendorffs Verlag, 1935); Definition: Total warfare a war that is unrestricted in terms of the weapons used, the territory or combatants involved, or the objectives pursued, especially one in which the laws of war are disregarded. (*Oxford Reference*).
[204] This legal catfight never has been satisfactorily resolved.
[205] *See* statements of Margarita Simonyan and Vladimir Soloviev on Russian state television, *reported by* Julia Davis "Top Kremlin Mouthpiece Warns of 'Inevitable' War With U.S. Over Another Ukraine Land Grab : 'Don't Even need the Nukes'" www.thedailybeast.com (13 April 2021).

"I do not believe that this will be a large-scale hot war, like World War II, and I do not believe that there will be a long Cold War. It will be a war of the third type: the cyberwar."[206]

The damage inflicted would be short of conventional or nuclear war, and as expected for reckless national security advisors who have not seen real war, the barriers to adopting a strategy expressed as a cyber-attack against the electrical grid consequently would seem to be lower. *This is a new development in strategic defense theory.* It envisions a central war between the superpowers without resorting to conventional or nuclear forces. Instead, they will rely on cyber-attacks.

Cyber Has Automated Espionage

Cyber has automated espionage. It now is hundreds of thousands of times more effective than any other type of spying.[207] Intelligence gathering[208] is aimed at both the opponent's Civil Society and government, including its military forces. Since the mid-1990s, a massive amount of information has been exfiltrated from even our most highly-protected and "secure" targets. The pilfered information covers a comprehensive range of topics including military, technological, political, industrial, strategic, personnel, and others. Cyber espionage has more than proven its worth. It is "cost effective." This would be beautiful in another context, but here, it is the United States that has been the victim harmed the most. A paradox of cyber is that the most advanced Nation States are the most vulnerable to attack with this quirky and asymmetric weapon.

For the purpose of understanding cyber-attacks against the electrical grid, we must note an important sub-class of espionage – the practice of gathering up technical intelligence regarding the networks and interconnected devices within the territory of one's opponent. At first, this sounds like a giant and overwhelming assignment, particularly if one is considering mapping and making sense of the networks within an entire Nation State. Indeed it is that. Nevertheless, with the use of automation, it is in fact possible to map such giant infrastructures, and even develop a database that contains basic information about many if not all of the connected devices.[209] Of course with technological developments such as the Internet of Things (IoT),[210] and IPv6,[211] the number of inter-connected devices theoretically can approach 10^{27} devices *per person*, yet this vast number also is within the range of automated mapping.

Apart from the technological wizardry of automated mapping, this form of espionage has an important and serious function. It makes it possible to pinpoint the best targets to attack. Automated mapping can locate the Internet-connected control devices in an electrical grid. Once that is done, the

---

[206] Margarita Simonyan quoted by Davis, Ibid.

[207] Human Intelligence (HUMINT); SIGINT; MASINT; ELINT, etc.

[208] In many models, this part of the process is referred to as "Reconnaissance", but that term refers to electronic surveillance of the network inside an organization once it has been penetrated, it is a *sub-set* of intelligence gathering.

[209] There are many examples. *See* Internet-map.net.

[210] The Internet of Things (IoT) describes the network of physical objects–"things, or objects"–that are embedded with sensors, software, and other technologies for the purpose of connecting and exchanging data with other devices and systems over the Internet.

[211] Internet Protocol Version 6 is vastly increasing the number of Internet addresses, and thus the number of possible interconnected devices. By 1998, the Internet Engineering Task Force had formalized the successor protocol. It designed IPv6 to use a 128-bit address, theoretically allowing 2^{128}, or approximately 3.4 x 10^{38} addresses. The old IPv4 used a 32-bit address space and allowed for 2^{32} unique addresses.

identity of these critical devices can be determined. Their identity known, internal cyber-dependent components can be dissected. When a hacker knows how something works, they can figure out how to stop it from working.

Next, malware can be created, then *inserted* into the foreign infrastructure. In some cases, such malware is designed merely to be there in case it is needed. It remains dormant. This is a type of pre-positioning that allows a Nation State to have code ready inside the infrastructure of an opponent. It is safe to assume that the infrastructure of the United States has been mapped, penetrated, and is full of pre-positioned code from enemies ready to strike.[212]

Even if there is no pre-positioning of malware, the use of cyber intelligence to identify key electrical grid control technologies has enabled enemies to write code that can be used to turn these devices into the equivalent of bombs.

Choice Of Cyber-Attack Vectors Depends On The Target

No matter what their underlying purpose, there are different types of cyber-attacks. Some are indiscriminate; others aimed at specific targets. Here, we assume that an attack against the electrical grid would be targeted, not indiscriminate. This narrows down the types of attack that might be used. For example, an indiscriminate DDoS[213] attack would be ruled out.[214]

A targeted attack against an important national security asset such as the electrical grid would require a number of phases. The target must be identified and its function understood. Preparation must be made, and a strategy for getting access to the target must be worked out. That being accomplished, the attack may be launched. Let us look at this in greater detail.

Pre-Attack Intelligence Gathering Selects The Target

Depending on the target, intelligence collection may be easy or difficult, or perhaps impossible.

Luckily for its enemies, the United States is one of the world's softest intelligence targets. An analyst's dream. So much information is freely available. In the Chi Mak Spy ring, for example, the spies found that in order to handle the pilfered technical information stolen from Boeing, it was necessary to rent multiple vans to drive the boxes upon boxes of documentation down to the Chinese Consulate

---

[212] There have been "multiple intrusions into US ICS/SCADA and smart grid tools [to] ... gather[] intelligence [and] develop capabilities to attack." *See* Timothy M. Wintch, "Perspective: Cyber and Physical Threats to the U.S. Power Grid and Keepng the Lights On" Homeland Security Today (20 April 2021) *quoting* Mission Support Center, *Cyber Threat and Vulnerability Analysis of the U.S. Electric Sector*, Idaho National Laboratory, 22 (2016), 22; There are rumors the United States has pre-positioned destructive dormant code into the electrical grids of its rivals, but this is impossible to determine with any reliability.

[213] Distributed Denial of Service (flooding a server with so many requests that it becomes over-loaded, thus making it impossible for regular customers/visitors to receive its service)

[214] A more restrictive model is the "Cyber Kill Chain" developed by Lockheed Martin. It involves a) Reconnaissance (harvesting email addresses, conference information, etc.); b) Weaponization (Coupling exploit with backdoor into deliverable payload); c) Delivery (Delivering Weaponized bundle to the victim via email, web, USB, etc.); d) Exploitation (Exploiting a vulnerability to execute code on victim's system); e) Installation (Installing malware on the asset); f) Command & Control (C2) (Command channel for remote manipulation of victim); and g) Actions on Objectives (With "Hands on Keyboard" access, intruders accomplish their original goals).

in San Francisco.[215] *Truckloads* of information, and that using the old fashioned "brick and mortar" type of espionage.

There are other important sources. Leaks abound. In the "Game of Thrones" cut-throat winner-takes-all environment of Washington, D.C., U.S. Government employees seeking to further one agenda or another routinely leak highly technical and strategically sensitive information, usually making it available over the World Wide Web. In the cyber world, the Government itself routinely publishes details on important computer exploits whereupon hackers use this information to conduct their work. America's industries also contribute to the softening process because they like to publicize their accomplishments and sales. As a consequence, when everything is added together, this ocean of information available in the United States gives an incomprehensible advantage to rivals. Go to a country such as Russia, and the situation is completely different. Information that Americans consider as being routine there is kept out of sight.

When getting ready for an attack, analysis of cyber intelligence goes through a narrowing-down process. First, there is an extended general scan of the environment. Here, it would involve probing and compiling an analysis of the target Nation State as a whole. At some point, a decision is made to hit the Electrical Grid.[216] After that, then cyber espionage becomes more specific. It narrows down collection activities to thoroughly examine the nature of the specific target. For the electrical grid in the United States, it would take only a short period of time to determine the gigantic scale of the network, and its organization into multiple units such as the a) Western Electricity Coordinating Council; b) Southwest Power Pool; c) Texas Reliability Entity; d) Reliability First Corporation; e) SERC Reliability Corporation;[217] f) Northeast Power Coordinating Council; and g) Florida Reliability Coordinating Council.

In an electrical grid, there are four major cyber systems that can serve as targets for attack including a) Supervisory Control and Data Acquisition Systems (SCADA) responsible for managing real-time measurements from substations and sending controlling signals to equipment such as circuit breakers or other control systems; b) Substation Automation Systems which are tasked with control of local equipment (in a single facility); c) Energy Management Systems responsible for real time analysis of the reliability of systems, usually by taking continuous samples of propagating electricity waves, *e.g.,* monitoring of frequency; and d) Market systems that are responsible for buying and selling of electricity on both a bulk and consumer basis, including the spot market. The highest priority for a cyber-attack is the SCADA equipment. These can turn off the power and possibly trigger a cascade of blackouts.[218]

Any of these systems provide a rich environment for launching a cyber-attack. For example, a Substation Automation System (SAS) links together in a network many substation devices including a) Intelligent Electronic Devices (IED); b) Network (ethernet) switches; c) Database and application servers; d) Front-End Processors (communications equipment that links an information system to one or more networks); e) Telecommunications gateways (equipment that links one network to an-

---

[215] *See* Edward M. Roche, *Snake Fish: The Chi Mak Spy Ring* (New York: Barraclough Ltd., 1996).

[216] The electrical grid could be the sole target; or merely one of many targets.

[217] Four organizations in the Southeast – the CARVA Pool, Tennessee Valley Authority (TVA), Southern Company, and the Florida Electric Power Coordinating Group – combine to form SERC.

[218] For an example of a cascading blackout, see below a description of the recent Texas blackout.

other and sometimes translates from one protocol to another); and f) Workstations for engineers and operators, sometimes referred to as the "HMI" or "Human Machine Interface."[219]

For a modestly sized system designed to provide 1,500 MW of power, the Substation Automation System will need to be capable at a minimum of processing 50,000 data points streaming in from more than 600 Intelligent Electronic Devices (IEDs).

It is popular to use the IEC 61850 communication protocol. Switchgear has numerical relays on this standard and the breakers are managed through the Distributed Control System (DCS).[220] A large amount of information travels back and forth reporting on the a) Status of the system components (circuit breaker open/close; circuit breaker in a testing routine or in service; motor speed switch); b) Protection data (breaker positions; thermal warning; Load-jam trip element; Phase under-voltage; breaker operation count); and c) Important measurement data (R-, Y-, and B-phase current; RYB Voltage and frequency; power; phase current measurements).[221]

Since these all are crucial factors for understanding the operation of the power plant, should these reporting data points be disturbed, there is a risk of power interruption. In addition, if these data points could be intercepted then the status of plant operations could be made to look different from what it actually is. Many of these systems also are part of an underlying alarm system, and if disabled would nullify any tip-off to plant operators of a problem.

For example, proud engineers describing operation of the Indira Ghandi Super Thermal Power Project in Jajjar announced to the world a serious potential vulnerability in their plant: *"Modern numerical relays ... capture all feeder data, report events, monitor the equipment ... Such near real-time data of the complete auxiliary system ... displayed on a human-machine interface (MHI) help monitor the system from remote locations."*[222]

Unfortunately, should these data paths be set up for remote access, there is a potential cyber-security problem because hackers can "dial in" and do their sabotage. This is what happened in the 2015 Ukraine incident.

The standard for delay in getting signals from these devices is 10 milliseconds or less.[223] The access to the Intelligent Electronic Devices (IED) is through the Ethernet switches which feed the SCADA servers and the Operator workstations.

How might this Intelligence analysis work? A network analysis, based on widely-available scanning tools, would reveal that the electrical grid of the United States could be broken into half with ten targeted attacks along a vertical line north from the mid-way point between El Paso and Tucson. Furthermore, by study of documents such as the North American Electric Reliability Corporation (NER-

---

[219] *See* Saroj Chelluri, Diego Rodas, Ala Harikrishna "Integration Considerations for Large-Scale IEC 61850 Systems" 2nd Annual Protection, Automation and Control World Conference (Dublin 27-30 June 2011).

[220] A DCS has high reliability because control processing is distributed to different nodes in the system, instead of having a single processor that might take down the entire system.

[221] Ibid.

[222] Ibid.

[223] Ibid. (noting that delay for CAT 5e/6 cables is 0.55 milliseconds per 100 meters; for fiber optics 0.49 and for wireless 0.33)

C)[224] Critical Infrastructure Protection (CIP) Standards[225] for the Bulk Electric System[226] it would be easy to identify all of the cyber defense activities underway at each major facility. For an enterprising hacker, it might be possible to penetrate the information system of the NERC and obtain copies of the self-studies and assessments benchmarking the CIP Standards as well as details of Reliability Standard Violations. This would quickly lead to the IEC 61850 standard of the International Electrotechnical Commission.[227] This, in turn, would lead to the detailed knowledge found in documents such as a) IEC TR 61850-90-1:2010 for communication between substations; b) IEC TR 61850-90-2:2016 for communication between substations and control centers; c) IEC TR 61850-90-5:2012 for transmission of synchrophasor information;[228] and d) IEC TR 61850-90-7:2013 for power converters in distributed energy resources (DER) systems.

Knowing the equipment to target and its possible vulnerability is insufficient. It is necessary to know the precise IP address of the equipment on the *internal* network of the facility. It may be necessary to exfiltrate this data after gaining preliminary access into the local system. In the Lockheed cybersecurity model, this is called the "Reconnaissance" phase.

For example, according to the E-ISAC Ukraine Report on Russia's cyber-attack on the Ukraine electric grid: *"After the attackers achieved the necessary freedom of movement and action in the IT infrastructure, they began exfiltrating the necessary information and discovering the hosts and devices to devise an attack concept to hijack the SCADA DMS to open breakers and cause a power outage."*[229]

Intelligence analysis would be able to find the location of all active Phasor Measurement Units.[230] Perhaps by using review of the trade press, the attacker would correlate the sales of IEC standard compliant equipment to various utility companies (and their locations). Perhaps it would target synchrophasor sites. Or perhaps it would target a Schweitzer Engineering Laboratories Software Defined Networking installation to *increase* its "Deny by Default" architecture response time from <0.1milliseconds to >0.5ms or even to >30ms. That should do it. There are many options to choose from.

---

[224] North American Electric Reliability Corporation (NERC). Created by the U.S. Government and designed to protect part of the electricity infrastructure of the United States.

[225] These standards apply specifically to the cybersecurity of the Bulk Electric System.

[226] Bulk Electric System (BES): Unless modified by the lists shown below, all Transmission Elements operated at 100 kV or higher and Real Power and Reactive Power resources connected at 100 kV or higher. This does not include facilities used in the local distribution of electric energy. *See* NERC, *Bulk Electric System Definition Reference Document*, Ver. 3 (August 2018).

[227] Work of its Technical Committee 57.

[228] Synchrophasor is a device (Phasor Measure Unit or PMU) that estimates the size and phase angle of an electrical phasor quantity (voltage; current) using a common time source for synchronization. It measures the frequency in the power grid. Typical measurement is 120 times per second. A phasor ("phase vector") is a complex number incorporating (1) amplitude (A); (2) angular frequency; and (3) initial phase.

[229] *See* Robert M Lee, Michael J. Assante, Tim Conway, "Analysis of the Cyber Attack on the Ukrainian Power Grid" E-ISAC (18 March 2016) p. 15, para. 5.

[230] *See* for example "The three different D[istribution] M[anagement] S[ystem] vendors were discoverable via opensource searching." *in* Robert M Lee, Michael J. Assante, Tim Conway, "Analysis of the Cyber Attack on the Ukrainian Power Grid" E-ISAC (18 March 2016) p. 10, fn. 28 (*hereinafter* "E-ISAC Ukraine Report" describing the identification of technology used in Ukraine in 2015).

Initial determination of the preferred scale of a cyber-attack is essential. Luckily for the attacker, they can determine that the electrical grid in the United States is subject to a cascading blackout effect. It is riddled with critical points that if disturbed will produce a chain reaction of one blackout causing another which in turn causes another. This was seen on August 10, 1996 in the Northwest United States (7.5 million customers), and August 14, 2003 in the Northeastern United States and Canada (50 million customers).[231]

Cascades happen because as each line is shut down, the electricity must be moved over to another transport route. "A line *overloads* if the absolute amount of power flowing in it exceeds a given *line threshold*." This leads to an immediate "outage of the corresponding line."[232] So if the electricity is passed over to a line without the capacity, the circuit will shut down, merely as a safety measure.

The potential for cascading blackouts in the electrical grid in the United States is a gift to the enemy. It would not be necessary to disable all of the utilities, or transmission switching points across the country. Instead it should be possible to damage the United States, its economy and its people merely by locating the handful of points that would cause a cascade of power failures.

Simulations have confirmed this approach. For example, a study in 2005 found that "an efficiency loss (damage) of up to 25% is possible after the loss of a *single* generator or transmission substation".[233] Another study of cascading effects in the electrical grid found that merely one-fifth of all failures were primary, and the rest were secondary, that is, they were caused by a blackout somewhere else on the network, usually next door.[234] The study found that larger cascades can be generated by an attack of multiple nodes that are close to each other, and close to the vulnerable set:

"[There is a] set of network components that are vulnerable to cascading failures under any out[age] of multiple conditions. ... [T]he vulnerable set consists of a small but topologically central portion of the network ... [L]arge cascades are disproportionately more likely to be triggered by initial failures close to this set. ... [L]arge cascades tend to be triggered by perturbations adjacent to the set of 'early adopters'."[235]

Here, the term 'early adopters' refers to parts of the grid that have blacked out first. Once these vital points in the electrical grid are identified, then the intelligence work can be focused on penetration of their supporting facilities. In the United States these vulnerable points in the electrical grid have been identified, but surprisingly do not appear to have been made public. Nevertheless, we must assume that through espionage, enemies have stolen copies of these classified studies and know precisely where to hit.

---

[231] *See* Ian Dobson, "Cascading Network Failure in Power Grid Blackouts," *Encyclopedia of Systems and Control* (London: Springer-Verlag, 2014).

[232] *See* Tommaso Nesti, Alessandro Zocca, and Bert Zwart "Emergent Failures and Cascades in Power Grids: A Statistical Physics Perspective" 120 Physical Review Letters 258301-1 (2018).

[233] *See* R. Kinney, P. Crucitti, R. Albert, V. Latora "Modeling Cascading Failures in the North American power grid" European Physical Journal B, Vol. 46 (2005) pp. 101-107, ("[T]he first node removed does the most damage while each successive removal does little to the worsening of the average efficiency. Similar behavior is recorded for generators." p. 106, para. 2).

[234] *See* Yang Yang, Takashi Nishikawa, Adilson E. Motter "Small Vulnerable Sets Determine Large Network Cascades in Power Grids" 358 Science, eaan3184 (2017).

[235] Ibid., p. 5

Intelligence collection also might focus on the personnel at target locations. Providing the Nation State has the resources, this information might lead to a recruitment or other inducement to cooperate on the part of persons with access to the facility. Over a long time, agents might be placed in key facilities.

The final work in the intelligence phase would be an analysis of the effects of a cyber-attack. Would it disable an intended target, such as a manufacturing plant, or military base? What would be the response from the target Nation State if the attacker were identified? Since this part of the analysis is little more than sophisticated guesswork, it will go quickly.

Nevertheless, the primary outcome of the intelligence phase of this operation would be an identification of the targets as well as the most promising technique for launching a successful cyber-attack that would have the desired effect. The bad news is that this work likely already has been done by enemies.

A Cyber Weapon Is Built With A Payload And Vector

In the next phase of the operation the attacker must a) build the cyber weapon; b) determine how to get it delivered; c) continue to assess the downstream effects of its use; d) develop contingencies for the operation if things do not go as planned.

The effect of a cyber-attack could be either less serious than anticipated, or could become much larger than anticipated. At the same time, intelligence monitoring if possible should continue to detect any material changes in underlying conditions, either technology-wise, politically, or as a detectable change in levels of security at a targeted site.

The most important part of the preparation phase is building the malware ("cyber-weapon") that will be used. Cyber weapons are similar to a biological virus; there are two crucial components. A virus such as Covid-19 has two essential elements. First, the RNA to be injected into the cell allowing it to cause replication of the virus itself. Second, a pathway ("vector") must be available to pass the RNA into the target cell. Any cyber weapon malware also has two essential components. First is the "payload." This refers to the [computer] code that will carry out the operations of the malware. In Stuxnet, the payload software was responsible for harming the centrifuges in Natanz, Iran. Second, the "Vector." This refers to the "exploit" that will be used to inject the damaging code into the target information system. Exploits are a "bug" in the operating system, applications or connected firmware-controlled devices. It can be exploited to sneak in the payload undetected.

There is much remarkable creativity in writing exploits. The recent SolarWinds attack used a novel vector of being put into commercial software *before* it was distributed from the factory to customers.[236]

---

[236] *See* Dina Temple-Raston, A 'Worst Nightmare' Cyberattack: The Untold Story Of The SolarWinds Hack" NPR website (16 April 2021). In attribution of the attack, the author writes that it was "Hackers *believed to be* directed by the Russian intelligence service" responsible (Emphasis Added). There is no indication regarding the identity of who believed the attack to originate in Russia and why they came to this conclusion. This means that attribution to Russia is either the product of analysis by U.S. intelligence services, or propaganda posing as a "leak" to feeder journalists. It is impossible to tell. All we know is that no evidence has been presented. How would someone know the precise details of how the SVR *in Russia* was directing a group of hackers *in Russia*? (SVR ``Sluzhba vneshney razvedki Rossiyskoy Federatsii", Foreign Intelligence Service of the Russian Federation).

Sourcing of these two components is completely different. For the most part, exploits ("vectors") for delivery of a payload may be obtained on the Dark Web ("Black Market") where they are auctioned off to the highest bidder. These markets operate with anonymity, or at least give the appearance of doing so. If these exploits are not yet known to the vendors of the software, they are given the name "Zero Day" exploits.[237]

Design of the payload is more complex. Here, the code must be written to the precise specifications that will accomplish the sabotage intended. To do that, the hacker must first obtain a realistic testbed to use for ensuring the software will work.[238] A diverse and skilled workforce is needed. It is a team effort, not that of an individual. There must be programming talent, but also knowledge of electricity, and operation of the grid, and also knowledge of the specific engineering characteristics of the device that is going to be penetrated and manipulated to inflict the intended damage.

There is a popular myth that cyber weapons can be made "by any teenager in a basement using software downloaded from the web." This is not at all true if we consider the target. It is not everyone who can write the specific code needed to disable an electrical grid. Apart from the programming skills, they need to have superb knowledge of the grid itself, how it works, and the specific equipment being made the target of the attack. They must understand the operational procedures of the specific facility being targeted.

For example, in the Stuxnet malware used to inhibit illegal uranium refinement (separation of U-235 from U-238) in Iran, the United States went through a number of steps including a) Interception on the high seas of identical gas centrifuges that were being shipped from North Korea to Libya; b) Transportation of the seized equipment to one of its national laboratories, probably Oak Ridge; c) Setting up the centrifuges and getting them to operate so they could be studied and used as a test bed; d) Intensive study of the SCADA systems controlling the equipment; e) Development of an attack plan for the malware (the attack was meant to remain hidden, so the centrifuges would appear to break randomly and naturally); f) Development of a systems design plan to create the software to do the intended task; g) Extensive testing of the malware; h) Intensive surveillance of the target facility in Iran for the purpose of determining the method for delivering the malware; i) Acquiring the Zero-Day exploits to serve as vectors for the malware payload; then j) Final Testing.

If the discovery and forensic analysis of Stuxnet is any guide, the programming expertise for its development required at least two separate domains of computer science including a) Traditional programming familiar with operating and networking systems of standard ICT equipment; and b) Specialized machine programming of the SCADA systems, written in different languages, and relying on a generally separate set of skills.

---

[237] Once an exploit is discovered (or purchased) by the vendor, they quickly rectify the vulnerability, and issue an update ("patch") to their software. After that, the countdown for the exploit begins. As days go by, users around the world gradually come to install the update on their system. When they do this, then the value of the malware decreases. Not everyone patches their system on a timely basis. So even if a particular exploit is known, and a solution issued in an update, still there always remain a large number of users who are negligent in doing the update. As a consequence, they remain vulnerable.

[238] *See* "The adversaries likely had systems *in their organization* that they were able to evaluate and *test their firmware against* prior to executing on December 23rd." E-ISAC Ukraine Report, p. 10, para. 5 (Emphasis Added).

This does not even account for all of the required engineering knowledge of how to operate a centrifuge. Apart from all of that extensive effort, there was a significant intelligence activity put into place including both collection, and either development or preparation of the human networks that would be used to introduce the malware into Iran. If those activities are added to the bill, and considering the intelligence work plus the engineering work, Stuxnet was probably a billion dollar weapon.

In sum, this was the type of work that could have been done only by a Nation State and definitely *not* by someone in a basement using off-the-shelf malware purchased from the sleaze merchants lurking on the Dark Web.

Obtaining Site Access Requires Intelligence Resources And Analysis

The next phase may just as well start up as the preparation phase is winding down. In order to accomplish this type of penetration of a sensitive electrical grid facility, the attacker can use a variety of tried and trusted techniques.

There are two methods of access for a cyber weapon. First, it can be introduced through the general Internet. If the systems being attacked are on the web, then they might come under attack. Spearphishing is the most common way hackers are able to get a foothold inside a target system. But security experts long have been aware of this problem and as a consequence have dis-connected many critical machines from the open Internet. This is done by setting up small Internets using the same underlying technology and standards, but with no gateways to the outside world. If this happens then a common way to cross this "air gap" is through an employee of the facility (or visitor) that might take in the malware on their own laptop or on a USB drive. One of the famous stories in this regard is the Nation State that placed invisible malware on USB drives, then scattered them in the parking lots of Department of Defense employees, whereupon these were picked up, taken into the facilities, and then plugged in so the curious (the unwitting "vector") could see their content. Once plugged into a network, the malware escaped into the closed system and the air gap had been breached.

There are other access techniques as well. These include a) Recruitment of human resources inside the facility;[239] b) Penetration of the facility with an operative using some form of social engineering (pretending to be someone they are not); c) Rigging of equipment shipped into the facility; or d) Some other method not known.[240]

All of these techniques for delivery of the malware take extensive resources, surveillance, analysis and sophistication. It is possible that extensive training would be required, raising further the complexity and barriers inhibiting a cyber-attack.

Cyber-Attacking The Electric Grid May Have Multiple Objectives

Finally, the time arrives to conduct the attack. The way this occurs is dependent on the larger theatre of conflict. In its simplest sense, the attack must be seen within the context of other parallel actions – political, diplomatic, military, economic – taking place at the same time. Here, the most fundamental

---

[239] Recruitment of human is done through the MICE framework: Money, Ideology, Blackmail or Ego. *See* Randy Burkett "An Alternative Framework for Agent Recruitment: From MICE to RASCLS" 57 Studies in Intelligence 7 (2013)

[240] *See* "[I]t is likely that the adversary will modify attack approaches in follow-on campaigns and these mitigation strategies may not be sufficient". E-ISAC Ukraine Report, p. 14, para. 1.

distinction is whether or not a cyber-attack against the electrical grid takes place as a stand-alone effort, or is within the context of a larger conflict involving conventional or nuclear weapons. In the Gulf Wars, cyber was used extensively to "soften up" the Iraqi targets before actual kinetic attacks were launched. In this classical model, exploitation of the vulnerabilities in information systems was merely one of many tools used by the military in conducting its compelling work.

Under the new strategic defense logic, it is possible that a cyber-attack against America's electrical grid might be fired off as a stand-alone event. Russia's reported repeated attacks on the Ukraine electric grid, and China's blackout of Mumbai, India, are attacks of this sort. Much depends on the overall political context, and the goals of the attacker. Stand-alone attacks could be aimed at accomplishing a number of goals including a) Doing damage to a specific region of a Nation State, perhaps one that is symbolic, such as the nation's capital; b) Sending a "warning signal" to deter some current or feared action by the Nation State being attacked; c) As punishment for a real or perceived confrontation with the attacker Nation State;[241] or d) As a prelude or diversion in preparation for an attack elsewhere.[242]

Lessons Learned From Past Cyber-Attacks Against Electric Grids

In the United States, cyber-attacks represent a major threat to the electrical grid.[243] Hackers have a number of types of equipment they can target including a) Supervisory Control and Data Acquisition (SCADA) systems; b) Emergency Management Systems, including the Energy Control System, Transmission Management System, and Generation Management System; c) Distributed Control Systems (DCS) found at generating plants; d) Substation Automation Systems, located at transmission substations; and e) Distribution Automation systems, found at distribution substations or on distribution pole tops. Most of these are connected using the Internet protocols.

The World's First Cyber-Attack On Critical Infrastructure

In December of 2015, the Ukraine suffered a number of cyber-attacks across its society.[244] One of the attacks went after its electricity power grid.

The electrical grid in the Ukraine is composed of more than 14,230 miles of High Voltage Lines and 135 Substations. In 2015 the consumption of electricity was as high as 187 TWh.[245] The peak load of the system was around 32GW.[246] It was powered by 14 Thermal plants (102 units of 800-150MW); 4 nuclear plants (15 units 1000-440MW); 7 Hydroelectric plants (94 units 117-19MW); 3 Pumped Storage facilities (9 units 325-37MW) and 3 Cogeneration plants (9 units 250-100MW).

---

[241] When there was a collision off the coast of China between a recklessly driven Chinese fighter jet and a U.S. reconnaissance aircraft, and also when there was an accidental bombing of the Chinese embassy in Yugoslavia (7 May 1999). NATO bombing. Operation Allied Force. Location: Belgrade: 3 killed 27 injured. There was a fierce cyber-attack against the United States launched by so-called "patriot hackers" in China.

[242] This list is by no means complete.

[243] See Marcus H. Sachs "Securing the North American Electric Grid" Lecture, RSA (Rivest-Shamir-Adelman) Conference, San Francisco (13-17 February 2017).

[244] December 6th (Ministry of Finance; State Treasury; State Pension Fund); December 12th (State Executive Service; Internet Service Provider Volya); December 13th (Defense Ministry); December 14-15 (Railways); 16th (Ministry of Infrastructure); 20th (Sea Port Authority; Stock Exchange).

[245] Terawatt-hour (TWh) is 10^{12} Watt-Hours.

[246] GW is Gigawatt or 10^9 Watts.

There appears to be a single large junction approximately at Uman linking the East with the West of the country.

On December 23, 2015, the electrical power plant servicing Ivano-Frankivsk, Ukraine, suffered a cyber-attack. Seven (7) 110 kV substations, and twenty-three 35 kV substations had been disconnected:[247]

"We started receiving calls from different regional energy operators, which was a surprise because they were not connected on the grid. It meant that something unusual was happening. When we looked at our computers, we saw that the mouse cursors were moving by themselves, randomly, and were disconnecting the power from different substations, disconnecting switchers, lines and transformers. What to do? We received information there was external interference."[248]

This cyber-attack left 225,000 Ukrainians without electrical power. The attackers used privileged access. They corrupted ICS systems in both the control room and field and wiped (erased) servers throughout the IT environment. All of this was accomplished without the need for even one attacker to set foot inside the facility. The steps in conducting the attack were are follows: a) Spear Phishing;[249] b) Establish persistent remote access;[250] c) KillDisk;[251] d) Credential Harvesting;[252] e) VPN Hack;[253] f) Learn Operations;[254] and g) Attack.[255] These are described below:

Like all Spear Phishing campaigns, it started with an innocent official-looking document sent out from an official-sounding email address. The email began "In accordance with the Presidential Decree 15/2015" which is the standard opening for an official document in the Ukraine. It then goes on to mention national "mobilization" to "strengthen the Ukraine."[256] The malware was a macro inside a Microsoft Office document. Once the attachment was opened, the malware was injected, thus infecting the endpoints in the information system.

This gave the attackers a compromise of the workstations in three electricity distribution control centers.[257] Once inside, the next step was to harvest the access credentials (login and password information). These included both credentials from the local workstations, but also those used for remote

---

[247] Data from Kyivoblenergo. This name is an abbreviation for "Kiev Region Energy Organization" [Kiev-Oblast-Energia-Organizatsi].

[248] NATO, What Happens When a Power Plant Comes Under Cyber Attack?, Video, Interview with Bohdan Soicuk, Operational Dispatcher Service, Prykarpattyaoblenergo Power Plant, 2016.

[249] Targeted systems administrators at local utility companies; (the attackers pretended to be either vendors or government employees).

[250] Installation of RATs ("Remote Access Trojan") to establish backdoor access.

[251] Attackers then installed "KillDisk" malware, making it possible to overwrite most files upon command of the attacker, thus rendering the system un-bootable.

[252] The attackers then guessed and stole credentials until they were able to obtain an administrator ("admin") credentials ("Credentials Harvesting").

[253] Attackers captured Virtual Private Network credentials; this allowed them remote access into control room systems without having to be inside the facility.

[254] Using this access, the attackers monitored operations for weeks, learning how the system was operated.

[255] After understanding the system, the attackers executed a highly coordinated attack.

[256] Author's translation.

[257] Note that this Phishing attack was being conducted throughout the Ukraine, not only against Electricity Grid targets.

access[258] to the SCADA systems. With this access, the attackers installed malware in the SCADA systems.

At the same time, the attackers disabled the uninterruptible power supply protecting the control centers. Later on, when the control room employees were attempting to restore their systems, there was no power.

Next, corrupt firmware was uploaded and put on the Serial-to-Ethernet gateways in the substations. These are the gateways that take sensing information from equipment and put it on the Ethernet on its way to the Human Machine Interface used on the workstations of the operators. Once this bad firmware was installed, the gateways were blocked, making it impossible for anyone trying later to get the electricity turned back on remotely to close the breakers, because those commands would not go through. To "close" a breaker means to connect the circuit allowing electricity to flow.

Once the access was verified, then an operator connected in from the outside using the compromised remote access system. They logged in and then shut down the power by opening the circuit breakers. This was an option in "dialogue mode" for an operator. An "open" breaker means that the circuit is cut. Using this technique, the power in every substation was shut down.

Since by now the breakers could no longer be closed by remote commands (the firmware upload had blocked this capability), the only way to restore power was to send actual repair personnel to the substations to manually close the breakers allowing the electricity once again to flow, thus losing much time.

The SCADA system in the control room then was taken down by more cyber malware. This was done using a "wiper" program, one that erases all of the data on a machine. Once the data was erased from a system, the situation could have been saved by using a backup program and re-installing all of the system. But here, that could not happen because the power had been cut, and its backup, the uninterruptible power supply, had been put out of service. Remember that cutting the power also had cut the power to the control center itself.

The attack had enabled the attackers to disconnect electricity breakers and cut power in regions across Ukraine. They also were able to lock out the control room operators from their own software, making it impossible for them to do their work.[259]

This was an artful attack because it was able to use the existing SCADA control system to shut down the power with the credentials of an authorized operator. Merely gaining control of the workstations and the credentials had been sufficient. In a sense, this was a less sophisticated attack than one that might have involved use of special malware to corrupt the SCADA systems and cause them to operate in an unpredictable way. This had happened at Natanz in Iran from the StuxNet malware attack. But in the Ukraine, during this attack, the SCADA systems operated correctly—it was the false commands from the hijacked workstations that were the source of the problem.

---

[258] "Remote Access" is used when a worker wishes to access their workstation from the outside, such as when they are working at home.

[259] *Source*: CyberArk "Threat Analysis: The Ukraine Shutdown" Video (23 March 2017).

The nature of the cyber-attack tells us something about the attackers. It is clear that detailed thought was given into not only turning off the power, but also on making it difficult for the operators to *restore* it. In order to conduct this operation, the attackers would have had to know the restoration procedures, and perhaps have gamed out the attack at a test facility. The remote attacker posing as a legitimate operator would by necessity have been trained on operation of the system. They would need to know how to issue the right commands and how to read the display. If the attackers were operating from any part of the former Soviet Union, it might have been easier for them to have obtained this training on a parallel testbed, since the Ukraine uses primarily Russian equipment for its electricity grid.[260]

This event, the world's first cyber-attack against a critical infrastructure facility could have been prevented if the Ukrainian company had put into practice a number of well-known precautions including a) Protecting against the Spear Phishing attack, which is one of the most commonly used ways of getting malware into target information systems; b) Setting of strict segregation of the IT network from the SCADA network using either a total separation approach or implementation of a DMZ.[261] (This would have prevented the attackers going through the network and installing the "Wiper" software on the SCADA system.); c) Either completely blocking any remote access to the system or improving the security of remote access through actions such as two-factor authentication, and the requirement that any remote access session be approved *each time* by local staff, (sensitive facilities probably should allow zero remote access; none whatsoever); d) Adding well-known network security controls for the Serial-to-Ethernet gateways by using either a firewall or an access control list which, for example, would have blocked the TCP port that was used for firmware uploads (The "Boreas" vulnerability);[262] e) Not having their Uninterruptible Power Supply connected to their network, because that is how the hackers disabled the power supply, leaving the control room dark when it should have been working on recovery of systems.[263]

It is regrettable that all of the above security precautions were well-known at the time, and they would have been effective, at least against this particular cyber-attack.

In essence, this plan involved a) Taking complete control of the Control Room systems; b) Then opening breakers, disabling the uninterruptible Backup Power Supply; updating the firmware in substations to disable communications so that afterwards no one would be able to issue restore commands; and activating the KillDisk malware throughout the IT environment causing erasure of workstations; and as icing on the cake; and c) Launching a telephone Denial of Service Attack that would prevent customers from reporting outages. It was altogether a professional and well-executed cyber-attack

---

[260] This is mere speculation, but plausible.

[261] In computer security, a DMZ or demilitarized zone ("perimeter network"; "screened subnet") is a subnetwork that limits exposure of internal network parts to the outside. Outsiders can access only what is exposed. Other things are hidden.

[262] *See* discussion in Goce Kiseloski, Dobre Blazhevski, Veno Pachovski "Protecting Power Grids: Will There Be Light In The Future" Working Paper, School of Computer Science and Information Technology, Skpoje, noting: "The vulnerability of ICS devices has its roots decade ago. U.S. Department of Homeland Security identified vulnerability in ICSs back in 2007 dubbed Boreas. This vulnerability allows permanent disabling controllers by simply loading manipulated firmware." (undated). *See also* Ralph Langner *Stuxnet und die FOLGEN* Hamburg: Langner Communications GMBH (August 2017) p. 38 para. 1.

[263] *Source*: Langner Group.

and obviously was meant to send a "signal" to the Government of the Ukraine. This perhaps was a type of "demonstration" attack. In a real conflict, one assumes the blackouts would have been much more extensive.

So in addition to the Ukraine electrical grid attack being the "world's first cyber-attack against critical infrastructure" it also was the "world's first use of an electrical grid blackout to send a powerful diplomatic signal."[264]

The Texas Blackout Shows What Can Happen And How Fast

A sketch of how a power grid disaster in the United States would work is found in the February 2021 blackout in Texas. It was caused by severe cold weather, and eventually left 4.5 million homes and businesses without electric power. Texas operates around 46,500 miles of electricity transmission lines connected with around 5,000 substations. It relies on a single balancing authority,[265] and is interconnected via only two links to other grids because it wishes to maintain independence from the Federal Government.[266] It receives almost one-half of its power from burning natural gas (51,667 MW, 47.45%). Surprisingly, Texas is a relatively "Green" state as it gets 31,390 MW from Wind (28.83%). Other sources include 13,630 MW (12.52%) from coal, 5,153 MW (4.73%) from nuclear and 6,177 MW (5.67%) from the Sun. Each of these different sources of electrical energy act differently when subjected to extreme weather.

Within an 8-hour period on February 15th, the Texas grid lost 15 GW of power from natural gas, and lost 3 GW from wind. The wind farms did not perform well in the poor weather. Coal eventually lost around 5,000 MW. Nuclear and solar also lost some power, but their shares are insignificant compared to natural gas.

Initiating the crisis was the demand for electricity which grew dramatically because for many it was the primary means of keeping warm. For various reasons, starting on February 15th, the amount of generation capacity *unavailable* increased dramatically. It quickly jumped from 30,000 MW up to 55,000 MW and remained there until the middle of the 17th at which point it started slowly to decrease. By the 20th, it had been reduced to approximately 29,000 MW *unavailable* for use.

In the United States, the electrical grid must operate at 60~cycles per second. Of course there is some variation allowed. As more electricity is demanded, it causes a decrease in the frequency of the grid. Unless there is a massive sudden change, the actions of individuals, or even buildings is not noticeable. The frequencies of the electricity being generated are carefully monitored, as this data is used to ramp up or ease off the amount of electricity generated. In a simple sense, as more people turn on their electric heaters, the frequency is pulled down, this is sensed, and the generators are ordered to increase production. These adjustments happen within seconds. It is not unlike "plate spinning."[267]

---

[264] This assumes the intention to carry out the operation truly was from Russia and the overall context involved the tense situation in the Eastern Ukraine, which is of vital strategic importance to Russia.

[265] A balancing authority ensures, in real time, that power system demand and supply are finely balanced. The Electric Reliability Council of Texas (ERCOT) covers most, but not all, of Texas and consists of a single balancing authority. *Source*: U.S. Energy Information Administration.

[266] The United States has approximately 60 balancing authorities.

[267] "Plate spinning" is a circus manipulation art where a person spins plates, bowls and other flat objects on poles, without them falling off.

It is a marvel of engineering that this happens across the giant electrical grid and the granularity of the measurements are in the milliseconds. On February 15th in Texas, the grid frequency went up to a little more than 60.1 (cycles per second) at around 1:26 in the morning. By 1:42 am it had dropped back down to 60.0, the standard rate. The term electricity companies use for turning off the power is "Load Shedding". By 1:45 am, only three minutes later, the frequency had dropped to 59.88, and this triggered a "Load Shed" order at around 1:47 am. Load shedding is a major event for an electricity utility because it means that power is being cut to customers.

Who gets their power cut? There is a system of prioritization, so certain critical facilities, such as hospitals, may remain connected to the grid. But a family living in their house will be cut. After all, most persons were sleeping at the time.

Unfortunately, this cut in power was not enough. The demand for electricity continued to jump up, thus pulling down the frequency of the grid, as more power was demanded. By 1:51 am, the frequency had dropped below the critical frequency of 59.4 cps. This is a type of "red line" for the grid, because as the frequency continued to drop from 60 cps, the electrical generation activity of the power station was rising to compensate, but at 59.4 cps, the maximum generation capacity of the power plant is reached, and it turns off as a safety measure in order to prevent damage to itself. To stop this, the response must be immediate Load Shedding, and that is what happened.

At 1:55 am, the grid frequency still was operating at 59.32 cps, dangerously low. So this massive shutdown of parts of the Texas grid had happened in a little less than nine minutes.

Demand for power continued to pull down the grid frequency and it remained in the 59.32 cps range through four more minutes, until 1:55 am at which time a *third* Shed Load order was executed. At that point, the grid frequency started to recover and by 1:57 it was in the 59.7 range, and by 1:59 it was at the 59.95 cps level, at which point a *fourth* Shed Load command was executed! By 2:01-2:02 am the frequency was still in the 59.5 range but by 2:03 it had recovered fully to 60cps and by 2:05 was up to 60.19 cps. The severe Shed Load orders had been executed between 1:51 to 1:59 am.

Only 8-9 minutes had been required to trigger the blackout.

The Load Shedding had allowed the total generation capacity of the grid to drop from 71,000 MW on the evening of February 14th to approximately 48,000 MW (-32%) the evening of the 15th where it stayed until mid-day on the 17th, when it rose again by the next day to around 65,000 MW. The Load Shed at first was small, but by the second order had jumped to 10,000 MW. It then rose to around 18,000 MW and hit as high as 20,000 MW the evening of the 15th and mid-day on the 16th. By the 17th, it was falling but remained at around 15,000 MW mid-day, then fell to zero by mid-night on the morning of the 18th.

The economic impact on the electricity industry was substantial. Between February 13th and 19th, the spot price for natural gas went up from a three-year average of less than $5 per MMBtu[268] to more than $230 dollars per MMBtu. This was a severe disruption to the market for natural gas.

---

[268] MMBTU is Million British Thermal Units (BTU); 1 BTU is the amount of heat required to rise the temperature of one pound of water by one degree Fahrenheit.

This change in the availability of electricity also had a substantial effect on its marketing. In Texas, as elsewhere, different companies supplying the grid purchase electricity from each other on an "as needed" basis. The prices remain generally low, but they are dynamically adjusted according to demand. If there is a "spike" in demand, then the spot price for wholesale electricity will go up. This is accounted for on a regular basis, as companies buy back and forth from each other, and reconcile periodically. On February 13th, the Texas Wholesale Electricity Spot Price jumped up to $1,000 per MWh.[269] It then quickly jumped as high as $8,900 per MWh which is an extraordinarily high price. By the 14th it was back down to the $900–$1,000 range, but then as night fell it jumped back up to $2,000, then $5,500, then $8,900 again. On the 15th, the price dropped for a short while to $4,000, but quickly jumped back up to $8,950. As the Load Shedding actions were undertaken, the spot price dropped back down as low as $1,500 but that evening jumped back up to the "ceiling" of $9,000 *and remained at that level* until the afternoon of the 19th at which time it dropped back down to a little above zero, which is the customary rate. For some facilities that had contracts to pay for electricity at a "market rate" instead of a fixed rate, they were subjected to some "Sticker Shock" when they received their electricity bills.

The lesson from Texas is that the electricity grid is more fragile than perhaps one may think. Out of range events such as an untoward surge in demand can cause a cascade of blackouts. It also indicates that an enemy attack against the U.S. electric grid would take place ideally in very cold weather, when electricity demand is at its highest. This would increase the chance of a catastrophic failure.

The Mumbai Blackout Confirms the Threat of Pre-Positioned Malware

India and China have a border dispute in India's North East. Some of the problem has its origin in the break-up of India and the spin-off of Pakistan in 1947.[270] In 1963 territory to the east of the Karakoram Range bordering Ladakh and Baltistan was ceded by Pakistan to China, but this was not recognized by India. This is the source of the border dispute. The problem stems from China's attempts unilaterally to seize Indian territory. A tense stand-off eventually led to several Indian deaths at the hands of the invading Chinese. Why these two great nations would have a military conflict over this desolate and unpopulated wasteland is difficult to understand. The conflict has been simmering for decades.

As the conflict and argumentation intensified, Chinese hacker groups developed a plan for a cyber-attack on India's power grid. In keeping with commonly used penetration techniques, the hackers set up a number of typosquat[271] domains. These were mimics of the domain names for Indian electrical power companies. For example, NTPC Limited is an Indian company in the electricity supply business. The typosquat used the the hackers was ntpc-co.com whereas the genuine web address was ntpc.co.in. There were at least 15 domains registered this way, and most were hosted by the same company HKBN Enterprise Solutions HK Limited. Three were hosted by EHOSTICT, another com-

---

[269] MegaWatt Hour.

[270] The British Indian Empire was partitioned into the Dominion of India and the Dominion of Pakistan.

[271] The term "typosquat" is a combination of Type and Squat. In Internet parlance, squatting is taking hold of the domain of another, and then refusing to release it until paid. It generally refers to a domain name that is similar enough to the targeted domain that the two easily are confused. Type (typo) refers to the way which squatting takes place, which is by slight modification of a protected domain name. An example of a typosquat would be Update-Microsoft. com or Microsofts.com.

pany in China.[272] The registrations were made by WEBCC, which offers registration for a number of domains such as ".cc", ".cn", ".sg", ".tw" and a number in Chinese characters such as ".香港"(xiang-gang) (Hong Kong), and ".公司" (gongsi.xianggang) (Company, Hong Kong).[273] The domains were registered through eznowdns.com, an "uncommon authoritative name server."[274]

The function of these installations was to work as Command and Control (C2) servers that direct malware covertly pre-positioned in target information systems. C2 servers work approximately in this sequence a) An exploit is found to load malware into a target information system; b) Once the malware is in position, it collects information about the host system it has infected; c) The malware then sends out signals to the C2 server; these signals contain important information about the targeted system (location; type of applications; name; other characteristics); d) The C2 server then "decides" if the target system shall become a target for attack; e) If yes, then the malware is sent a signal to activate; f) If activated, then the malware module begins to download and execute further malicious code to do things such as exfiltrate data, erase all of the data in the information system, change important settings, steal credentials, etc.[275] g) If not, then the malware remains sleeping and perhaps at some point erases itself.

If the presence of the malware within the target system is not known, nevertheless this type of operation may be detected when the concealed malware sends out its signals to the C2 server.[276] At some point in the host environment, the signal must pass through a router. But routers can be trained to look for specific IP addresses or even for IP addresses that are not "ordinary." For example, if the process within the host system in India generally is designed to interact with workstations within its facility, then why would a packet of information be heading out the door to an unknown server registered in Hong Kong?

Attempts are made to avoid this type of detection, and this is done by spacing out the signals to only 2-3 per day, and from a data point of view, these are very small messages, probably encrypted.

But this type of flying under the radar does not always work.

---

[272] It is not known when these domains were first operational.

[273] Using pinyin for romanization.

[274] *See* analysis by Insikt Group, *Cyber Threat Analysis China*, White Paper, Recorded Future, Doc. No. CTA-CN-2021-0228, *hereinafter* "Insikt Rpt.". *NB:* A name server refers to the server component of the Domain Name System (DNS), one of the two principal namespaces of the Internet. The most important function of DNS servers is the translation (resolution) of human-memorable domain names (example.com) and hostnames into the corresponding numeric Internet Protocol (IP) addresses (93.184.216.34), the second principal name space of the Internet which is used to identify and locate computer systems and resources on the Internet.

[275] *See* Kaspersky "ShadowPad: How Attackers hide Backdoor in Software used by Hundreds of Large Companies around the World" cyber news blog at kaspersky.com: "Following the installation of an infected software update, the malicious module would start sending DNS-queries to specific domains (its command and control server) at a frequency of once every eight hours. The request would contain basic information about the victim system (user name, domain name, host name). If the attackers considered the system to be 'interesting,' the command server would reply and activate a fully-fledged backdoor platform that would silently deploy itself inside the attacked computer. After that, on command from the attackers, the backdoor platform would be able to download and execute further malicious code."

[276] *See* Insikt Rpt., ("Using a combination of proactive ... infrastructure detections, domain analysis, and ... Traffic Analysis" p. 1).

The advantage of this type of "scatter seeds then evaluate" approach for the attacker lies in the lack of discrimination in the initial attack. Rather than being forced to do the extensive research in advance to find the precise cyber-locations[277] of the target systems, one may merely spew out a giant attack all over the Internet, and this attack may have little if any need for discriminating between systems before infecting them. In the Mumbai power matter, the attackers were using ShadowPad, which is a "backdoor planted in a server management software ... used by hundreds of large businesses around the world."[278] The software was planted in NetSarang[279] technology. It was possible for someone to determine that there were a large number of IPs resolving to Indian critical infrastructure.[280]

It appears that these China-based C2 servers were able to pre-position malicious software on "10 distinct Indian power sector organizations, including 4 of the 5 Regional Load Dispatch Centres ... responsible for operation of the power grid."[281] This happened at approximately the same time as Indian soldiers were fighting off encroachments from invading Chinese troops near Chushul. In May of 2020, the tense stand-off resulted in the first combat deaths between China and India in 45 years.

On October 13, 2020, the electricity failed in central Mumbai. It happened in the center of the vibrant business district. Train and emergency services had their electrical power disrupted. The stock exchange itself managed to continue operation, most likely because it had reserve back-up power, but its trading volume took a nose dive. The power outage started at 10 am and lasted for two hours. At this time, the Covid crisis was at its peak in Mumbai, and as hospitals lost power, there was a sudden wave of fear and panic. The power outage had hit India's financial capital, and surrounding areas.

An investigation by Tata Power later determined there was a simultaneous tripping of circuits at two substations, Kalwa and Kharghar. This caused a large dip in grid frequency in the Mumbai transmission system and led to a cut off of the power supply.

The Maharashtra Government investigated the blackout and concluded it was the result of cyber sabotage. Its Home Minister, Anil Deshmukh provided a briefing based on a confidential report concerning the blackout incident:

"Fourteen Trojan Horse malware [programs] may have been installed in the server. Similarly, 8 GB [of] unaccounted data may have been transferred from [a] foreign server. ... Many blacklisted IP Firms may have tried to log into [Indian power] server[s]."

The research had been done by Ernst & Young working with a cybercrime unit of the Maharashtra government.[282] The 100-page preliminary report from the cybercrime unit depicted three poten-

---

[277] IP Addresses.

[278] *See* Kaspersky "ShadowPad: How Attackers hide Backdoor in Software used by Hundreds of Large Companies around the World" cyber news blog at kaspersky.com.

[279] Netsarang Computer at www.netsarang.com. This was discovered in July, 2017 by Kaspersky Lab.

[280] Insikt Rpt., Ibid.

[281] Insikt Rpt. *assessing that* "Pre-positioning on energy assets may support several potential outcomes, including geo-strategic signaling during heightened bilateral tensions, supporting influence operations, or as a precursor to kinetic escalation."

[282] Several months later, March 2, 2021, the Union Power Minister R. K. Singh stated that the power outage had been caused by human error and that there was "no evidence" that the attack had been caused by China. Governments and utilities often routinely deny or cover-up cyber-attacks as they are reluctant to acknowledge vulnerabilities.

tial sabotage methods, a malware attack on the server of the Maharashtra State Electricity Board (MSEB), a transfer of 8 GB of unaccounted data from a foreign server to the MSEB, and attempts by several blacklisted IP addresses to login into the MSEB server.

After the attack, it was reported that the Central Electricity Authority sent out alerts informing operators that 40 sub-stations had detected malware entering their information systems. India's Computer Emergency Response Team (CERT-In) reported that Command and Control (C2) servers in China were making contact with systems in the Telangana State Load Dispatch Centre. It identified the presence of the ShadowPad malware. Later India's National Critical Information Infrastructure Protection Centre (NCIIPC) issued a warning pointing to a Chinese state-sponsored group and circulated a list of IPs and registered domains that should be blocked. It advised all power utilities to take protection and safety measures. The Indian operators dutifully took the list of Chinese C2 servers and reconfigured their firewalls to shut them out. As part of the house-cleaning, all of the control centers on the electricity grid not only blocked the listed IPs and domains, they also scanned all of their software to search for any installed malware. Some installations removed discovered malware from their systems. Their firewall settings then were strengthened even further. In addition, other protective measures were put in place.[283] India is re-evaluating its use of Chinese-manufactured equipment in its grid.

It was not the first incident. The Telangana power system had been attacked previously by hackers in April of 2019. Their Greater Hyderabad service area had been subjected to a ransomware incident.[284]

The message was clear. Shutting down an electricity grid is a possibility for China in its attacks on India. In diplomatic terms, the two-hour blackout was considered by many to be a "warning" to India.

Attacks On America's Grid Will Come From Nations And Terrorists

The type of cyber-attack that may be launched by an opponent against the United States also varies with the capabilities of the attacker. It is dependent on such factors as a) the strength and motivation of the attacker; b) their strategic situation; c) the intensity of the conflict; d) the type of effect sought, *e.g.,* either tangible or primarily symbolic; and e) the co-dependency of the cyber-attack with other events.

Non-State Actors Have Limited Means But Can Do Substantial Damage

The Non-State Actor does not have the capabilities of a superpower, or of any Nation State.[285] It lacks the engineering skills, money, and infrastructure to develop a cyber-weapon as complex and sophisticated as Stuxnet. This paucity of resources available to devote to a cyber-attack means that it will be more difficult to engage in that comprehensive cyber-intelligence work needed to choose a target and determine its vulnerabilities. Without automatic network scanning capabilities, it would be problematical to pre-position logic bombs into the American electrical grid. In addition, it would be much

---

[283] The Indian power companies were not specific regarding the details of their counter-measures.

[284] The Indians did not pay. They simply suspended services for 3-4 days while they rebuilt their IT system.

[285] If the Non-State Actors were acting on behalf of a Nation State, then we would consider this to be a Nation State attack.

more challenging to assemble the resources and skills needed for systems development of a sophisticated cyber-weapon such as StuxNet. This would make it difficult to create a device-specific attack.

This leaves us to expect that a Non-State Actor cyber-attack against the electrical grid of the United States would have the following characteristics: a) It would be organized by a small team; b) There is a high probability that the attack would take place on-site instead of remotely; c) Social engineering and recruitment of fellow-travelers might well be used to gain site access and to collect intelligence; d) Attacks are more probable against Civil Society targets instead of against the military because (i) there is a perceived lesser change of devastating retaliation; and (ii) attacks against Civil Society targets have a larger psychological and propaganda effect; e) The ability to attack the entire electrical grid of the United States is non-existent, consequently attacks would at most be against a regional facility, although multiple attacks, perhaps 2–3, might be launched in different locations at the same time.

In sum, cyber-attacks by Non-State Actors against the entire electrical grid are an unlikely event; any attacks against regional (or city) electrical grids from a cyber point of view are more probable but would be unsophisticated and primitive.

Iran Has A Proven Record Of Large Cyber-Attacks

The capabilities of Iran for conducting a cyber-attack are considerably better than those of the rag-tag bands of terrorists and revolutionary brigades mulling around the world. For a small country, it has scored a few notable cyber-attacks, including the highly-successful "Shamoon" attack in 2012 against Saudi Aramco and Qatar's RasGas. Also known as W32.DistTrack, the computer virus scooped up valuable files, transmitted them to the attacker, erased all of the data on the infected system, then wiped out its master boot record, making it impossible to re-start those computer workstations running Saudi Arabia's national oil company. The attackers claimed to be the "Cutting Sword of Justice." More than 30,000 workstations were wiped clean. The attack had been timed to coincide with Ramadan, so there were less personnel on site, allowing the malware to spread more extensively without being detected. Note that this timing was generally contextual in nature, and thus did not require extensive intelligence-gathering *inside* the targeted facilities.

This attack was successful, but also may show the limitations in Iranian skills, at least at that time: a) The attack was a general attack against workstations, and not directed at specific process control (SCADA) equipment, which would have required more sophistication in the engineering of the payload; b) Although wiping out the hard disks of workstations certainly qualifies as an attack, the most it accomplished was a week's delay while Saudi technologists restored the information infrastructure, implying that although the attack was an irritation, ultimately it did little harm; and c) The attackers publicized on PasteBin.com[286] the purpose of the attack and their motivation; this done before the attack took place, thus lessening or eliminating altogether the chances of anonymity.

Nevertheless, thus far, Iran has a proven cyber-attack record in: a) website defacement; b) data breach and theft; c) denial of service attacks; and d) destructive attacks, such as a "wiper" attack that will erase the victim's information systems. For example, apart from the Saudi Aramco (2012) attack, Iran

---

[286] "We ... an anti-oppression hacker group ... want to hit the ... Al-Saud corrupt regime [that has] ... hands ... infected with the blood of innocent children and people."

has scored a number of attacks against the United States. These include: a) the 2014 attack against the Sands Casino in Las Vegas which destroyed data on its internal network;[287] b) a number of DDoS attacks against U.S. banks (Bank of America; Wells Fargo; PNC Financial; SunTrust Banks) between 2011 and 2013 (done under the name "Qassam Cyber Fighters"); c) massive information operations (influence activities) involving Twitter and Facebook between 2009 and 2019; d) cyber-espionage against the U.S. Department of Labor, and the Federal Energy Regulatory Commission; and e) access and manipulation of the SCADA systems of the Bowman Dam in Rye, New York in 2013. This latter attack indicates Iranian efforts to develop cyber-attack capabilities against critical infrastructure.

We can expect that an Iranian cyber-attack against the electrical grid of the United States would have the following characteristics: a) It likely would rely on use of relatively indiscriminate tools for access that could be employed from a distance, such as the use of phishing emails; b) Iran would focus on information systems disruption and then rely on the secondary effects against the deeper infrastructure of the electrical grid, rather than attempting to cause those secondary effects itself; c) Iran's most probable attack point using cyber would be low-criticality services such as those market systems involved in the buying and selling (brokering) of electricity; d) Iran's progress in science and technology[288] would suggest it has the technical capabilities to target high-criticality systems such as Supervisory Control and Data Acquisition Systems (SCADA) or medium-criticality systems such as Substation Automation or Energy Management Systems;[289] e) Iran has a moderate chance of inflicting temporary but substantial damage to the electrical grid, primarily in its supporting information processing operations; f) It is unlikely that Iran would be capable of attacking the entire electrical grid of the United States.

In sum, Iran can be a serious irritant against the electrical grid, but does not have yet the capability of launching a coordinated nation-wide cyber-attack. Iran should be considered capable of doing substantial damage to secondary processes associated with electricity generation.

It is expected that under current U.S. policy, Iran will develop thermonuclear weapons within half a decade or so along with the missile capabilities necessary for their delivery. As such, Iran theoretically could explode such a weapon in the atmosphere over the United States causing an electromagnetic pulse (EMP) to harm significant portions of the electrical grid. It is assessed that: a) Iran has the technical understanding of how to employ EMP effects generated from setting off atomic bombs in the atmosphere and continues to seek acquisition of an EMP device that might be used, providing it could get it delivered into the United States; b) Iran continues to work hard to develop cyber exploits into the U.S. electrical grid and has been successful in the implantation of malware; c) In spite of its relentless jingoistic posturing, Iranian leadership would be cautious of the response from the United States, which without question would react forcefully.

---

[287] The owner (53%) of the Sands Casino at the time was Sheldon Adelson (1933–2021), a supporter of Israel.

[288] In 2013, 1,505,030 engineering students in university; 509 doctorates produced in 2012 (latest data); exceeds Turkey in number of scientific (refereed) publications cited (2008-2012); around 40 scientific industrial parks. *Source*: UNESCO Science Report: Towards 2030 (2015). In addition, the Government of Iran has developed a number of offensive cyber capabilities including the IRGC Electronic Warfare and Cyber Defence Organization; Basij Cyber Council (paramilitary cyber force); Cyber Defence Command; Ministry of Intelligence and Security (MOIS), similar to the U.S. National Security Agency (NSA) and Islamic Revolutionary Guard Corps (IRGC) with overseas cyber activities.

[289] Iran has by now had a chance to reverse-engineer the StuxNet.

In Cyber, China Is A Mortal Threat To The United States

The People's Republic of China appears to be the world's leader in cyber-espionage, at least if measured by volume of pilfered information.[290] In addition, it is the world's largest manufacturer and consumer of electrical power and electrical equipment. It is reasonable to assume that in the course of China's R&D on electrical grid systems, it has conducted extensive technical research (patent analysis; tear-downs of foreign-manufactured equipment; evaluation of operational procedures; industrial espionage of newer technologies). In addition, after the Gulf Wars, China's military establishment adopted a "crash" program to develop cyber capabilities. China also has sent to the United States many scientists who have penetrated the control chambers of America's electrical grid operators. This access has given China's agents numerous opportunities to collect extensive intelligence on the U.S. grid, including both operating and recovery procedures as well as characteristics (specific machine and hardware identities) of its supporting ICT control systems.

China has the money, national laboratory network, trained personnel, and strategic necessity to develop the highest quality cyber-weapons capable of severely disrupting the electrical grid throughout the United States. The Chinese diaspora in the United States has placed potential Chinese agents[291] into virtually every part of the engineering and R&D associated with the electrical grid. In addition, China is not deterred from hitting the United States, as seen in the massive cyber-attack launched in retaliation for the April 2011 collision between a U.S. intelligence platform and a Chinese jet. The Chinese pilot flew recklessly close to the U.S. aircraft and was said to have crashed, killing the pilot, although the death was not confirmed.[292] Shortly thereafter, the United States suffered a number of massive cyber-attacks. These were organized and supported by the Government of China, although under the laughable fiction they were "spontaneous" actions of patriotic and concerned Chinese citizens. The attacks, motivated by such slogans as "Hack it Great Chinese!!", and hastily constructed web-sites such as KillUSA.com were meant to serve as a warning to the United States.

Another factor in understanding the danger of cyber-attacks made by China is the contextual framework of its overall strategy, or lack of one. In the past half-decade, Chinese diplomacy has done what no other nation was capable of doing: It stimulated formation of a cooperative alliance-like system between Japan, India, Vietnam, South Korea, The Philippines and others aimed at resisting Chinese hegemonic expansionism. These countries combined have more population, more technology, and more money than China.[293] Rather than physical confrontation, China prefers as a default use of "soft power," *e.g.,* propaganda and corruption of elites by bribery. In Texas, Chinese owned corporations have purchased very large tracts of land and are setting up wind-farms to take advantage of subsidies for green energy paid by the U.S. government. As such, we can expect there will be no let-up of in-

---

[290] *See* "We assess that China presents a prolific and effective cyber-espionage threat, possesses substantial cyber-attack capabilities ... [and] can cause localized, temporary disruptions to critical infrastructure within the United States" ODNI 2021 Rpt. p. 8, para. 5-6

[291] The Government of China uses the extended family remaining in China to coerce cooperation from family members living in the United States, even if they are U.S. citizens.

[292] *See* Shirley A. Kan, et al., China-U.S. Aircraft Collision Incident of April 2001: Assessments and Policy Implications CRS Report for Congress, No. RL30946 (10 October 2001).

[293] *See* extensive discussion and analysis in Edward N. Luttwak, *The Rise of China vs. the Logic of Strategy* (Cambridge: Belknap Press, 2012).

tensive cyber-espionage conducted by the Chinese government itself against the United States and its industries, including the electrical grid.

We can expect that a cyber-attack by China against electricity in the United States would have the following characteristics: a) China has the capability to disable all or at least very large parts of the electrical grid (Eastern, Western, Texas Grid Interconnects) as well as target specific areas, such as power in a single metropolitan area; b) A massive cyber-attack against the entire electrical grid would take place within the context of a general war between the United States and China, but a large-scale conventional or nuclear war is highly unlikely; c) More likely is a massive cyber-attack against the entire U.S. electric grid prior to the outbreak of conventional or nuclear war, or during an extreme international crisis, to deter or defeat the U.S. with "gray-zone aggression" instead of or prior to outbreak of a "real shooting war" consistent with China's military doctrine that Cyber Warfare is an unprecedented and decisive Revolution in Military Affairs; d) China is prepared to use targeted attacks against America's electrical grid as a stand-alone method of fighting what it calls "U.S. Hegemony"; e) There is a moderate chance of some irritating event such as an accidental boat collision on the high sea leading to a repeat of the Hainan Island incident, leading to another fabricated "patriotic" cyber-attack against the United States, perhaps against a small portion of the electrical grid (but not against the entire system, and only if there was significant loss of Chinese life in the incident); f) China might engage in a cyber-attack against electrical grid systems of low-criticality as a symbolic warning if it feared an attack from the United States; g) China may engage in brokering of vulnerability information about the electrical grid in the United States as an unscrupulous profit-making activity, with exploits being sold to Non-State Actors or nations such as Russia.

Russia Is The Best Prepared To Defend Against Cyber-Attack And Use Cyber As A Strategic Weapon

Russia does not have the amount of money or human resources of China but it does have superior strategy-making capabilities. In addition, Russia has a long-proven track record of being able to develop world-class offensive capabilities in any field using a fraction of the resources of the United States. Russia does not brag and publicize its cyber warfare capabilities as does the United States, but from examination of publicly available documents, we know that if needed, it can closely integrate its military with all resources in civil society, including all of its hackers.[294]

Russian cybersecurity companies routinely monitor the world's Internet, and are sensitive to any threats. Unlike the United States, Russian law passively encourages development of robust hacking skills because it is not illegal for its citizens to hack computing resources *outside* in other countries.[295] Finally, Russia has a reliable habit of *always* launching a counter-strike if it has been attacked, and this includes in the cyber domain.[296]

---

[294] *See* ODNI 2021 RPT. p. 10, para. 8-9 ("Russia will remain a top cyber threat … [and] continues to target critical infrastructure, including underwater cables and industrial control systems … [giving it] ability to damage infrastructure during a crisis").

[295] The criminal system in Russia successfully deters Russian hackers from applying their skills against Russian targets.

[296] For example, recent discussion of Russian interference in the U.S. election system rarely mentioned the preceding use of the Internet and social media by the United States as official policy to influence events inside Russia.

We can expect that a cyber-attack by Russia against the electrical grid of the United States would have the following characteristics: a) Russia is capable of launching a massive attack that would shut down in one coordinated attack at least 80% of America's electrical grid; b) Russia has developed the capabilities of attacking high-criticality SCADA systems in the electrical grid, as well as all other systems; c) Russia likely knows more about EMP than the United States given its extensive testing and development of EMP weapons;[297] d) A massive Russian attack against the entire electrical grid would occur within the context of a major strategic conflict between Russia and the United States; e) During an extreme international crisis, a massive Russian cyber-attack against the entire U.S. electric grid prior to the outbreak of conventional or nuclear war is likely, to deter or defeat the U.S. with "gray-zone aggression" instead of or prior to outbreak of a "real shooting war" consistent with Russia's military doctrine that Cyber Warfare is an unprecedented and decisive Revolution in Military Affairs; f) Russia's response to a major cyber-attack made by the United States is likely to be at least proportional but more likely disproportional and massive, possibly even resulting in Russian nuclear retaliation as threatened in their military doctrine; g) Like China, Russia possibly would use a targeted cyber-attack against a low-criticality electrical grid system as a show of force and warning to deter escalation in a conflict by the United States; h) Russia likely has experimented with placement of cyber logic-bombs in portions of America's electrical grid; i) Russia is more capable than other countries in placement of assets (human agents) into critical parts of the management structure of the American electrical grid.

For U.S. relations with both nations, Russia and China, the emergence of viable paths to cyber-attacks against critical infrastructure as a new strategic weapon has lowered the barriers to conflict, and presents a heightened danger with the potential to disrupt the long-standing balancing calculus dependent upon nuclear deterrence.

---

[297] *See* reports of the 1961 testing in Russia at Vasily N. Greetsai, Andrey H. Kozlovsky, Vadim M. Kuvshinnikov, Vladimir M. Loborev, Oleg A. Parfenov, Oleg A. Tarasov, and Leonid N. Zdoukhov "Response of Long Lines to Nuclear High-Altitude Electromagnetic Pulse (HEMP)" 40 IEEE Transactions on Electromagnetic Compatibility pp. 348–354 (1998).

PHASE	SCALE OF CYBER ATTACK AGAINST ELECTRICAL GRID		CHINA	RUSSIA	IRAN	NON-STATE ACTOR (TERRORIST)
INTELLIGENCE (TARGET SELECTION)	CYBER ESPIONAGE	NETWORK MAPPING	YES	YES	YES	NO
		DEVICE IDENTIFICATION	YES	YES	NO	NO
PREPARATION	ENGINEER MALWARE		YES	YES	NO	NO
	PRE-POSITION LOGIC BOMBS		YES	YES	NO	NO
SITE ACCESS	SOCIAL ENGINEERING ATTACK		YES	YES	NO	YES
	ZERO DAY EXPLOITS		YES	YES	YES	NO
ATTACK	KINETIC ATTACK	KINETIC ATTACK	NO	NO	NO	YES
		DEVICE SPECIFIC	YES	YES	NO	NO
	STAND ALONE CYBER ATTACK	INFORMATION OPERATIONS	YES	YES	NO	NO
		MASS BRIGADE	YES	NO	NO	NO
		DDOS AND SIMILAR	YES	YES	YES	YES
	IN TANDEM WITH CONVENTIONAL OR NUCLEAR FORCES	MILITARY TARGET	YES	YES	NO	NO
		CIVIL SOCIETY TARGET	YES	YES	NO	YES

TABLE 1 PHASES OF CYBER ATTACK AND CAPABILITIES OF ATTACKERS

LEVEL OF CRITICALITY	CYBER VULNERABILITY POINTS IN THE ELECTRICAL GRID	
HIGHEST	SUPERVISORY CONTROL AND DATA ACQUISITION SYSTEMS (SCADA	REAL-TIME MEASUREMENTS FROM SUBSTATIONS
		SEND CONTROL SIGNALS TO EQUIPMENT (CIRCUIT BREAKERS; OTHER CONTROL SYSTEMS)
MEDIUM	SUBSTATION AUTOMATION SYSTEMS	CONTROL OF LOCAL EQUIPMENT
	ENERGY MANAGEMENT SYSTEMS	REAL TIME ANALYSIS OF RELIABILITY OF SYSTEMS
LOW	MARKET SYSTEMS	BUYING AND SELLING OF ELECTRICITY

TABLE 2 LEVELS OF CRITICALITY FOR INFORMATION SYSTEMS IN THE ELECTRICAL GRID

FIGURE 1 SYSTEM DEVELOPMENT CYCLE FOR MALWARE

SUPPLEMENTARY ROLE FOR CYBER	NUCLEAR AND CONVENTIONAL WEAPONS	WARFARE BETWEEN NATION STATES; CYBER IN SUPPORTING ROLE TO ASSIST IN TRADITIONAL COMBAT
CYBER-ONLY OPERATIONS	CYBER KINETIC ATTACKS	CYBER ATTACKS DESIGNED TO HAVE REAL-WORLD PHYSICAL CONSEQUENCES; NEW AND DANGEROUS REALM OF NATION-STATE CONFLICT
	INFORMATION OPERATIONS	USE OF CYBER FOR INJECTING PROPAGANDA OR MANIPULATING SOCIAL MEDIA AND THE POLITICAL MOVEMENTS DEPENDENT UPON IT.
	CYBER ESPIONAGE	PASSIVE COLLECTION OF GOVERNMENT, MILITARY, AND COMMERCIAL INFORMATION. MONITORING OF ONE'S NATIONALS LIVING IN OTHER NATION STATES.

TABLE 3 CYBER KINETIC ATTACKS REPRESENT POTENTIALLY A NEW FORM OF WARFARE BETWEEN NATION STATES

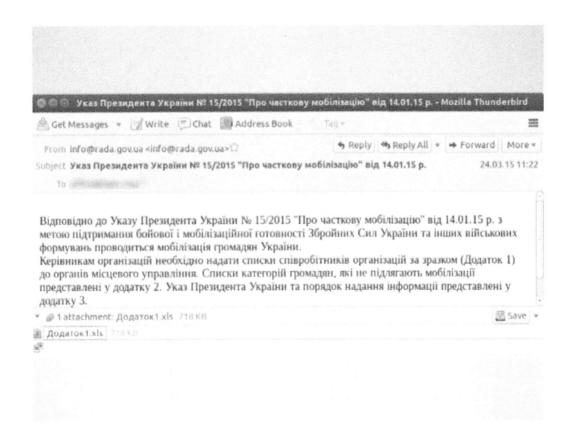

FIGURE 2 A COPY OF THE PFISHING EMAIL SENT TO THE UKRANIAN GRID OPERATORS (THE LANGUAGE APPEARS AS MIGHT AN OFFICIAL GOVERNMENT DOCUMENT)

III

PHYSICAL SECURITY: THE ELECTRIC GRID'S DIRTY LITTLE SECRET

by Michael Mabee

One of the easiest ways for a terrorist organization, a state actor or a homegrown radicalized group to really hurt the United States and kill thousands, tens of thousands or even millions of people would be a coordinated physical attack against the U.S. electric grid. What is perhaps most disturbing is that the government has known for over 4 decades about the vulnerability of the electric grid to physical attacks, yet very little has been done to protect it.

The North American electric grid is an amazing human accomplishment. It is the largest machine in the history of the world, built piece by piece over many generations. This machine is literally the life support system for the United States.

The "electric grid" is actually thousands of entities, both public and private sector, that operate in an interconnected system to facilitate the generation, transmission and distribution of electrical power. The grid is made up of power generation—such as nuclear, coal and gas-fired power plants, hydroelectric facilities, wind turbines and solar farms, high voltage transmission lines that span long distances across the country and local distribution lines which bring the power to our homes and businesses.

This interconnected—and vulnerable—patchwork is what allows the United States to support her human population. Everything that enables 330 million people in the country to survive is wholly reliant on the electric grid. All of our critical infrastructures, including food, water, fuel, transportation, financial, communications, medical systems and our national defense infrastructure, are all completely dependent on the electric grid. This cannot be overemphasized: *Our national security is dependent on the electric grid.*

Much of the electric grid is self-regulated (similarly to Wall Street). The federal government under current law can't mandate that "the grid" protect itself from threats. The North American Electric Reliability Corporation (NERC) is a not-for-profit corporation. It acts as the self-regulatory organization "whose mission is to assure the reliability of the bulk power system (BPS) in North America." The Federal Energy Regulatory Commission (FERC) is an independent federal agency that regulates the interstate transmission of electricity, natural gas, and oil. FERC's specific authority over the electric grid is to "oversee the reliability of the bulk power system." The regulatory scheme of the grid between NERC and FERC is mind-numbingly complex. (Just the way most industries prefer their relationship with the federal government to be.)

Just to add another layer of complexity, the bulk power system consists of approximately 1,500 entities operating at 100 kilovolts or higher which are regulated by NERC, overseen by FERC. However, the bulk power system does not include distribution to end-users. Distribution is under the jurisdiction of state public utility commissions. This means that there are over 60 state and federal government agencies as well as a number of non-profit corporations involved in the regulation of the electric grid. Talk about herding cats! Finally, there are almost incomprehensible complexities in the regulation of electricity markets.

In the current self-regulatory regime, the electric utility industry writes their own standards, which are then enforced by NERC. NERC is funded and largely controlled by the industry it regulates.

Believe it or not, there are no physical security requirements for most of the electric grid. It is just a big, fat, juicy, soft target. The only enforceable federal standard that exists applies to *only a few* facilities in the "Bulk Power System" (the interstate transmission system). There are no physical security standards for the generation or distribution portions of the electric grid, and most of the transmission system is exempted from the one weak standard that does exist.

The 2013 Metcalf Attack

At approximately 1:00 A.M. on April 16, 2013, a major PG&E transformer substation in Metcalf California was attacked. The attack was well-planned and sophisticated. Former Federal Energy Regulatory Commission (FERC) Chairman Jon Wellinghoff called the attack "the most significant incident of domestic terrorism involving the grid that has ever occurred."[298]

The attackers were never caught. They entered a manhole and cut communications wires before exiting and using precisely aimed rifle fire, damaged the substation, taking it off line for almost a month. They vanished without a trace just before police arrived. PG&E dismissed the incident as "vandalism." However, multiple government agencies and Congress were sufficiently concerned that the attack on Metcalf "could have been a dress rehearsal for a larger event."[299]

One year later, the Metcalf station was struck again when the fence was cut open and, the facility entered and tools were stolen.[300] Obviously, the physical security situation had not improved much in the intervening year. In fact, PG&E's credibility was shot when its public statements about its physical security improvements were contradicted by a leaked internal memo.[301]

The April 2013 Metcalf attack was not the only physical attack on critical components of the North American electric grid. According the Department of Energy (DOE) OE-417 reports[302], there were 721 physical attacks against the grid reported from January 1, 2010 through December 31, 2020.[303]

However, the attack on the Metcalf substation—and the other attacks—shouldn't have been a surprise. On May 12, 1981, the General Accounting Office (GAO) issued a report entitled: *Federal Electrical Emergency Preparedness Is Inadequate*.[304] GAO noted in 1981:

---

[298] Smith, Rebecca. The Wall Street Journal. *"Assault on California Power Station Raises Alarm on Potential for Terrorism."* February 5, 2014. https://www.wsj.com/articles/assault-on-california-power-station-raises-alarm-on-potential-for-terrorism-1391570879

[299] Ibid.

[300] Wald, Matthew L. The New York Times "California Power Substation Attacked in 2013 Is Struck Again." August 28, 2014. https://www.nytimes.com/2014/08/29/us/california-power-substation-attacked-in-2013-is-hit-again.html

[301] NBC Bay Area "Internal Memo: PG&E Years Away from Substation Security." May 15, 2015 https://www.nbcbayarea.com/on-air/as-seen-on/internal-memo_-pg_e-years-away-from-substation-security_bay-area/69201/

[302] Utility companies and grid operators are required to submit reports on electric disturbance events to the Department of Energy (DOE) on a form known as an OE-417.

[303] See report: "OE-417 Electric Disturbance Events Database" https://michaelmabee.info/oe-417-database/

[304] Available at: https://www.gao.gov/assets/emd-81-50.pdf

"If saboteurs, terrorists, or an enemy attacked the Nation's electric power system, would the Federal Government be prepared to handle the resulting energy disruptions? Probably not, because the Department of Energy has failed to prepare required electric emergency preparedness plans. A national plan to cope with the problems caused by a loss of electricity–which would virtually halt communication, transportation, and distribution systems–is essential, because utilities and the States cannot be expected to deal with such emergencies on their own."

At least as far back as 1981, GAO was concerned about the physical security of our substations. GAO found:

"Electric power systems are highly dependable, but are very vulnerable to disruptions from acts of war, sabotage, or terrorism. In the region GAO looked at:

- *An attack on just eight substations could disrupt power to the entire region for a long time. (See p. 8.)*

- *Damage to just four substations could disrupt power to one city for up to a year. (See p. 8.)*

- *Damage to just one substation could leave a key military facility without power. (See p. 8.)"*

Further, a year before the Metcalf attack, the National Academies published a report titled: *Terrorism and the Electric Power Delivery System.*[305] The report discussed physical security of high-voltage transformers noting:

"High-voltage transformers are of particular concern because they are vulnerable to attack, both from within and from outside the substation where they are located. These transformers are very large, difficult to move, custom-built, and difficult to replace. Most are no longer made in the United States, and the delivery time for new ones can run to months or years."

Then, one year *after* the Metcalf attack, the Wall Street Journal ran two alarming stories, headlined:

- "Assault on California Power Station Raises Alarm on Potential for Terrorism. *April Sniper Attack Knocked Out Substation, Raises Concern for Country's Power Grid"*[306]

- "U.S. Risks National Blackout From Small-Scale Attack. *Federal Analysis Says Sabotage of Nine Key Substations Is Sufficient for Broad Outage"*[307]

In the second article, the Wall Street Journal noted:

"The U.S. could suffer a coast-to-coast blackout if saboteurs knocked out just nine of the country's 55,000 electric-transmission substations on a scorching summer day, according to a previously unreported federal analysis."

---

[305] Available at: https://www.nap.edu/catalog/12050/terrorism-and-the-electric-power-delivery-system

[306] Smith, Rebecca. Wall Street Journal. February 5, 2014. Available at: https://www.wsj.com/articles/assault-on-california-power-station-raises-alarm-on-potential-for-terrorism-1391570879

[307] Smith, Rebecca. Wall Street Journal. March 12, 2014. Available at: https://www.wsj.com/articles/u-s-risks-national-blackout-from-small-scale-attack-1394664965

"The study by the Federal Energy Regulatory Commission concluded that coordinated attacks in each of the nation's three separate electric systems could cause the entire power network to collapse, people familiar with the research said."

The threat of physical attack on the electric grid is not theoretical: there have been hundreds of physical attacks *reported* against the electric grid in the last decade, according to federal records.

Historically, we have seen spectacular and sophisticated physical attacks against the electric grid such as

- **2013 The Metcalf Sniper Attack.**[308] No arrests have ever been made in one of the most alarming physical attacks against the electric grid. The attack on the PG&E Metcalf substation raised Congressional concern which lead to the Commission directing the North American Electric Reliability Corporation (NERC) to develop a physical security standard. Unfortunately, as I will explain below, the standard is fraught with loopholes and covers very few facilities.

- **2013 The Arkansas grid attacks.**[309] In a period of a few weeks, attacks occurred against a two transmission lines and a substation. The perpetrator was eventually arrested but the attacks demonstrate the extreme vulnerability of transmission lines and substations to physical attack.

- **2014 The Nogales IED attack.**[310] An improvised explosive device (IED) was used in an attempt to blow up a 50,000-gallon diesel fuel tank at a critical transformer substation. The bomb failed to ignite the fuel, but called into larger question the physical security of the grid.

- **2014 The Hydro-Québec attack by airplane.**[311] While the details of the attack are under court seal, the attacker used an airplane to short out two major transmission lines, cutting off power to over 180,000 customers. This incident demonstrated the vulnerability of the grid to an attack by air.

While these four particular attacks took place prior to the effective date of NERC's subsequently issued physical security standard (CIP-14-2), it is debatable whether the present standard would have

---

[308] Smith, Rebecca. The Wall Street Journal. *"Assault on California Power Station Raises Alarm on Potential for Terrorism."* February 5, 2014. https://www.wsj.com/articles/assault-on-california-power-station-raises-alarm-on-potential-for-terrorism-1391570879

[309] Pentland, William. Forbes. Weekend Attacks on Arkansas' Electric Grid Leave 10,000 Without Power; 'YOU SHOULD HAVE EXPECTED U.S.' Oct 7, 2013. https://www.forbes.com/sites/williampentland/2013/10/07/weekend-attacks-on-arkansas-electric-grid-leave-10000-without-power-you-should-have-expected-u-s/; Pentland, William. Forbes. Vandals Attack Electric Grid In Arkansas. Sep 26, 2013. https://www.forbes.com/sites/williampentland/2013/09/26/terrorists-attack-electric-grid-in-arkansas/#35a862fd35ef; FBI: Attacks on Arkansas Power Grid - Perpetrator Sentenced to 15 Years. August 10, 2015. https://www.fbi.gov/news/stories/attacks-on-arkansas-power-grid

[310] Holstege, Sean. The Republic. Sabotage at Nogales station puts focus on threats to grid. June 12, 2014. https://www.azcentral.com/story/news/arizona/2014/06/12/sabotage-nogales-station-puts-focus-threats-grid/10408053/; Sobczak, Blake and Behr, Peter. E&E News. 'Crude' bomb at Ariz. substation stokes broader security concerns. June 13, 2014. https://www.eenews.net/stories/1060001267.

[311] Freeman, Alan. The Washington Post. Pilot to be sentenced in sabotage that crippled Quebec power grid. November 2, 2018. https://www.washingtonpost.com/world/2018/11/02/pilot-be-sentenced-sabotage-that-crippled-quebec-power-grid/; Behr, Peter. E&E News. Outage on Quebec power grid traced to airborne attacker. June 17, 2015. https://www.eenews.net/stories/1060020352

stopped them if they occurred today. In fact, in the case of PG&E's Metcalf station, the following year the Metcalf station was successfully attacked for a second time.[312]

And the fact remains that *since* the effective date of CIP-14-2, there have been hundreds of physical attacks on the grid. This simply cannot be ignored.

Moreover, the threat of a coordinated physical attack is not theoretical. There are numerous recent and historic examples of terrorists or "inferior forces" using well-planned sophisticated attacks against multiple targets with great effect:

—The Tet Offensive on January 30, 1968 was a coordinated surprise attack on over 100 cities and outposts in Vietnam. The attack caught the U.S. totally by surprise and it is widely attributed to turning the tide of the war against the U.S.[313]

—On September 11, 2001, terrorists attacked the U.S. in a sophisticated, well-coordinated attack against multiple targets.[314] The impacts to the U.S. from the 9/11 attacks were dramatic and society changing.

—On October 27, 2013, the Knights Templars, a terrorist drug cartel, used small arms and explosives to blackout Mexico's Michoacan state, putting 420,000 people in the dark and isolating them from help from federal police, so the drug cartel could publicly assassinate town and village leaders. Ironically, that evening in the United States, the National Geographic aired a television docudrama "American Blackout" that accurately portrayed the catastrophic consequences of a cyber-attack that blacks-out the U.S. grid for ten days. The North American Electric Reliability Corporation (NERC) and some utilities criticized "American Blackout" for being alarmist and unrealistic, apparently unaware that life had already anticipated art just across the largely unprotected U.S. border with Mexico.[315]

—On June 9, 2014, for the first time in history, a terrorist attack blacked-out an entire nation. Al Qaeda in the Arabian Peninsula (AQAP) used small arms and explosives to black-out temporarily the entire electric power grid of Yemen, plunging a nation of 16 cities and 24 million people into darkness.[316]

—On January 25, 2015, terrorists in Pakistan sabotaged key transmission towers causing a nearly nationwide blackout across 80 percent of Pakistan's electric power grid for several days, causing widespread disruption in government, business, and society.[317] Pakistan is a nuclear weapons state.

---

[312] Wald, Matthew L. The New York Times. "California Power Substation Attacked in 2013 Is Struck Again." August 28, 2014. https://www.nytimes.com/2014/08/29/us/california-power-substation-attacked-in-2013-is-hit-again.html

[313] History Channel. Tet Offensive. October 29, 2009. https://www.history.com/topics/vietnam-war/tet-offensive

[314] The National Commission on Terrorist Attacks Upon the United States. "The 9/11 Commission Report." July 22, 2004. http://bit.ly/3bjibKW

[315] Patrick Corcoran, "Lights Out In Western Mexico" Christian Science Monitor (5 November 2013). Patrick Corcoran, "Who Turned The Lights Out In Michoacan, Mexico?" InSight Crime (5 November 2013). Dr. Peter Vincent Pry, *The Power And The Light: The Congressional EMP Commission's War To Save America* (2020) pp. 77-78. National Geographic, "American Blackout" (25 October 2013). Frank Gaffney, "Keeping Americans In The Dark" Washington Times (14 November 2013).

[316] Peter Kelly-Detweiler, "Terrorist Attack Left All Of Yemen In Darkness Last Week: Another Wake-Up Call" Forbes (19 June 2014).

[317] Salman Masood, "Rebels Tied To Blackout Across Most Of Pakistan" New York Times (25 January 2015). NBC News, "Massive Pakistan Power Blackout Leaves 80 Percent In Darkness" (25 January 2015). "Massive Power Failure Plunges 80% Of Pakistan Into Darkness" The Guardian (25 January 2015).

More recently, on September 14, 2019 two oil production facilities in Saudi Arabia were attacked by drones and missiles causing a substantial temporary loss of Saudi Arabia's oil production.[318] Responsibility for this attack was claimed by Houthi rebels in Yemen. However, the United States and other countries have accused Iran of involvement.[319] Terrorist organizations such as ISIS (a.k.a. "Islamic State") are also known to have deployed weaponized drones.[320]

The U.S. electric grid, built over generations in which domestic terrorism was not a concern, was not designed to thwart physical attacks. That physical security must now be put into place for the entire electric grid: generation, transmission and distribution. But it just hasn't been done and is not being done.

The electric grid is a wide open target. For example, in 5 minutes using Google Maps, I was able to trace transmission lines from two generating plants to various equipment and substations on the grid. I was able to see the equipment and locations in excellent detail.

Here are several screen shots from my 5-minute Google Maps "reconnaissance" of part of the grid:

---

[318] Reid, David. CNBC. Saudi Aramco reveals attack damage at oil production plants. September 20, 2019. https://www.cnbc.com/2019/09/20/oil-drone-attack-damage-revealed-at-saudi-aramco-facility.html.

[319] Reuters. U.S. blames Iran for Saudi oil attack, Trump says 'locked and loaded.' September 15, 2019. https://www.reuters.com/article/us-saudi-aramco-attacks/u-s-blames-iran-for-saudi-oil-attack-trump-says-locked-and-loaded-idUSKB-N1W00SA

[320] Rassler, Don. United States Military Academy. The Islamic State and Drones: Supply, Scale and Future Threats. https://ctc.usma.edu/app/uploads/2018/07/Islamic-State-and-Drones-Release-Version.pdf

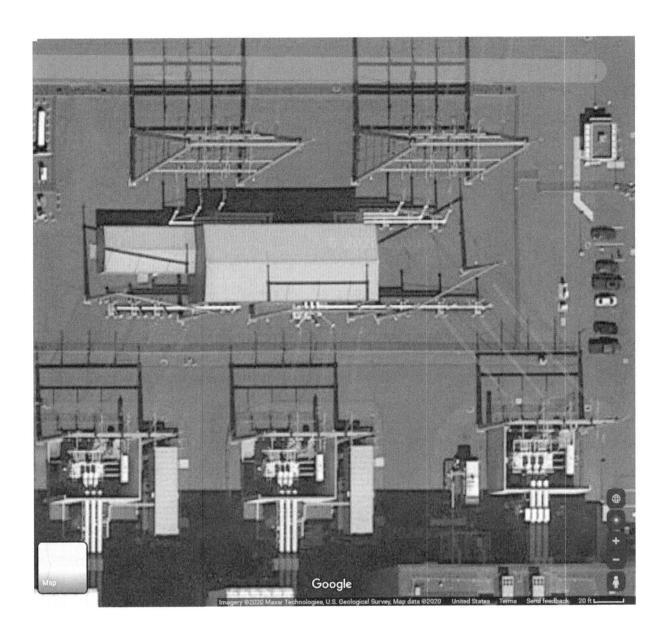

Terrorists can easily map out sections of the grid and locate critical equipment simply using satellite photos and mapping available on the internet. With drones, they could attack these facilities from several kilometers away.[321] Even without drones, a terrorist organization can map out and attack numerous facilities with small teams using a variety of means to disable or destroy equipment.

The federal government was already concerned about the vulnerability of the critical infrastructures and on February 12, 2013, President Barack Obama implemented Presidential Policy Directive 21 (PPD-21)[322] – Critical Infrastructure Security and Resilience. PPD-21 identifies the 16 critical infrastructures in the U.S. and mandates that:

The Federal Government shall work with critical infrastructure owners and operators and SLTT [state, local, tribal, and territorial] entities to take proactive steps to manage risk and strengthen the security and resilience of the Nation's critical infrastructure, considering all hazards that could have a debilitating impact on national security, economic stability, public health and safety, or any combination thereof.

PPD-21 identifies the energy sector as uniquely critical due to the enabling functions it provides across all 16 critical infrastructure sectors. The electric grid is the lynchpin: All 16 critical infrastructures, including the rest of the energy sector and our national security apparatus, depends on the electric grid. Therefore, any threat to the electric grid is a threat to U.S. national security. The Department of Energy is designated as the Sector Risk Management Agency for the energy sector.[323]

However, PPD-21 does not mandate physical security protections for the electric grid. After Metcalf, Congressional pressure built for the Federal Energy Regulatory Commission to mandate that NERC write a physical security standard for the Bulk Power System.

What Was Done After Metcalf?

(Spoiler Alert: Physical security requirements for the electric grid—and their enforcement—are largely non-existent 8 years after the Metcalf attack and 4 decades after the May 12, 1981 GAO report.)

After the February 5, 2014 Wall Street Journal article, the Senate sent a letter on February 7, 2014 to the Federal Energy Regulatory Commission (FERC), to ask them what they were doing to protect the grid.[324] And FERC Responded on February 11, 2014 telling the Senate that:

"Since the attack on the Metcalf facility in April 2013, the Commission's staff has taken responsive action together with NERC, other federal and state agencies, and transmission and generation asset owners and operators."[325]

---

[321] See: King, Llewellyn. InsideSources. "Drones Pose a New, Deadly Threat to Energy Infrastructure." September 20, 2019. https://www.insidesources.com/drones-pose-a-new-deadly-threat-to-energy-infrastructure/; Bean, Tim. PowerGrid International. "Energy Industry also Faces Threats from Drones." October 9, 2018. https://www.power-grid.com/2018/10/09/energy-industry-also-faces-threats-from-drones/#gref; Sobczak, Blake. E&E News. "Feds to energy companies: Beware drones made in China." May 21, 2019. https://www.eenews.net/stories/1060369689

[322] Available at: http://bit.ly/2NUr04k

[323] See: https://www.cisa.gov/energy-sector

[324] Available at: https://www.ferc.gov/industries/electric/indus-act/reliability/chairman-letter-incoming.pdf

[325] Available at: https://www.ferc.gov/industries/electric/indus-act/reliability/chairman-letter-feinstein.pdf

Despite the Congressional hearings and press scrutiny after the spectacular physical attack against the transformer in Metcalf, California in 2013,[326] the industry advised *against* a mandatory physical security standard.[327]

FERC, under immense pressure from Congress, directed NERC to develop a standard anyway. So, the industry went to work writing the physical security standard it didn't want. We shouldn't be surprised at the result – if you force a person, organization or industry to do something they don't want to do, expecting them to rip into the task with zeal is probably a stretch. NERC submitted their proposed standard (known as CIP-014-1[328]) on May 23, 2014.

FERC issued an order on November 20, 2014[329] literally ordering NERC to change one word. (The word was: "widespread" and was used 30 times in the proposed standard. This word—a slight of pen by NERC's attorneys—would have excluded many more facilities from falling under the standard.)

On October 2, 2015, FERC approved the "Physical Security" standard, known as CIP-014-2.

What we know is that according to the Department of Energy OE-417 Electric Emergency Incident and Disturbance Reports there have been hundreds of physical attacks against the electric grid since the standard became effective.[330] And we know that to date there have been very few citations for violations of the physical security standard.

Notwithstanding FERC's assurances to the senate in 2014, the physical security of our critical transformers and facilities appears to remain inadequate in 2021.

Problem #1: There is no mandatory physical security standard for the entire electric grid.

The problem starts with the fact that the physical security standard only applies to the "bulk power system" and not the entire electric grid. Moreover, most facilities in the "bulk power system" are exempted, so very few facilities are actually even covered.

CIP-14-2 admittedly expects the population of facilities covered by the standard "will be small and that many Transmission Owners that meet the applicability of this standard will not actually identify

---

[326] Smith, Rebecca. The Wall Street Journal. *"Assault on California Power Station Raises Alarm on Potential for Terrorism."* February 5, 2014. https://www.wsj.com/articles/assault-on-california-power-station-raises-alarm-on-potential-for-terrorism-1391570879 and Smith, Rebecca. Wall Street Journal. "U.S. Risks National Blackout From Small-Scale Attack." March 12, 2014. https://www.wsj.com/articles/SB10001424052702304020104579433670284061220

[327] NERC's then CEO Gerry Cauley told Congress in a February 12, 2014 letter: "I do not believe it makes sense to move to mandatory standards at this time. There are more than 55,000 substations of 100 Kv or higher across North America, and not all those assets can be 100% protected against all threats. I am concerned that a rule-based approach for physical security would not provide the flexibility needed to deal with the widely varying risk profiles and circumstances across the North American grid and would instead create unnecessary and inefficient regulatory burdens and compliance obligations." Letter available at: https://michaelmabee.info/wp-content/uploads/2021/05/NERC-Response-to-Senators-Letter-Reid-2-11-14-v4.pdf

[328] Available at: https://www.nerc.com/pa/Stand/Reliability Standards/CIP-014-1.pdf

[329] Available at: https://www.ferc.gov/whats-new/comm-meet/2014/112014/E-4.pdf

[330] To the extent that anybody wishes to argue that some of these incidents were "mere vandalism," this is hardly comforting. If a couple of 13-year-olds can break in and damage equipment, it does not bode well for our protective posture against terrorists.

any such Facilities."[331] And, unbelievably, "the SDT[332] determined that it was not necessary to include Generator Operators and Generator Owners in the Reliability Standard."[333]

Most alarmingly, FERC has admitted that: "Reliability Standard CIP-014-1 does not require responsible entities to assess the criticality of Bulk-Power System facilities based on a simultaneous attack on multiple facilities."[334] Although the issue of simultaneous attacks was raised strenuously in rulemaking, FERC declined to address it.

Moreover, the March 7 Order "anticipate[d] that the number of facilities identified as critical will be relatively small compared to the number of facilities that comprise the Bulk-Power System ... [and that the Commission's] preliminary view is that most of these would not be 'critical' as the term is used in [the March 7 Order]." Accordingly, NERC was not required to address in the physical security Reliability Standards scenarios of simultaneous physical attacks involving multiple critical facilities.[335] [Internal footnotes omitted.]

There are over 2000 EHV LPTs[336] (Extra High Voltage Large Power Transformers) in the United States and tens of thousands of LPTs. But according to CIP-14-2's applicability, very few of these would meet the criteria for coverage. That is a lot of critical targets for a potential simultaneous terrorist attack which are not covered by the standard.

But it gets worse.

Power generation plants are not covered under CIP-14-2. OE-417 data from the Department of Energy shows that there have been 74 disturbances cause by fuel supply deficiency since 2010.[337] There have also been at least 17 disturbances cause by "generation interruption" during the same period.[338] During times of extreme weather, we have seen the systems in New England, Texas and California strained to the limits. And this is in "normal times."

Then FERC Chairman Cheryl LaFleur testified on September 22, 2014 before the Senate Energy Committee and admitted: "A carefully planned and executed attack on a single or multiple generation plants could cause cascading outages..."[339]

If, as FERC admits, an attack on *one generation plant* could cause a cascading failure, a simultaneous terrorist strike on several generation facilities is a grave danger. If such an attack occurs in conjunction with a "public appeal" to reduce electricity consumption – which have occurred at least 65 times

---

[331] CIP-14-2 "Guidelines and Technical Basis," page 22.

[332] Standard Drafting Team.

[333] CIP-14-2 "Guidelines and Technical Basis," page 23.

[334] Order Denying Rehearing in Docket RM14-15-001. Page 4 (April 23, 2015).

[335] Order Denying Rehearing in Docket RM14-15-001. Page 5 (April 23, 2015).

[336] U.S. Department of Energy "Large Power Transformers and the U.S. Electric Grid." June 2012. https://www.energy.gov/sites/prod/files/Large Power Transformer Study - June 2012_0.pdf

[337] See: https://michaelmabee.info/oe-417-database/

[338] See: https://michaelmabee.info/oe-417-database/

[339] Testimony of FERC Chairman Cheryl LaFleur, to U.S. Senate Energy Committee in a letter dated June 4, 2014. https://www.energy.senate.gov/public/index.cfm/files/serve?File_id=86e83c32-636a-40b6-8e5d-c072f2f95a8c; Full April 10, 2014 hearing is available at https://www.govinfo.gov/content/pkg/CHRG-113shrg87851/pdf/CHRG-113shrg87851.pdf.

since 2010,[340] or in conjunction with a weather-related event – which have occurred 961 times since 2010,[341] the consequences for an already stressed grid are dire.

Transmission lines are not covered under CIP-14-2. While it may not be feasible to fully secure 240,000 miles of high voltage transmission lines, this does not mean that they should be completely excluded from the CIP standard. There are actions that should be required.

For example, Transmission Owners and Operators should be required to coordinate with all law enforcement agencies through whose jurisdiction the lines pass. They should be required to provide these law enforcement agencies with maps, access points and have a standing "no trespassing" enforcement request. Signage should be required. In critical access areas, gates should be installed to limit vehicular access to authorized vehicles.

Critical military bases and other critical infrastructures may lose power. CIP-14-2's "applicability" will not protect the grid from a coordinated attack on smaller facilities.

"The purpose of Reliability Standard CIP-014 is to protect Transmission stations and Transmission substations, and their associated primary control centers that if rendered inoperable or damaged as a result of a physical attack could result in instability, uncontrolled separation, or Cascading within an Interconnection."[342]

This means that the standard only applies to each individual facility *that if disabled alone* would meet this applicability. Moreover,

"The Standard Drafting Team (SDT) expects this population will be small and that many Transmission Owners that meet the applicability of this standard will not actually identify any such Facilities."[343]

A coordinated attack against uncovered facilities could threaten our key military bases in that area and other critical infrastructures. FERC admits that:

"Reliability Standard CIP-014-1 does not require responsible entities to assess the criticality of Bulk-Power System facilities based on a simultaneous attack on multiple facilities."[344]

CIP-14-2's "applicability" leaves unprotected large swaths of the critical components of the electric grid which are susceptible to a coordinated terrorist attack, including:

- Generation plants

- Transmission lines

- Most transformer stations and substations

---

[340] See: https://michaelmabee.info/oe-417-database/
[341] See: https://michaelmabee.info/oe-417-database/
[342] CIP-14-2 Guidelines and Technical Basis. Page 22.
[343] CIP-14-2 Guidelines and Technical Basis. Page 22.
[344] Order Denying Rehearing in Docket RM14-15-001. Page 4 (April 23, 2015).

- Some control facilities

- Distribution networks nationwide

A standard with an "applicability" to so little of the most critical of our critical infrastructures cannot be deemed "adequate" under any circumstances.

Problem #2: The standard—CIP-014-2 (Physical Security)—is a joke.

As a result of Metcalf, FERC ordered NERC to develop a physical security standard. NERC submitted their proposed standard (known as CIP-014-1[345]) on May 23, 2014. Remember, this standard only applies to the "bulk power system" - not the entire electric grid.

FERC issued an order on November 20, 2014[346] literally ordering NERC to change one word. (The word was: "widespread" and was used 30 times in the proposed standard. This word—a slight of pen by NERC's attorneys—would have excluded many facilities from falling under the standard.)

On October 2, 2015, FERC approved the "Physical Security" standard, known as CIP-014-2.[347] Unfortunately, the physical security standard requires very little:

1. Requirement 1: Each Transmission Owner shall perform a risk assessment of its Transmission stations and Transmission substations.

2. Requirement 2: Each Transmission Owner shall have an unaffiliated third party verify the risk assessment *[e.g., a peer grid company would meet the requirement—"Hey, if you verify mine, I'll verify yours"]*.

3. Requirement 3: If a Transmission Owner operationally controls an identified Transmission station or Transmission substation, it must notify the Transmission Operator that has operational control of the primary control center.

4. Requirement 4: Each Transmission Owner shall conduct an evaluation of the potential threats and vulnerabilities of a physical attack to each of their respective Transmission station(s), Transmission substation(s), and primary control center(s).

5. Requirement 5: Each Transmission Owner shall develop and implement a documented physical security plan(s) that covers their respective Transmission station(s), Transmission substation(s), and primary control center(s).

6. Requirement 6: Each Transmission Owner shall have an unaffiliated third party review the evaluation performed under Requirement R4 and the security plan(s) under Requirement R5 *[again, a peer grid company would meet the requirement]*.

---

[345] Available at: https://www.nerc.com/pa/Stand/Reliability Standards/CIP-014-1.pdf

[346] Available at: https://www.ferc.gov/whats-new/comm-meet/2014/112014/E-4.pdf

[347] Available at: https://www.nerc.com/pa/Stand/Reliability Standards/CIP-014-2.pdf

That's it. All the infrastructure owner must do is to have a binder with a bunch of papers labeled "Physical Security Plan" and have any peer utility they choose review the "risk assessment," "evaluation" and "security plan(s)". No need for it to be anybody who knows anything significant about physical security.

And there is no requirement as to what the "Physical Security Plan" must include—or even that it be effective. Nobody with regulatory authority even has to even approve it—All you need is somebody to "review" it. What if the "reviewer" happens to say "this plan sucks?" It doesn't matter. The only requirement is that the three-ring binder be "reviewed." (I guess most any papers in a three-ring binder will do.)

That unapproved three-ring binder of papers is what is standing between the United States and a catastrophic widespread power outage caused by a terrorist attack. (Also, it is worthy of note that generation plants and most other facilities are specifically exempted from NERC's physical security standard – so most won't even have the three-ring binder to protect them from terrorists.)

Problem #3: Enforcement of CIP-014-2 seems nonexistent.

One would think that after the public and Congressional interest in the Metcalf attack, FERC and NERC would take a special interest in the enforcement of the physical security standards. Unfortunately, one would be wrong. How many times since Metcalf have utilities been cited for violations of standard CIP-014-2?

Six.

We have had 721 physical attacks to the grid (that have been publicly disclosed) yet, utilities have been cited for violations of the standard only six (6) times in the eight years since the Metcalf attack. It would appear that this standard and regulatory scheme are not working. Here are the facts.

- There are close to 1,500 entities regulated by NERC.

- There are over 2000 EHV LPTs[348] (Extra High Voltage Large Power Transformers) in the United States and tens of thousands of LPTs.

- There have been six (6) citations for non-compliance with the physical security standard (CIP-014-2) since Metcalf.

The American people are not stupid. We see these transformers unguarded behind chain-link fences as we drive up the road or walk our dogs.

So, let's take a look at the six times NERC found CIP-014-2 violations:

---

[348] U.S. Department of Energy "Large Power Transformers and the U.S. Electric Grid." June 2012. https://www.energy.gov/sites/prod/files/Large Power Transformer Study - June 2012_0.pdf

- In FERC Docket No. NP19-4-000[349] (one Violation—which everybody knows is Duke Energy Corp.[350]), Duke apparently excluded one substation from its risk assessment because they didn't think it met the criteria for inclusion.

- In FERC Docket No. NP18-14-000[351] (one violation), the "Unidentified Registered Entity" failed to do a risk assessment on one substation due to a "management oopsy."

- And in FERC Docket No. NP17-29-000[352] (two violations), the "Unidentified Registered Entity" failed to include one control center in its 1) risk assessment and 2) security plan (two violations) because an employee who knew what they were doing left the company, leaving nobody else at the company who knew what they were doing.

- And in FERC Docket NP20-18-000[353] (two violations) "The root cause of this violation was a less than adequate understanding of how to document mitigating activities to specifically address identified vulnerabilities and threats pursuant to CIP-014-2 R5 Part 5.1."

One will notice that all six of these "violations" are administrative in nature and have nothing to do with whether there is actually meaningful physical security in place.

Brief History Of The "Physical Security" Standards

CIP-001-1 (Sabotage Reporting)[354] became effective on June 4, 2007. Utilities were cited for its violation 404 times between 6/4/2008 and 5/26/2011. It them morphed into CIP-001-1a (February 2, 2011)[355] and CIP-001-2a (August 2, 2011)[356]—neither of which were EVER cited.

Meanwhile, EOP-004-1 (Disturbance Reporting)[357], which covered "equipment damage" among other things, had violations 16 times between 2009 and 2013.

NERC began to look at merging CIP-001 and EOP-004 "to eliminate redundancies" and on June 20, 2013, FERC approved[358] merging CIP-001-2a (Sabotage Reporting) and EOP-004-1 (Disturbance Reporting) into EOP-004-2 (Event Reporting)[359]. (CIP-001-2a Sabotage Reporting and EOP-004-1 Disturbance Reporting were then "Retired.") EOP-004-2 covers reporting "damage or destruction of a facility." EOP-004-2 and its successors have never been found to be violated.

Here is the enforcement history of these various standards:

---

[349] Available at: https://elibrary.ferc.gov/idmws/file_list.asp?document_id=14739324

[350] Sobczak, Blake and Behr, Peter. E&E News. "Duke agreed to pay record fine for lax security — sources." February 1, 2019. https://www.eenews.net/stories/1060119265

[351] Available at: https://elibrary.ferc.gov/idmws/file_list.asp?document_id=14675460

[352] Available at: https://elibrary.ferc.gov/idmws/file_list.asp?document_id=14605551

[353] Available at: https://elibrary.ferc.gov/eLibrary/filelist?document_id=14867867

[354] Available at: https://www.nerc.com/files/CIP-001-1.pdf

[355] Available at: https://www.nerc.com/files/CIP-001-1a.pdf

[356] Available at: https://www.nerc.com/files/CIP-001-2a.pdf

[357] Available at: https://www.nerc.com/files/EOP-004-1.pdf

[358] FERC Order Approving Reliability Standard. 143 FERC ¶ 61,252. https://www.ferc.gov/whats-new/comm-meet/2013/062013/E-8.pdf

[359] Available at: https://www.nerc.com/files/EOP-004-2.pdf

- 404 Citations issued for CIP-001-1 (Sabotage Reporting) between 2008 and 2011

- 16 Citations were issued for EOP-004-1 (Disturbance Reporting) between 2009 and 2013—not all related to damage.

Metcalf happened on April 16, 2013, but then…

- No citations have been issued for EOP-004-2 (effective June 20, 2013)

- No citations have been issued for EOP-004-3 (effective November 19, 2015)

- No citations have been issued for EOP-004-4 (effective January 18, 2018)

And adding in the CIP-014 physical security Standard:

- No violation citations have been issued for CIP-014-1

- Six violation citations have been issued for CIP-014-2:

    —FERC Docket NP19-4-000 (one violation)
    —FERC Docket NP18-14-000 (one violation)
    —FERC Docket NP17-29-000 (two violations)
    —FERC Docket NP20-18-000 (two violations)

Why Don't "They" Fix It?

I am usually asked the same question when I do presentations. When made aware of the various threats to the electric grid—cyberattack, physical attack, geomagnetic disturbance (GMD), electro-magnetic pulse (EMP), vegetation management, extreme weather, pandemic, etc.—people invariably ask: "why don't they fix it?"

Indeed, "they" have known for decades that the electric grid is vulnerable to a variety of threats. In fact, there have been decades of Congressional hearings and federal reports on the known threats to the grid.[360]

So why don't "they" fix it? Excellent question. First of all, let's define "they." There are a few of "them."

1. "They" could mean the regulators

2. "They" could mean Congress

3. "They" could mean the electric utility industry

So why can't the regulators, Congress and the industry fix grid security? The regulators actually *can* fix grid security with legislation through meaningful mandatory regulations. Congress actual-

---

[360] See Database of Federal Grid Security Documents at: https://michaelmabee.info/government-documents-emp-and-grid-security/

ly *can* fix grid security with legislation. The industry also *can* fix grid security voluntarily. They haven't. So, as it turns out, the more appropriate question is *why won't* any or all of these groups fix grid security?

This is the greatest example that I can think of "special interests" co-opting our government and endangering us. According to The Center for Responsive Politics, the electric utilities in the 2020 cycle:

- Spent $108,468,019 on lobbying the U.S. Congress.[361]

- Made total contributions to the U.S. Congress of $28,562,003:[362]

    —Made $11,626,034 in political contributions to members of the U.S House.

    —Made $5,140,906 in political contributions to members of the U.S. Senate.

- Total lobbying and contributions in the 2020 cycle: over $137 million.

In the last decade the electric utility industry has spent *$1.2 billion* lobbying the U.S. Congress and another $150 million in "contributions." (Not including lobbying and contributions at the state level.) Imagine if this $1.2 billion, which largely originated from the bills of ratepayers, was put towards electric grid security rather than lobbying against further regulation.

The industry's lobbyists have embedded themselves over the years, as "partners" in DOE and FERC via the Electric Subsector Coordinating Council ("ESCC") and trade organizations such as the Edison Electric Institute ("EEI"), the American Public Power Association ("APPA"), the National Rural Electric Cooperative Association ("NRECA"), the Large Public Power Council ("LPPC"), the Transmission Access Policy Study Group ("TAPS"), the Electric Power Supply Association ("EPSA"), WIRES, and the Electricity Consumers Resource Council ("ELCON"). These industry groups have actively *fought against* grid security regulation, mandatory critical infrastructure protection standards and public transparency.

That is why our electric grid is not secure from the threats outlined in this book, including the physical security threats discussed in this chapter.

Conclusion

We have known for four decades about the grave danger posed by physical attacks on the electric grid, and yet today there is no physical security standard for the vast majority of the grid.

A coordinated physical attack on multiple grid facilities can be achieved by an unsophisticated domestic group or a sophisticated terrorist organization or in a covert operation by a state actor. A coordinated physical attack could cause wide area and long-term blackouts, impacting critical infrastructures and endangering the public.

---

[361] See: https://www.opensecrets.org/industries/lobbying.php?cycle=2018&ind=E08
[362] See: https://www.opensecrets.org/industries/contrib.php?ind=E08&Bkdn=DemRep&cycle=2020

There have been 721 physical attacks against the electric grid reported to the Department of Energy between 2010 and 2020. There have been only six (6) NERC Physical Security standard violations cited since the Metcalf attack in 2013.

Despite the well-documented physical security problem in the critical electric infrastructure[363], the industry continues for fight *against* stronger physical security regulations. The multiple gaps and loopholes of the physical security standard were highlighted in a complaint filed with the Federal Energy Regulatory Commission (FERC) on January 29, 2020 alleging that grid physical security was inadequate.[364]

At the urging of the industry, on June 9, 2020 FERC dismissed the complaint.[365] The U.S. national electric power grid remains perilously vulnerable to sabotage by special forces or terrorists using low-tech weapons like rifles, RPGs, or explosives.

---

[363] See for example: Smith, Rebecca. Wall Street Journal. "How America Could Go Dark." July 14, 2016. https://www.wsj.com/articles/how-america-could-go-dark-1468423254

[364] See Complaint at: https://michaelmabee.info/complaint-filed-electric-grid-physical-security/ and Supplemental Information at https://michaelmabee.info/loopholes-in-grid-physical-security-identified/

[365] See 171 FERC ¶ 61,205. https://elibrary.ferc.gov/eLibrary/idmws/file_list.asp?document_id=14867700

IV

NON-NUCLEAR EMP ATTACK

by Dr. Peter Vincent Pry

Non-Nuclear Electromagnetic Pulse (NNEMP) weapons, more commonly known as Radio-Frequency Weapons, are non-nuclear weapons that use a variety of means, including explosively driven generators or high-power microwaves, to emit an electromagnetic pulse similar to the E1 HEMP from a nuclear weapon, except less energetic and of much shorter radius. The range of NNEMP weapons is rarely more than ten kilometers.[366]

International scientific and electronic engineering organizations describe the NNEMP threat as "Electro-Magnetic (EM) Terrorism" and, less dramatically, as "Intentional Electro-Magnetic Interference" (IEMI).[367] Non-Nuclear Electromagnetic Pulse (NNEMP) weapons is the term used here to emphasize that the NNEMP threat has significant similarities to nuclear HEMP, similar technical solutions, and poses a much greater threat than implied by the word "Interference" in IEMI.

"There is enormous diversity in possible electromagnetic weapon designs, for both large scale and highly focused attacks, both against civil and military targets," according to Dr. Carlo Kopp, one of the world's leading experts on NNEMP weapons, "There are many possible taxonomical divisions for electromagnetic weapons":

—"Directed Energy Weapons vs. 'one shot' E-Bombs;"
—"Nuclear (HEMP) E-Bombs vs. Non-nuclear E-Bombs;"
—"Narrow Band Weapons vs. Wideband or UWB [Ultra-Wide Band] weapons;"
—"High Power Microwave vs. 'Low Band' weapons;"
—"Persistent Area Denial (AD) weapons vs. Non-Persistent weapons;"
—"Explosively pumped vs. Electrically pumped weapons."[368]

Unlike the nuclear HEMP threat, NNEMP weapons are much more readily available to and easily exploitable by terrorists and the least sophisticated state actors.

NNEMP weapons can be built relatively inexpensively using commercially available parts and design information available on the internet. In 2000, the Terrorism Panel of the House Armed Services Committee conducted an experiment, hiring an electrical engineer and some students to try building

---

[366] U.S. FERC Interagency Report, Wiliam Radasky and Edward Savage, *Intentional Electromagnetic Interference (IEMI) and Its Impact on the U.S. Power Grid* (Meta-R-323) Metatech Corporation (January 2010). Carlo Kopp, *The Electromagnetic Bomb—A Weapon of Electrical Mass Destruction* (Melbourne, Australia). Jerry Emanuelson, "Non-nuclear Electromagnetic Pulse Generators" www.futurescience.com. Tom Harris, "How E-Bombs Work" www.science.howstuffworks.com.

[367] Ibid, U.S. FERC Interagency Report, pp. 1-2. R.L. Gardner, "Electromagnetic Terrorism: A Real Danger" Proceedings of the XIth Symposium on Electromagnetic Compatibility" (Wroclaw, Poland: June 1998).

[368] Dr. Carlo Kopp, "E-Bombs vs. Pervasive Infrastructure Vulnerability" Briefing, Pacific Theater Air, Sea, Land Battle Concept: IO/EW/Cyber Operations International Conference (Monash University/Air Power Australia) carlo.kopp@monash.edu.

an NNEMP weapon on a modest budget, using design information available on the internet, made from parts purchased commercially, available to anyone.[369]

They built two NNEMP weapons in one year, both successfully tested at the U.S. Army proving grounds at Aberdeen. One was built into a Volkswagen bus, designed to be driven down Wall Street to disrupt stock market computers and information systems and bring on a financial crisis. The other was designed to fit in the crate for a Xerox machine so it could be shipped to the Pentagon, sit in the mailroom, and burn-out Defense Department computers.[370]

EMP simulators that can be carried and operated by one man, and used as an NNEMP weapon, are available commercially.

For example, one U.S. company advertises for sale an "EMP Suitcase" that looks exactly like a metal suitcase, can be carried and operated by one man, and generates 100,000 volts/meter over a short distance. The EMP Suitcase is not intended to be used as a weapon, but as an aid for designing factories that use heavy duty electronic equipment that emit electromagnetic transients, so the factory does not self-destruct.[371]

But a terrorist or criminal armed with the "EMP Suitcase" could potentially destroy electric grid SCADAs, possibly shutdown transformers, and blackout a city. Thanks to NNEMP weapons, we have arrived at a place where the technological pillars of civilization for a major metropolitan area could be toppled by a single madman.

The "EMP Suitcase" can be purchased without a license by anyone.

According to the Wall Street Journal, a classified study by the U.S. Federal Energy Regulatory Commission found that damaging as few as 9 out of 2,000 EHV transformers could trigger cascading failures, causing a protracted nationwide blackout of the United States.[372] Terrorists armed with NNEMP weapons might use unclassified computer models to duplicate the reported U.S. FERC study and figure out which nine crucial transformer substations need to be attacked in order to blackout the entire national grid for weeks or months.

Big blackouts in the U.S., including the Great Northeast Blackout of 2003 that put 50 million people in the dark, caused by a tree branch, and the 2021 Texas blackout, caused by an ice storm, highlight the fragility of the national power grid. Malevolent actors are surely cognizant of this fragility.

Even random attacks using NNEMP weapons against less than 100 EHV transformer control substations located in all three U.S. grid systems—Eastern, Western, and Texas—would probably suffice to inflict a protracted nationwide blackout.

NNEMP weapons could offer significant operational advantages over assault rifles and bombs. Something like the "EMP Suitcase" could be put in the trunk of a car, parked and left outside the fence of

---

[369] Kenneth R. Timmerman, "U.S. Threatened With EMP Attack" ktimmerman@InsightMagazine.com and EMPwar.com U.S. Congress, "Radio Frequency Weapons and Proliferation: Potential Impact on the Economy" Hearing before the Special Oversight Panel on Terrorism, House Armed Services Committee (February 25, 1998) www.house.gov/jec/hearings/02-25-8h.htm.

[370] Ibid.

[371] Applied Physics Electronics, "High-Power RF Suitcase EMP Pulse Generator" www.apelc.com/rf-suitcase. Dr. Peter Vincent Pry, *Electric Armageddon* (EMP Task Force on National and Homeland Security, 2013) p. 13.

[372] Rebecca Smith, "U.S. Risks National Blackout From Small-Scale Attack" Wall Street Journal (March 12, 2014).

an EHV transformer or SCADA colony, or hidden in nearby brush or a garbage can, while the bad guys make a leisurely getaway. Or a single NNEMP weapon could be driven from one transformer substation to another (the substations are unguarded) to knock-out enough SCADAs and transformers to cause a regional or even national protracted blackout.

If the EMP fields are strong enough, an NNEMP weapon could be more effective, and far less conspicuous, than using explosives or small arms to attack transformers and controls at substations. Since all electronics within the field of the NNEMP could be damaged, precision targeting would be unnecessary, as is the case for firearms and explosives. Unlike firearms and explosive munitions, damage inflicted by NNEMP weapons might be mistaken as a freak accident or unusual systemic failure.

Some documented examples of successful attacks using NNEMP weapons, and accidents involving electromagnetic transients, are described by the Department of Defense:

—"In the Netherlands, an individual disrupted a local bank's computer network because he was turned down for a loan. He constructed a Radio Frequency Weapon the size of a briefcase, which he learned how to build from the Internet. Bank officials did not even realize that they had been attacked or what had happened until long after the event."
—"In St. Petersburg, Russia, a criminal robbed a jewelry store by defeating the alarm system with a repetitive RF generator. Its manufacture was no more complicated than assembling a home microwave oven."
—"In Kyzlyar, Dagestan, Russia, Chechen rebel commander Salman Raduyev disabled police radio communications using RF transmitters during a raid."
—"In Russia, Chechen rebels used a Radio Frequency Weapon to defeat a Russian security system and gain access to a controlled area."
—"Radio Frequency Weapons were used in separate incidents against the U.S. Embassy in Moscow to falsely set off alarms and to induce a fire in a sensitive area."
—"March 21-26, 2001, there was a mass failure of keyless remote entry devices on thousands of vehicles in the Bremerton, Washington, area...The failures ended abruptly as federal investigators had nearly isolated the source. The Federal Communications Commission (FCC) concluded that a U.S. Navy presence in the area probably caused the incident, although the Navy disagreed."
—"In 1999, a Robinson R-44 news helicopter nearly crashed when it flew by a high frequency broadcast antenna."
—"In the late 1980s, a large explosion occurred at a 36-inch diameter natural gas pipeline in the Netherlands. A SCADA system, located about one mile from the naval port of Den Helder, was affected by a naval radar. The RF energy from the radar caused the SCADA system to open and close a large gas flow-control valve at the radar scan frequency, resulting in pressure waves that traveled down the pipe and eventually caused the pipeline to explode."
—"In June 1999 in Bellingham, Washington, RF energy from a radar induced a SCADA malfunction that caused a gas pipeline to rupture and explode."
—"In 1967, the USS Forrestal was located at Yankee Station off Vietnam. An A4 Skyhawk launched a Zuni rocket across the deck. The subsequent fire took 13 hours to extinguish. 134 people died in the worst U.S. Navy accident since World War II. EMI [ElectroMagnetic Interference] was identified as the probable cause of the Zuni launch."[373]

North Korea used an NNEMP "cannon" purchased from Russia to attack airliners and impose an "electromagnetic blockade" on air traffic to Seoul, South Korea's capitol. The repeated attacks by

---

[373] Department of Defense, *Pocket Guide for Security Procedures and Protocols for Mitigating Radio Frequency Threats* (Technical Support Working Group, Directed Energy Technical Office, Dahlgren Naval Surface Warfare Center).

NNEMP also disrupted communications and the operation of automobiles in several South Korean cities in December 2010; March 9, 2011; and April-May 2012.[374]

In July 2019, the USS Boxer downed an Iranian drone using a powerful new jammer, in the latest demonstration that the United States has incorporated Non-Nuclear EMP weapons into its armed forces.[375]

In 2019, the U.S. Air Force deployed at least 20 CHAMP cruise missiles, armed with NNEMP warheads, advertised as being capable of paralyzing North Korean or Iranian missiles and their military command, control, and communications: "The U.S. Air Force has deployed at least 20 missiles that could zap the military electronics of North Korea or Iran with high-power microwaves, rendering their military capabilities useless without causing any fatalities. Known as the Counter-electronics High Power Microwave Advanced Missile Project (CHAMP), the missiles were built by Boeing's Phantom Works for the U.S. Air Force Research Laboratory and tested successfully in 2012. They have not been operational until now."[376]

Since the Department of Defense clearly recognizes the utility of NNEMP weapons for offensive operations—and given the history of use of NNEMP weapons by criminals, terrorists, and North Korea—continued failure by the Department of Homeland Security to assign high priority to national EMP preparedness is inexplicable and intolerable.

NNEMP Technological Revolution

Special mention must be made of the ongoing technological revolution in Non-Nuclear EMP weapons, which are becoming more powerful, more miniaturized and lighter-weight, and deliverable by cruise missiles or drones. The marriage of NNEMP warheads to drones or cruise missiles, preprogrammed or equipped with sensors to follow high-power electric lines and to target control centers and transformers, introduces a major new threat to national power grids.[377]

A non-explosive High-Power Microwave warhead, for example, can emit repeated bursts of electromagnetic energy to upset and damage electronic targets. Such a warhead, attached to a programmable drone or cruise missile, could follow the powerlines to attack numerous transformer and control substations, until its energy is exhausted.

Relatively small numbers of NNEMP cruise missiles or drones—perhaps only one capable of protracted flight—could inflict a long nationwide blackout. Reportedly, as noted earlier, according to a classified study by the U.S. Federal Energy Regulatory Commission, disabling just 9 of 2,000 U.S. EHV transformer substations could cause cascading failures that would crash the North American power grid.[378]

The "Cascade Failure" problem, warns Dr. Carlo Kopp, makes modern digital societies highly vulnerable to NNEMP attack: "Digital infrastructure is highly interconnected and thus interdependent." Because of: "Common reliance on power grid, telecommunications cabled and wireless connections,

---

[374] "Massive GPS Jamming Attack By North Korea" www.gpsworld.com (May 8, 2012).

[375] Ben Watson, "New U.S. Jammer Downs Alleged Iranian Drone in Gulf" Defense One (July 19, 2019).

[376] Ron Kessler "USAF Deploys New Champ Missile" (May 17, 2019) www.neogaf.com/threats/usaf-deploys-new-champ-missile. See also Dave Majumdar, "CHAMP: America's EMP Missile that Might Be Able to Fry North Korea's Nukes" National Interest (December 11, 2017).

[377] Carlo Kopp, The Electromagnetic Bomb – A Weapon of Electrical Mass Destruction (February 8, 2003). Though dated, Kopp is still among the best for background.

[378] Rebecca Smith, "U.S. Risks National Blackout From Small-Scale Attack" Wall Street Journal (March 12, 2014).

local and remote servers, single and multiple site Clouds and Grids," consequently, "A mass destruction effect in one geographical area can cause cascading failures as interdependent systems fail… *Damage effects are thus no longer localized in extant, e.g. destroying a server or Cloud in Washington DC may cripple dependent systems globally.*"[379]

Thus, NNEMP might be able to achieve results similar to a nuclear HEMP attack in blacking-out power grids, though the NNEMP attack would probably take hours instead of seconds.

"The technology used in conventional E-Bombs is within reach of any nation capable of designing nuclear weapons and high power radars—e.g. China, Iran, DPRK, Russia," according to NNEMP expert Dr. Kopp:

—"OSINT source material very scarce on E-Bomb technology and designs, effort is usually well hidden from scrutiny;"
—"Potentially large area footprints of many square miles for GigaWatt class weapons, with the usual lethality prediction caveats—targets not tested may be unexpectedly resistant or susceptible at specific weapon frequencies/polarisations;"
—"Terrorist attacks predicated on the availability of proven designs or inventory of E-Bomb munitions—emerging risk;"
—*"The high payoff in using E-Bombs as disruptive or area suppression weapons points to common use in future nation state conflicts involving developed nations.*"[380]

The technology for non-nuclear EMP generators and drones is widely available for purchase as civilian equipment which can easily be weaponized, even by non-state actors.

As noted earlier, one U.S. company sells a NNEMP device for legitimate industrial purposes called the "EMP Suitcase" that looks like a suitcase, can be carried and operated by one person, generates 100,000 volts/meter over a short distance, and can be purchased by anyone. NNEMP devices like the "EMP Suitcase" could become the Dollar Store version of weapons of mass destruction if turned against the national electric grid by terrorists.[381] A German version of the "EMP Suitcase" weighs only 62 pounds, easily deliverable by a drone or cruise missile.[382]

In 2020, Northeastern University's Global Resilience Institute (GRI) tested in an EMP simulator numerous electronic components vital to the operation of electric grids and other critical infrastructures. The GRI tests "confirmed the ability for non-state actors to outfit commercially-available platforms to conduct localized tactical EMI attacks against electronics that support critical systems…identified the thresholds at which the functioning of representative electronics in common use across multiple infrastructures could become compromised, generating catastrophic outcomes. This includes, but is not limited to, disruption in cybersecurity safeguards for critical infrastructure to include key components of the electric power grid and telecommunications system."[383]

---

[379] Emphasis original in Dr. Carlo Kopp, "E-Bombs vs. Pervasive Infrastructure Vulnerability" Briefing, Pacific Theater Air, Sea, Land Battle Concept: IO/EW/Cyber Operations International Conference (Monash University/Air Power Australia) carlo.kopp@monash.edu.

[380] Ibid, emphasis original.

[381] Applied Physics Electronics, "High-Power RF Suitcase EMP Pulse Generator" www.apelc.com/rf-suitcase.

[382] U.S. FERC Interagency Report, Wiliam Radasky and Edward Savage, *Intentional Electromagnetic Interference (IEMI) and Its Impact on the U.S. Power Grid* (Meta-R-323) Metatech Corporation (January 2010) p. 2-5.

[383] Global Research Institute Northeastern University, *Mobilizing a National Response to the Vulnerability of Critical Infrastructure to Non-nuclear Electromagnetic Pulse/Electromagnetic Interference Attacks* (April 2020) p. 4.

GRI's tests of the non-nuclear EMP threat "confirm that a small EMI emitter that could be carried on a commercially-available drone or terrestrial vehicle, is capable of compromising electronic components, in common commercial use, at very low-energy levels from a considerable distance."[384]

Most NNEMP generators have limited range, less than 10 kilometers.[385] But if mated to a cruise missile or drone capable of protracted flight to target electric grid key nodes, the results can be spectacular.

For example, Boeing's Counter-electronics High Power Microwave Advanced Missile Project (CHAMP) cruise missile can be viewed on the internet where CHAMP "navigated a pre-programmed flight plan and emitted bursts of high-powered energy, effectively knocking out the target's data and electronic subsystems."[386] The U.S. Air Force has purchased CHAMP cruise missiles, deployed to Japan, reportedly to prevent North Korean missile attacks by "frying" their missiles, command and control, and power grid electronics.[387]

Russia may still be the world leader in NNEMP weapons, as was the USSR during the Cold War. Russia's nuclear-powered cruise missile, the Burevestnik (Storm Petrel, NATO designation SSC-X-9 Skyfall), now under development, makes little sense as yet another missile to deliver nuclear warheads, as advertised by Moscow. The Storm Petrel's engines, powered by a nuclear reactor, theoretically will give it unlimited range and limitless flying time for crossing oceans and cruising over the U.S. The Storm Petrel could be a nuclear-powered version of CHAMP, able to fly much farther and longer and armed with a more potent NNEMP warhead, electrically supercharged by the nuclear-reactor.[388]

Iran has demonstrated sophisticated cruise missiles and drones, using over 20 to make highly precise and coordinated attacks on Saudi Arabia's oil processing facilities on September 14, 2019.[389] Such delivery vehicles could easily be armed with NNEMP warheads, to make a less sophisticated version of CHAMP.

India's Institute for Defence Studies and Analysis worries about being attacked with NNEMP weapons anonymously to defeat deterrence, but also sees possession of such weapons as a possible deterrent:

"EMP weapons could also be used clandestinely to take out important targets during peace time, when the use of conventional weapons would be considered outrageous, as it will be difficult to prove who exactly was responsible. Such incapacitating applications of EMP could also prove to be an effective deterrent against enemies contemplating military action."[390]

India's IDSA recommends: "Looking at the gross asymmetrical advantage it provides against adversaries, India should actively consider developing an offensive NNEMP capability."[391]

---

[384] Ibid.

[385] "Range of Russian EMP Weapons Increased to 10 km" Russia Today Military News TASS (July 5, 2020).

[386] "Boeing: CHAMP – Lights Out" www.boeing.com.

[387] Ron Kessler, "USAF Deploys New CHAMP Missile" (May 17, 2019) www.neogaf.com/threats/usaf-deploys-new-champ-missile. Dave Majumdar, "CHAMP: America's EMP Missile that Might Be Able to Fry North Korea's Nukes" The National Interest (December 11, 2017).

[388] Dr. Peter Vincent Pry, "When Will DC Awaken To Putin's Nuclear Aim For US?" Newsmax (August 21, 2019).

[389] "Arms Seized by U.S., Missiles Used to Attack Saudi Arabia 'of Iranian Origin'" Reuters and New York Times (June 11, 2020).

[390] Group Captain Atul Pant, "EMP Weapons and the New Equation of War" Indian Defence Review (October 16, 2017).

[391] Ibid.

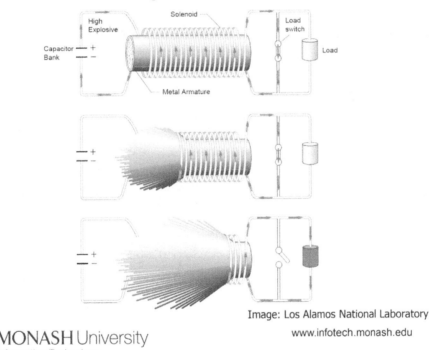

Source: Dr. Carlo Kopp, "E-Bombs vs. Pervasive Infrastructure Vulnerability" briefing to Pacific Theater Air, Sea, Land Battle Concept: IO/EW/Cyber Operations International Conference (Monash University, Air Power Australia) Carlo.Kopp@monash.edu.

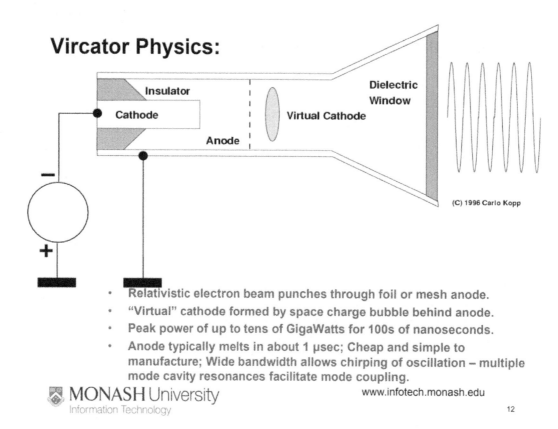

Vircator Physics:

Insulator

Cathode

Anode

Virtual Cathode

Dielectric Window

(C) 1996 Carlo Kopp

- Relativistic electron beam punches through foil or mesh anode.
- "Virtual" cathode formed by space charge bubble behind anode.
- Peak power of up to tens of GigaWatts for 100s of nanoseconds.
- Anode typically melts in about 1 μsec; Cheap and simple to manufacture; Wide bandwidth allows chirping of oscillation – multiple mode cavity resonances facilitate mode coupling.

MONASH University
Information Technology

www.infotech.monash.edu

12

Source: Dr. Carlo Kopp, "E-Bombs vs. Pervasive Infrastructure Vulnerability" briefing to Pacific Theater Air, Sea, Land Battle Concept: IO/EW/Cyber Operations International Conference (Monash University, Air Power Australia) Carlo.Kopp@monash.edu.

HPM (Microwave) E-Bomb Layout

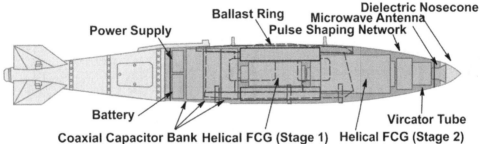

HIGH POWER MICROWAVE E-BOMB - GENERAL ARRANGMENT MK.84 PACKAGING WARHEAD USING VIRCATOR AND 2 STAGE FLUX COMPRESSION GENERATOR

HPM E-BOMB WARHEAD (GBU-31/Mk.84 FORM FACTOR)

MONASH University
Information Technology

www.infotech.monash.edu

13

Source: Dr. Carlo Kopp, "E-Bombs vs. Pervasive Infrastructure Vulnerability" briefing to Pacific Theater Air, Sea, Land Battle Concept: IO/EW/Cyber Operations International Conference (Monash University, Air Power Australia) Carlo.Kopp@monash.edu.

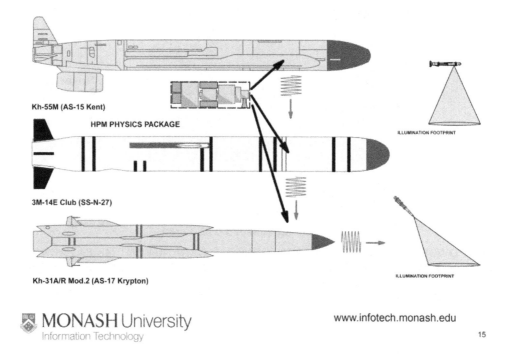

Source: Dr. Carlo Kopp, "E-Bombs vs. Pervasive Infrastructure Vulnerability" briefing to Pacific Theater Air, Sea, Land Battle Concept: IO/EW/Cyber Operations International Conference (Monash University, Air Power Australia) Carlo.Kopp@monash.edu.

Dozens of nations reportedly have NNEMP weapons or are developing them. Some of these are Russia, China, North Korea, Iran, Pakistan, India, Israel, Germany, the United Kingdom, France, Australia, and Switzerland. Ukraine's Yuri Tkasch, Director of the Kharkov Institute of Electromagnetic Research, which was the leading design bureau for the USSR's NNEMP weapons, is a one-man worldwide proliferator of NNEMP technology to any buyer.[392]

The technological revolution in NNEMP weapons threatens to become an electromagnetic "Pearl Harbor" for nations, like the United States, that fail to fully comprehend the threat and have not protected civilian critical infrastructures and military systems.

"Since the term E-Bomb was coined in 1992, the scale of vulnerable infrastructure and systems has multiplied many times over, yet there has been no systematic effort to harden the infrastructure or military systems using COTS [Commercial Off-The Shelf] hardware," warns NNEMP expert Dr. Kopp:

—"Widespread skepticism and disbelief concerning weapon feasibility and infrastructure vulnerability, wholly a result of *technical illiteracy in electromagnetism;"*
—"The notion that a technology which is available and profitable to use in combat would not be used is wishful thinking."
—"*Legislation for electromagnetic hardening of infrastructure and systems for military, dual use and critical civil applications should be introduced immediately.*"[393]

NNEMP: A Clandestine Threat

Non-Nuclear EMP weapons, as a cutting-edge military technology, are being developed largely clandestinely, with relatively little detailed open source reporting on specific national programs, let alone on what terrorists may be doing. So the worldwide status of the NNEMP threat, the power and capabilities of NNEMP weapons in the inventories of state and non-state actors, is largely unknown.

However, the U.S., always more open than most nations, has demonstrated its CHAMP, noted earlier. This NNEMP cruise missile is clearly a threat to electric power grids. CHAMP is well within the technological capabilities of Russia and China. More primitive versions are well within the capabilities of North Korea and Iran.

China, as an example of the clandestine threat, has been working on NNEMP weapons for at least 20 years secretly.

Twenty years ago, the U.S. intelligence community detected China's NNEMP weapons program. According to a previously classified SECRET/NORFORN/XI U.S. defense intelligence report, now declassified, in April 2001: "The Chinese could assemble COTS [Commercial Off-the-shelf Technology] radiofrequency weapons at any time, and may have already done so without our knowledge since it is unlikely that fabrication of such devices would be detected by standard intelligence methods"[394]

Moreover, the U.S. intelligence report assesses that the first NNEMP weapon developed by China will likely be designed to attack critical infrastructures, like electric power grids: "…the first systems

---

[392] "Kiev Gave Riyadh Technology To Create Microwave Weapons" en.topwar.ru (23 January 2019).

[393] Emphasis original in Dr. Carlo Kopp, "E-Bombs vs. Pervasive Infrastructure Vulnerability" Briefing, Pacific Theater Air, Sea, Land Battle Concept: IO/EW/Cyber Operations International Conference (Monash University/Air Power Australia) carlo.kopp@monash.edu.

[394] Department of Defense, *Assessment of Chinese Radiofrequency Weapon Capabilities* National Ground Intelligence Center, NGIC-1867-0285-01 (April 2001) p. 9.

functioning as RF [Radio Frequency] weapons that the Chinese have the capability to deploy…could be effective for launching attacks at short range against critical elements of civilian and military infrastructure including electric-power distribution facilities, telecommunications networks and satellite ground terminals."[395]

Furthermore, according to the previously classified U.S. intelligence report, assessing the NNEMP threat from China 20 years ago:

—*"The Chinese are conducting research on high-power RF generation, susceptibility, and propagation that is relevant to the development of RF weapons."*
—*"…the Chinese have written about the use of radiofrequency (RF) weapons for waging information warfare and government officials have been quoted as stating that RF weapons that would defeat the enemy's electronics are among those weapons that China will need in the 21st century."*
—*"Clearly the purpose of the NINT [acronym for China research institute] measurements is to determine the optimum operating parameters for RF weapons designed to upset computers. In the same vein, an earlier paper from the National University of Defense Technology described experiments in which gigawatt HPM [High-Power Microwave] pulses from a VCO were used to induce upset and damage in computer components—a microprocessor, two sets of binary counters, and individual transistors and CMOs."*
—*"The NUDT [National University of Defense Technology] authors state explicitly that their purpose is to gain a better understanding of HPM effects on electronics in order 'to develop high-power microwave weapons and harden our vulnerable components.'"*
—*"The unclassified publications discussed above leave no doubt the Chinese are contemplating the development of RF weapons to defeat computers and electronic mines…for air defense and for antisatellite applications."*
—*[Illustration of a Chinese RF weapon] "concealed inside a truck so that it may be employed clandestinely."*
—*"…there is evidence of Chinese interest [in] a repetitively-pulse RF system deployed in a cruise missile or unmanned aerial vehicle flying at low altitude and that is used to attack ground targets such as air-defense sites and command and control infrastructure."*[396]

The last quote above indicates that, 20 years ago, China was working toward an NNEMP cruise missile or Unmanned Aerial Vehicle (UAV) resembling the new U.S. CHAMP. China may have eclipsed CHAMP, as it has developed weaponized UAVs capable of evading radar and traveling intercontinental distances, 15,000 miles, from Beijing to Chicago and back, while carrying smart bombs, jamming radars, and conducting electronic warfare.[397]

Russia is proliferating NNEMP weapons technology worldwide, offering their Rosa-E and Ranets-E high-powered microwave "cannons" for sale at international arms shows as long ago as 2001, almost certainly not Russia's most sophisticated NNEMP weapons.[398]

Electric Grid Vulnerability To NNEMP Attack

Perhaps the best unclassified report on the vulnerability of the U.S. electric power grid to NNEMP attack is Metatech's *Intentional Electromagnetic Interference (IEMI) and Its Impact on the U.S.*

---

[395] Ibid.

[396] Ibid, pp. iii, 1, 5, 6, 7-9, 11.

[397] "China Reveals Chilling New 'Sharp Sword' Stealth Drone" www.mirror.co.uk (19 January 2017). "Losing World War III Inside America's Borders" Washington Times (8 September 2020).

[398] John Keller, "Russia Offers To Develop New Types Of Radio Frequency Weapons—If Buyers Pay For Research" Military and Aerospace Electronics (1 January 2002).

Power Grid (January 2010). This interagency report, sponsored and coordinated with the U.S. Federal Energy Regulatory Commission (FERC), the Department of Defense and Oak Ridge National Laboratory, is based on comprehensive testing and analysis of SCADAs, PLCs and other electronics vital to electric power grid operations.[399]

The bottom-line is that the U.S. electric power grid is vulnerable, potentially highly vulnerable, to exactly the kind of electromagnetic fields that can be generated by NNEMP attack. Critical electric grid components experience upset and damage when exposed to NNEMP fields of 10,000 volts/meter (10 kilovolts/meter or 10 kV/m) or much less, in many cases less than 1,000 volts/meter (1 kV/m).

The empirical results of *Intentional Electromagnetic Interference (IEMI) and Its Impact on the U.S. Power Grid* deserve quoting at length:

"While this report aims to inform the reader about the threat of IEMI against commercial electronic equipment and systems in general, it is clear that the biggest threat is against the civil infrastructure, as shutting down the control electronics associated with the power grid, the telecom network or other parts of the critical infrastructure could have widespread impacts."[400]

The *IEMI* report notes some examples of accidental electromagnetic transients causing: explosions and fire on a U.S. aircraft carrier that killed 134 sailors, the failure of anti-lock braking (ABS) systems on Germany's autobahn, and a death resulting from electromagnetically induced failure of a monitor and defibrillator in an ambulance, caused by the radio.[401]

While governments have ignored or been unaware of the threat from NNEMP, the *IEMI* report notes that, more than 20 years ago, in 1999, the International Radio Scientific Union (URSI) passed a "Resolution of Criminal Activities using Electromagnetic Tools" warning of:

—*"The existence of criminal activities using electromagnetic tools and associated phenomenon."*
—*"The fact that criminal activities using electromagnetic tools can be undertaken covertly and anonymously and that physical boundaries such as fences and walls can be penetrated by electromagnetic fields."*
—*"The potentially serious nature of the effects of criminal activities using electromagnetic tools on infrastructure and important functions in society such as transportation, communication, security, and medicine."*
—*"That the possible disruptions of the health and economic activities of nations could have major consequences."[402]*

Some important technical findings from test results and analysis in *Intentional Electromagnetic Interference (IEMI) and Its Impact on the U.S. Power Grid* are that even small electromagnetic generators like the "EMP Suitcase" are a potential threat:

—*"For radiated fields, it seems clear that frequencies above 100 MHz are of primary concern in that they are able to penetrate unshielded or poorly protected buildings very well and yet couple efficiently to the equipment inside of the building. In addition, they have the advantage that antennas designed to radiate efficiently at these frequencies are small."[403]*

---

[399] U.S. FERC Interagency Report, Wiliam Radasky and Edward Savage, *Intentional Electromagnetic Interference (IEMI) and Its Impact on the U.S. Power Grid* (Meta-R-323) Metatech Corporation (January 2010).

[400] Ibid, p. 1-2.

[401] Ibid, p. 1-3.

[402] Ibid, p. 1-4.

[403] Ibid, p. 2-4.

—"*With regard to actual threat 'weapons'…Figure 2-6 illustrates a briefcase weapon (mesoband) developed by a German company for anti-terrorist actions.*"[404]
—"*…existing briefcase test generators are sufficient to create operational problems, if the facility and its internal equipment are not properly grounded.*"[405]
—"*For wideband radiated threat waveforms, buildings can be exposed externally to hyperband waveforms with peak field levels on the order of 10 kV/m. For briefcase devices, the same level of peak field in the hyperband to the mesoband range can be delivered and should be considered.*"[406]

The *IEMI* report warns that, while non-nuclear EMP weapons can deliver thousands of volts on target: "The modern civil infrastructure is very dependent on computers, which operate at logic levels of a few volts. So an intentional interference can occur at a few volts in critical circuits, causing logic upset…If one raises the interfering signal to some tens of volts, then one may expect permanent damage to occur in the circuit elements by some type of breakdown, which in turn provides a path for the power supply to insert much more energy than provided initially by the incident waveform."[407] Unprotected systems are vulnerable to "functional upset from radiated fields as low as 30 V/m [30 volts/meter]."[408]

The *IEMI* report notes that testing has proven the vulnerability of a wide range of modern electronic equipment, including: "cash machines, industrial control equipment, power supplies, Ethernet components, WIFI networks, automobiles, GPS electronics, cellular phones, PDAs and different types of sensors." Automobiles experience upset (engine stop) at 500 V/m and permanent damage at 15-24 kV/m.[409]

Intentional Electromagnetic Interference (IEMI) and Its Impact on the U.S. Power Grid finds from testing: "For conducted IEMI threats, it seems clear that if access to external telecom or power cables is not prevented, it is fairly easy to inject harmful signals into a building. Experiments have shown that narrowband voltages injected into the grounding system of a building can cause significant equipment malfunctions inside. Frequencies below 100 Hz and levels below 100 volts have been known to cause problems."[410]

Moreover: "While these failure values may seem low, they should not be a surprise. When one examines the EMC (Electro-Magnetic Compatibility] test requirements for immunity…it is unusual to see a narrowband radiated field level immunity requirement above 10 V/m [10 volts/meter]…This is also the current recommended immunity level for medical devices that are needed to support life."[411]

Summarizing the vulnerability of modern electronic equipment generally, the *IEMI* report finds:

—"*For narrowband, radiated fields, it appears that modern electronic equipment will have serious upsets at 0.5 kV/m for a frequency of 1 GHz. At 400 MHz upsets occur as low as 0.3 kV/m. Above 1 GHz, higher levels are required.*"
—"*For wideband, radiated fields, the onset of upsets occurs at [about] 2 kV/m. Damage occurs at levels only a factor of 2-3 higher ([about] 5 kV/m).*"

---

[404] Ibid, p. 2-5.

[405] Ibid, p. 2-8.

[406] Ibid, p. 2-10.

[407] Ibid, p. 3-1.

[408] Ibid, p. 3-2.

[409] Ibid, p. 4-1.

[410] Ibid, p. 4-3.

[411] Ibid, p. 4-4.

—"For conducted, wideband voltages, fast pulses with 5/50 ns pulse characteristics (rise time/pulse width), show serious malfunctions at peak levels of [about] 2kV/m and damage at [about] 4/kV. There is not much data for faster pulse injection waveforms at this time, so it is possible that the susceptibility levels could be even lower for faster pulses. Slower pulses (10/700 microseconds) have shown damage as low as 0.5 k/V with rare upsets."
—"For conducted narrowband voltages, only limited testing has been performed, but severe upsets have occurred when the grounding system of buildings were injected at levels of 100 V for frequencies below 100 Hz."[412]

The *IEMI* report notes that, at much shorter range, non-nuclear EMP weapons are comparable to the effects of nuclear E1 HEMP: "It is clear that there are many similarities between the peak field levels that can be produced by EM weapons at close ranges and by E1 HEMP. The IEMI waveforms tend to have higher frequency content than E1 HEMP, so they are likely to create equipment and system failures at lower peak levels than E1 HEMP."[413]

Assessing vulnerability of the U.S. electric power grid to non-nuclear EMP weapons, the *IEMI* report analyzed data testing:

1. High voltage substation controls and communication

2. Power generation facilities

3. Power control centers

4. Distribution transformers

5. Distribution line insulators

"Of these 5 portions of the power system, items 1-3 are of the biggest concern due to IEMI," according to the report.[414]

Intentional Electromagnetic Interference (IEMI) and Its Impact on the U.S. Power Grid found that high voltage substation controls and communication, crucial to the operation of the U.S. power grid, are most vulnerable, including:

1. "Computers, of various kinds."

2. "PLCs—programmable logic controllers—basically computers, but specialized with I/O ports, such as A/D and D/A converters (A=analog, D=digital) so that they can process controllers."

3. "Communication devices—modems, routers, switches, etc."

4. "Solid-state safety relays (increasingly used as replacements for the older electromechanical power relays)."

5. "SCADA systems (Supervisory Control And Data Acquisition)—this involves communication of data and controls between unmanned substations and manned control centers."[415]

---

[412] Ibid, p. 4-5.
[413] Ibid, p. 5-1.
[414] Ibid, p. 5-1
[415] Ibid, pp. 5-2-5-3.

Testing finds: "Such devices can be vulnerable to either upset or damage from IEMI pulses coming in on the connected wiring. (There is always the possibility that some functional upsets might actually lead to damage, in which the system's own energy is turned against itself, such as for devices controlling moving structures or burning of fuels, for example)."[416]

A few examples from the many test results that damaged critical electric grid equipment, from the *IEMI* report:

—*"The IRGC ports for both the SEL 331L and SEL 2032 [relays] were broken at a level of a few hundred volts (600 volts open circuit). The Ethernet connection on the SCADA unit was also damaged at the low level (1.2 kV open circuit). In this case we heard a 'bang' associated with the damage, and further testing showed that a resistor on the circuit board had blown up."*[417]

—*"Figure 5-7 shows the Fisher ROC809 unit…The effects ranged from some that were localized to the port that was pulsed, up to effects occurring on other parts of the device. Damage was as low as 1 kV for the analog out port. The analog out card damage was subtle at first—its output was more and more inaccurate as the pulse level was increased, until finally (at 1 kV) the level was too high, and it would no longer work."*

—*"A computer was also tested…The Ethernet switch was upset (stopped working) at the 2.0-2.5 kV level. The full 8-port unit stopped communicating…On the computer two different network circuits were tried…These upset at the 4.5-5.0 kV level…The serial port on the computer died at a very low level—750 volts."*[418]

Intentional Electromagnetic Interference (IEMI) and Its Impact on the U.S. Power Grid bottom-line: "Given the vulnerability levels for such equipment, and the levels of coupled signal that IEMI can produce, it can be seen that the 'brains' and communication systems of any modern power facility could be vulnerable to IEMI. This applies to power substations, control centers, and power generation facilities…It is important to evaluate the IEMI threat to high voltage power networks throughout the world, and to develop protection methods against this threat."[419]

NNEMP Attack On The U.S. Electric Grid

Described here are two possible technical scenarios for Non-Nuclear EMP attacks on the U.S. electric grid, out of many possible scenarios. The political-military scenarios are also many.

Political-Military Scenarios

Political-military scenarios for NNEMP attack on the U.S. national power grid include:

—Surprise attack "bolt from the blue" in peacetime, based on adversary calculation that war is eventually inevitable;
—NNEMP attack during a crisis but prior to outbreak of a "shooting war" as a warning and/or preemptive strike designed to cripple U.S. power projection capabilities;
—NNEMP attack coordinated with the outbreak of a traditional "shooting war";

---

416 Ibid, p. 5-3.

417 Ibid, p. 5-4.

418 Ibid, p. 5-5.

419 Ibid, p. 5-13.

—NNEMP attack as a last-ditch effort to reverse the tide of a losing war;
—NNEMP attack in the aftermath of a lost war, for revenge.

The scale of an NNEMP attack on the U.S. electric grid could include:

—Temporary blackout of a city to send a warning (as China did to Mumbai, India in October 2020 by cyber-attack)[420];
—Protracted blackout of a state or region to send a bigger warning and/or to cripple particular U.S. military capabilities;
—Protracted nationwide blackout of the U.S. electric grid to defeat the U.S. without a traditional "shooting war" and possibly to eliminate the U.S. as an actor on the world stage (as described in the military doctrines of Russia, China, North Korea, and Iran).[421]

There are many possible political-military scenarios. The focus here is on technical scenarios including adversary capabilities.

Technical Scenario: Nationwide Blackout

The most difficult technical scenario for the NNEMP threat is an attack on the U.S. power grid nationwide, against all three major parts comprising the national grid—the Eastern grid, Western grid, and Texas grid—that inflicts against all three grids simultaneously a protracted blackout, lasting weeks, months, or longer. As shall be demonstrated, since an NNEMP attack can achieve this worst-case scenario, all the lesser scenarios described earlier are also possible.

In both scenarios described here, the technical objective is to damage SCADAs and other vital electronics in EHV transformer substation control centers, of which there are 2,000 in the U.S. national electric power grid. EHV transformers themselves are unlikely to be damaged by NNEMP attack, but damaging the SCADAs and other control systems can stop transformer operations. As shown earlier, extensive testing of SCADAs and other control electronics proves they are highly vulnerable to the NNEMP threat.

In both scenarios, the tactical objective is to damage as many EHV transformer substation control centers as possible in a period of 24 hours. Near simultaneous damage of enough substations will at some point inevitably trigger cascading failures, as more and more load gets dumped on undamaged substations. Cascading failures result rapidly in a nationwide blackout, like the Great Northeast Blackout of 2003 writ larger and lasting much longer because of much deeper damage to the national electric power grid.[422]

A useful point of reference for assessing the likely effectiveness of the two NNEMP attacks described below is a classified study by the U.S. Federal Energy Regulatory Commission, leaked to the press, that found a protracted nationwide blackout could result from sabotage against EHV transformer substations that targets just 9 of 2,000 substations.[423]

---

[420] "China Appears To Warn India: Push Too Hard and the Lights Could Go Out" New York Times (28 February 2021).

[421] EMP Commission, *Nuclear EMP Attack Scenarios and Combined-Arms Cyber Warfare* (17 July 2017) pp. 1-11. "Russia: 'War Is Inevitable…Cyberwar'" Newsmax (19 April 2021).

[422] U.S.-Canada Power System Outage Task Force, *Final Report on the August 14, 2003 Blackout in the United States and Canada* (Canada: April 2004).

[423] Rebecca Smith, "Transformers Expose Limits In Securing Power Grid" Wall Street Journal (14 March 2014).

Scenario #1: Lower-Tech NNEMP Attack

Scenario #1 is the kind of threat that is well within the technological and operational capabilities of Iran, North Korea, virtually any nation state, and major terrorist or criminal organizations.

Scenario #1 entails a lower-tech NNEMP threat employing weapons which must be man-delivered by automobile or panel truck. The postulated NNEMP weapons are lower-tech also in power, requiring about 10 minutes to maximize damage against the electronics in unmanned electric grid control substations associated with EHV transformers.

Scenario #1 postulates that every panel truck armed with an NNEMP weapon has a two-man crew, one to drive and one to operate the weapon. The NNEMP weapon illuminates the target—an EHV transformer control substation—for 10 minutes. Then the panel truck moves to the next target, the nearest next substation, located on average 40 road miles away, traveling on average 50 mph.

Given these conditions, a single panel truck carrying an NNEMP weapon and 2-man crew can attack 30 EHV transformer control substations in 24 hours. Below find the capabilities for an NNEMP attack performed by up to 30 vehicles in 24 hours:

—1 NNEMP truck can attack 30 EHV transformer control substations in 24 hours;
—2 NNEMP trucks can attack 60 substations;
—3 NNEMP trucks can attack 90 substations;
—4 NNEMP trucks can attack 120 substations;
—5 NNEMP trucks can attack 150 substations;
—6 NNEMP trucks can attack 180 substations;
—7 NNEMP trucks can attack 210 substations;
—8 NNEMP trucks can attack 230 substations;
—9 NNEMP trucks can attack 260 substations;
—10 NNEMP trucks can attack 280 substations;
—11 NNEMP trucks can attack 310 substations;
—12 NNEMP trucks can attack 340 substations;
—13 NNEMP trucks can attack 370 substations;
—14 NNEMP trucks can attack 400 substations;
—15 NNEMP trucks can attack 430 substations;
—16 NNEMP trucks can attack 460 substations;
—17 NNEMP trucks can attack 490 substations;
—18 NNEMP trucks can attack 520 substations;
—19 NNEMP trucks can attack 550 substations;
—20 NNEMP trucks can attack 580 substations;
—21 NNEMP trucks can attack 610 substations;
—22 NNEMP trucks can attack 640 substations;
—23 NNEMP trucks can attack 670 substations;
—24 NNEMP trucks can attack 700 substations;
—25 NNEMP trucks can attack 730 substations;
—26 NNEMP trucks can attack 760 substations;
—27 NNEMP trucks can attack 790 substations;
—28 NNEMP trucks can attack 820 substations;
—29 NNEMP trucks can attack 850 substations;
—30 NNEMP trucks can attack 880 substations.

As noted earlier, reportedly a classified U.S. FERC study calculates that damaging 9 of 2,000 EHV transformer substations (0.45% of all transformers) is enough to cause a protracted blackout nationwide. Just one NNEMP truck could damage over three times this many (30) substations in 24 hours, but in only one of the three big grids.

At minimum, three NNEMP trucks would be required to attack the Eastern, Western, and Texas grids. These collectively could damage 90 substations, 30 substations damaged in each of the major grid systems, ten times the number of substations damaged in the U.S. FERC study.

The NNEMP attack would probably focus on areas that have the highest concentration of EHV transformer control substations, to maximize opportunities for inflicting the most damage in 24 hours.

In the Eastern grid, the seaboard area between Washington, DC and New York City has the highest concentration of substations. In Texas, substations are most highly concentrated around Dallas, Houston, and Austin. In the Western grid, substations are more geographically dispersed, but most concentrated around Los Angeles and Seattle and on the seaboard in between.

Since the Eastern grid generates about 75% of U.S. electricity, an NNEMP attack, or any other kind of attack, would probably focus most of its effort there. Logically, if the attack is proportioned to the percentage of the U.S. electric power supply, about 75% of the effort would attack the Eastern grid, 20% the Western grid, and 5% the Texas grid.

So in Scenario #1, if 20 NNEMP trucks are employed to attack the three big grids in proportion to their electric generating power, 15 would attack the Eastern Grid, 4 would attack the Western grid, and 1 would attack the Texas grid. Collectively, 20 NNEMP trucks could damage 580 EHV transformer substations in 24 hours, 430 substations in the East, 120 substations in the West, 30 substations in Texas—29% of all substations nationwide.

Scenario #1 requires very few operational personnel, just six men for three NNEMP trucks to attack all three big grids. The "army" manning 30 NNEMP trucks would number just 60 men. By way of comparison, al Qaeda's September 11, 2001, attacks on New York and Washington, that started the long War on Terrorism, was executed by 19 terrorists.

Scenario #1 and this chapter focuses exclusively on NNEMP attacks. But it is highly likely, if this scenario were to occur, the NNEMP attack would be supplemented by a kinetic attack on the EHV transformers too, using for example rocket propelled grenade launchers or a high-powered 0.50 caliber rifle firing explosive bullets, to destroy the EHV transformers while their control substations are also being attacked by NNEMP.

Scenario #2: Higher-Tech NNEMP Attack

Scenario #2 is the kind of threat that is well within the technological and operational capabilities of Russia and China, plausibly within the capabilities of North Korea and Iran, and even possibly within the capabilities of major terrorist or criminal organizations.

Scenario #2 entails a higher-tech NNEMP threat employing CHAMP-like drones or Unmanned Aerial Vehicles (UAVs) that can be preprogrammed or guided to attack EHV transformer control substations. The postulated NNEMP weapons are higher-tech also in power, requiring about 1-5 minutes to maximize damage against the electronics in unmanned electric grid control substations associated with EHV transformers.

Scenario #2 postulates an NNEMP drone or UAV that can fly 100 mph, locate the target, pause to make an NNEMP attack, and sustain these operations continuously for 24 hours. China's Pterodactyl UAV is exactly the kind of drone/UAV capable of such operations, if armed with an NNEMP warhead. Russia has similar UAVs, including the Skyfall cruise missile, powered by a nuclear reactor, that could conceivably energize a super-charged NNEMP warhead. Iran has demonstrated drones, UAVs, and cruise missiles capable of precision attacks on Saudi Arabian oil facilities, that could be modified to make an NNEMP attack.[424]

Scenario #2 postulates, after illuminating the target for 1-5 minutes, the drone or UAV moves to the next target, the nearest next substation, located on average 20 flight miles away, traveling on average 100 mph.

Given these conditions, a single drone/UAV armed with an NNEMP weapon, illuminating each target for 1 minute, can attack 110 EHV transformer control substations in 24 hours. If the time on each target lasts 5 minutes, a single drone/UAV can attack 85 targets in 24 hours. Below find the capabilities for an NNEMP attack, lasting 1-5 minutes on each substation, performed by up to 10 drones/UAVs in 24 hours:

SUBSTATIONS ATTACKED IN 24 HOURS

# DRONES/UAVs:	1	2	3	4	5	6	7	8	9	10
MINUTES										
ON TARGET										
1	110	220	330	440	550	660	770	880	990	1100
2	103	203	306	409	512	615	718	821	924	1027
3	96	192	288	384	480	576	672	768	864	960
4	90	180	270	360	450	540	630	720	810	900
5	85	170	255	340	425	510	595	680	765	850

In the case of Russia or China, drones or UAVs could travel intercontinental distances, fly under radar, to make the NNEMP attacks. As noted earlier, China has a stealthy intercontinental UAV that can fly 15,000 miles, from Beijing to Chicago and back, to make attacks with missiles and conduct electronic warfare.[425]

NNEMP drones/UAVs could be launched off false-flagged freighters from U.S. coastal waters, for greater anonymity and plausible deniability. Freighter-launching would bring the U.S. in range of the kind of drones/UAVs currently available to Iran and North Korea. The freighter could carry all the technical personnel needed to perform the attack. Drones/UAVs could be disguised as cargo, hidden in and launched from shipping containers, like Russia's Club-K missile system, designed to convert ordinary freighters into missile launching platforms. The Club-K has been purchased by Iran.

Alternatively, NNEMP drones/UAVs could be shipped into the United States undetected, stored in warehouses located nearest targets in the electric grid, launched and operated from secure warehouses. This scenario would require three secure warehouses, one located in the Eastern grid, one in the Western grid, and one in the Texas grid.

---

[424] "China Reveals Chilling New 'Sharp Sword' Stealth Drone" www.mirror.co.uk (19 January 2017). "Losing World War III Inside America's Borders" Washington Times (8 September 2020). "When Will DC Awaken To Putin's Nuclear Aim For US?" Newsmax (21 August 2019). "Russia's Top Long-Range Attack Drones" airforce-technology.com (27 November 2020). "Drone Attacks Cripple Production At Giant Saudi Oil Plants" www.abc.net.au (14 September 2019). "2019 Abqaiq-Khurais Attack" en.wikipedia.org.
[425] Ibid.

For drones/UAVs that are range-limited, like those currently inventoried by Iran and North Korea, a minimum of three drones/UAVs would be required to make NNEMP attacks on the three big grids—Eastern, Western, and Texas. If NNEMP illumination on each substation lasts 1 minute, 3 drones/UAVs can attack 330 of 2,000 substations in 24 hours.

As noted earlier, a U.S. FERC study reportedly found that sabotaging just 9 of 2,000 EHV transformer substations could start catastrophic cascading failures, causing a protracted nationwide blackout.

10 drones/UAVs making NNEMP attacks, illuminating each target for 1 minute, could in 24 hours attack 1,100 substations, 55% of all EHV transformer control substations. If the NNEMP attack allocates 10 drones/UAVs roughly according to the percentage of electric power generated by each of the big grids, the Eastern grid would get 7 drones/UAVs, the Western grid 2 drones/UAVs, and Texas 1 drone UAV. Consequently, 770 substations would be attacked in the East, 220 substations in the West, and 110 substations in Texas.

A protracted nationwide blackout of the U.S. electric power grid, lasting weeks, months, or longer, would be inevitable.

Aftermath

Unlike the Great Northeast Blackout of 2003, the nationwide blackout from NNEMP attack will not be quickly recoverable because of widespread damage to numerous EHV transformer control substations. Many transformers, additional substations not attacked by NNEMP, and other electric grid equipment not attacked by NNEMP, may nonetheless be damaged by system-generated over-voltages as the grid collapses, as often happens during severe weather, like hurricanes.

Unlike hurricanes, that only have regional impact, a nationwide blackout induced by NNEMP attack will cause much deeper and more widespread systemic damage to all three parts of the North American grid—Eastern, Western, and Texas. Identifying damaged substations, locating and accurately diagnosing damage to equipment, will take time, probably many weeks. Replacing damaged equipment may not even be possible because of insufficient spares.

Acquiring replacement equipment and installation will require many weeks or months, if even possible when all critical infrastructures—communications, transportation, petroleum and natural gas, business and finance, food and water infrastructures—are inoperable or severely crippled due to protracted nationwide blackout.

Utility emergency crews are typically too few and inadequately resourced to repair and recover electric grids from damage inflicted by hurricanes, let alone a nationwide NNEMP attack. Utility workers are not the police or firefighters, and may not even report to work from concern for their families as a nationwide blackout quickly becomes growing chaos. After Hurricane Katrina, many on duty police and firefighters stayed home with their families instead, 24 hours after the lights went out.

U.S. military power projection capabilities would be severely crippled or altogether paralyzed by a protracted nationwide blackout. CONUS military bases depend upon the civilian electric grid for 99% of their electric power.[426]

Any rational American president, faced with a ticking clock toward societal chaos and mass starvation, would likely give highest priority to mobilizing all remaining operating resources, including the Defense Department, to recovering the national electric grid and other life-sustaining critical infrastructures, instead of fighting World War III.

---

[426] Loren Thompson, "Critical U.S. Military Sites Can't Cope With A Prolonged Power Outage" Forbes (18 May 2018). Peter Huessy, "Electronic Doomsday for the U.S.?" Gatestone (13 January 2016).

Locations of EHV transformer substations 345 kilovolts or higher.

Source: Adapted from Edward Savage, James Gilbert, and William Radasky, *The Early Time (E1) High-Altitude Electromagnetic Pulse (HEMP) and Its Impact on the U.S. Power Grid*, Meta-R-320 (January 2010) p. 7-20.

NORTH AMERICAN ELECTRIC GRIDS

The Eastern, Western, and Texas grids are called "interconnects" although they are not interconnected. The Eastern and Western North American grids include the USA and Canada.

V

HIGH-ALTITUDE ELECTROMAGNETIC PULSE (HEMP) ATTACK

by Dr. Peter Vincent Pry

A Revolution In Military Affairs

Nuclear HEMP attack is part of the military doctrines, plans and exercises of Russia, China, North Korea, and Iran for a revolutionary new way of warfare against military forces and civilian critical infrastructures by cyber, sabotage, and HEMP. This new way of warfare is called many things by many nations. In Russia, China, and Iran it is called Sixth Generation Warfare, Non-Contact Warfare, Electronic Warfare, Total Information Warfare, and Cyber Warfare. Some U.S. analysts, the very small number paying attention, call it Cybergeddon, Blackout War, or Combined-Arms Cyber Warfare.[427]

Significantly, because HEMP attack entails detonating a nuclear weapon at such high altitude that no blast or other prompt effects injurious to humans are delivered, only the HEMP that immediately damages only electronics, potential adversaries do not appear to regard nuclear HEMP attack as an act of nuclear warfare.

Potential adversaries understand that millions could die from the long-term collateral effects of HEMP and cyber-attacks that cause protracted black-out of national electric grids and other life-sustaining critical infrastructures. At least some regard this relatively easy, potentially anonymous, method of inflicting mass destruction as an attractive feature of what they describe as a "Revolution in Military Affairs".

Ignorance of the military doctrines of potential adversaries and a failure of U.S. strategic imagination, as noted in military writings of potentially hostile powers, is setting America up for an HEMP Pearl Harbor.[428] Russia, China, North Korea and Iran appear to regard nuclear HEMP attack as the ultimate weapon in an all-out "Cyber War" aimed at defeating U.S. and allied military forces on the battlefield and in a theater of operations. They also see HEMP and Combined-Arms Cyber Warfare as a means of defeating entire nations by blacking-out their electric grids and other critical infrastructures for longer periods of time than technologically developed societies, including the U.S., can tolerate without major disruption and loss of life.[429]

---

[427] While many analysts are paying attention to cyber warfare, narrowly defined as the use of computer viruses and hacking and other such techniques, relatively few conceive of "cyber warfare" as potential adversaries do— as Combined-Arms Cyber Warfare entailing coordinated use of computer viruses etc., sabotage and kinetic attack, non-nuclear and nuclear EMP weapons. EMP Commission, *Nuclear EMP Attack Scenarios and Combined-Arms Cyber Warfare* (July 2017). Dr. Peter Vincent Pry, *Blackout Wars* (Task Force on National and Homeland Security, 2015).

[428] For Example: Zhang Shouqi and Sun Xuegui, "Be Vigilant Against 'Pearl Harbor' Incident In The Information Age" Jiefangjun Bao (Official newspaper of the PRC People's Liberation Army, May 14, 1996) translated in FBIS FTS19960514000049

[429] Ambassador R. James Woolsey, "Heading Toward An EMP Catastrophe" Statement for the Record before the Senate Homeland Security and Governmental Affairs Committee, July 22, 2015.

Russia

For example, Russian General Vladimir Slipchenko in his military textbook *Non-Contact Wars* describes the combined use of cyber viruses and hacking, physical attacks, non-nuclear EMP weapons, and ultimately nuclear HEMP attack against electric grids and critical infrastructures as a new way of warfare that is the greatest Revolution in Military Affairs (RMA) in history. Slipchenko sees HEMP as such a departure from traditional ways and means of warfare that he describes HEMP weapons and warfare as "based on new physical principles"—a phrase that has become ubiquitous in Russian literature to describe the RMA that is HEMP:

"In practically all preceding generations of wars...weapons were employed that acted against targets primarily by kinetic, chemical and thermal energy. In addition to these arms...new ones will also appear in...wars of the future....Weapons based on new physical principles having an electromagnetic effect will see considerable development. They will represent a form of casualty and damage producing effect on targets through the energy of electromagnetic emissions of various wavelengths and levels of power generated by radio frequency and laser weapons and by means of electronic countermeasures using a conventional or high-altitude nuclear burst....Depending on the power of emission, such weapons will be capable of...suppressing practically all classic electronic equipment...causing the melting or evaporation of metal in the printed circuit boards...or causing structural changes of electronic elements..."[430]

Like Nazi Germany's Blitzkrieg ("Lightning War") Strategy that coordinated airpower, armor, and mobile infantry to achieve strategic and technological surprise that nearly defeated the Allies in World War II, the New Blitzkrieg is, literally and figuratively, an electronic "Lightning War" so potentially decisive in its effects that an entire civilization could be overthrown in hours.

According to General Slipchenko, HEMP and the new RMA renders obsolete modern armies, navies and air forces. For the first time in history, small nations or even non-state actors can humble the most advanced nations on Earth.

An article in Military Thought, the flagship journal of the Russian General Staff, "Weak Points of the U.S. Concept of Network-Centric Warfare" points to nuclear HEMP attack as a means of defeating the United States:

"American forces may be vulnerable to electronic warfare attacks, in particular, an electromagnetic pulse that is a brief powerful electromagnetic field capable of overloading or destroying numerous electronic systems and high-tech microcircuits that are very sensitive to the electromagnetic field, even if transmitted from a distance. A single low-yield nuclear weapon exploded for this purpose high above the area of combat operations can generate an electromagnetic pulse covering a large area and destroying electronic equipment without loss of life that is caused by the blast or radiation."[431]

Moreover: "Today, too, a considerable body of administrative information in the U.S. armed forces goes through the civilian Internet. Many commercial communication satellites, particularly satellites

---

[430] General Vladimir Slipchenko, Non-Contact Wars (Moscow: January 1, 2000) translated in FBIS CEP20001213000001.
[431] Colonel A.V. Kopylov, Weak Points of the U.S. Concept of Network-Centric Warfare" Military Thought, Volume 3, 2011.

in low orbits, can have their functions impaired or they can be disabled by electromagnetic shocks from high altitudes."[432]

According to another Russian article: "Nuclear war strategy has already planned nuclear explosions at an altitude of 50-100 km to destroy enemy satellites' electronic instruments with electromagnetic pulse":

"There are now 683 space craft in near-earth orbit. Of these about 150 are Russian and about 400 American. In the estimation of specialists, for every 100 of our 'purely' military espionage artificial earth satellites there are 300 civilian satellites. Clearly, this discrepancy will increase both quantitatively and qualitatively (considering the state of the Russian military-industrial complex)....Nuclear war strategy has already planned nuclear explosions at an altitude of 50-100 km to destroy enemy satellites' electronic instruments with an electromagnetic pulse."[433]

A 2015 article from Russia's A.A. Maksimov Scientific Research Institute for Space Systems, alludes to "cyber weapons in the nuclear variant" as the most effective cyber weapon: "Even more effective are remote-controlled cyber weapons in the nuclear variant, but in this case a warhead is required with a capacity many times smaller by comparison with the charges of the typical strategic missiles."[434] The low-yield nuclear weapon described sounds like what Russians call a "Super-EMP" warhead maximally designed, not to make a big explosion, but to emit enhanced-gamma rays to generate HEMP.

Russia made a thinly veiled HEMP threat against the United States on May 2, 1999, in an apparent effort to blackmail the U.S. to stop the Balkans War. During the spring of 1999, tensions between the United States and Russia rose sharply over Operation ALLIED FORCE, the NATO bombing campaign against Yugoslavia. A bipartisan delegation from the House Armed Services Committee of the U.S. Congress met at Vienna with their Russian counterparts on the Duma International Affairs Committee, headed by Chairman Vladimir Lukin. The object of the meeting was to reduce U.S.-Russia tensions and seek Russian help in resolving the Balkans War.

On May 2, during the Vienna meeting, Chairman Lukin and Deputy Chairman Alexander Shabanov chastised the United States for military aggression in the Balkans, and warned that Russia was not helpless to oppose Operation ALLIED FORCE. LUKIN—"Hypothetically, if Russia really wanted to hurt the United States in retaliation for NATO's bombing of Yugoslavia, Russia could fire a submarine launched ballistic missile and detonate a single nuclear warhead at high-altitude over the United States. The resulting electromagnetic pulse would massively disrupt U.S. communications and computer systems, shutting down everything. No internet. Nothing." SHABANOV—"And if that didn't work, we'd just launch another missile."[435]

---

[432] Ibid.

[433] Aleksandr Khokhlov, "If There Are Star Wars Tomorrow," Novyye Izvestiye, November 5, 1997, p. 2 translated in FBIS FTS19971106000897.

[434] Department Chief Dr. Grigoriy Vokin, "Remote Custodian. Warheads with Artificial Intelligence for Reconnaissance, Guaranteed Destruction of Targets, and Human Rescue" A.A. Maksimov Scientific Research Institute (2015).

[435] HASC Transcript On Vienna Conference (May 2, 1999). Interview with Vienna Conference participants Rep. Curt Weldon and Rep. Roscoe Bartlett.

"Super-EMP Is A…First-Strike Weapon"

"The further direction of the work on the development of Super-EMP was associated with the increase of its kill effect by focusing Y-radiation, which should have resulted in an increase of the pulse's amplitude. These properties of Super-EMP make it a first strike weapon, which is designed to disable the state and military command and control system, the economy, ICBMs, especially mobile based ICBMs, missiles on the flight trajectory, radar sites, spacecraft, energy supply systems, and so forth. So, Super-EMP is obviously offensive in nature and is a destabilizing first-strike weapon."

"The Russian nuclear component relies on the Super-EMP factor, which is the Russian response to U.S. nuclear blackmail."

From Aleksey Vaschenko, "A Nuclear Response To America Is Possible" Zavtra (November 1, 2006) translated in CEP20061108358006.

China

China's military doctrine sounds an identical theme about the revolutionary implications of HEMP and Information Warfare. According to People's Liberation Army textbook *World War, the Third World War—Total Information Warfare*, written by Shen Weiguang (allegedly, according to the PRC, the inventor of Information Warfare) "Therefore, China should focus on measures to counter computer viruses, nuclear electromagnetic pulse...and quickly achieve breakthroughs in those technologies...":

"With their massive destructiveness, long-range nuclear weapons have combined with highly sophisticated information technology and information warfare under nuclear deterrence....Information war and traditional war have one thing in common, namely that the country which possesses the critical weapons such as atomic bombs will have "first strike" and "second strike retaliation" capabilities.... As soon as its computer networks come under attack and are destroyed, the country will slip into a state of paralysis and the lives of its people will ground to a halt. Therefore, China should focus on measures to counter computer viruses, nuclear electromagnetic pulse...and quickly achieve breakthroughs in those technologies in order to equip China without delay with equivalent deterrence that will enable it to stand up to the military powers in the information age and neutralize and check the deterrence of Western powers, including the United States."

An article from the People's Republic of China's Air Force Engineering University describes nuclear HEMP weapons as the most powerful and effective variant of electronic warfare weapons for waging Information Warfare. Nuclear and non-nuclear EMP weapons in the context of Information Warfare are the crucial instruments for implementing this Revolution in Military Affairs:

"In future high-tech warfare under informatized conditions, information warfare will span multiple dimensions, including ground, sea, air, and the EM spectrum. Information superiority has already

become central and crucial to achieving victory in warfare…If the communications equipment used for the transmission of battlefield information were attacked and damaged by an opponent's EMP weapons, then the one attacked would face the danger of disruption in battlefield information transmission. EMP severely restricts the tactical performance and battlefield survivability of informatized equipment."[436]

Moreover, the article clearly makes a distinction between nuclear weapons and nuclear HEMP weapons, describing the latter as "a new type of weapon" like non-nuclear EMP weapons, all for waging Information Warfare:

"As opposed to conventional and nuclear weapons, EMP weapons are a new type of weapon capable of causing mass destruction by instantly releasing high-intensity EMP…They can interfere, damage, and overheat electronics, resulting in logic circuit dysfunctions, control malfunctions, or total failure. The unique destructive effect that EMP have on electronic equipment was unintentionally discovered by the United States in the 1960s during a nuclear test. In July 1962, the United States conducted a high-altitude nuclear explosion in the Pacific Ocean. This…unexpectedly overloaded the Honolulu power grid in Hawaii, 1,400 km away, even overheating lightning protection devices on powerlines. On a battlefield, this new-type weapon will cause devastating damage to electronic systems, including computers, communications and control systems, and radars, resulting in immeasurable losses."[437]

Furthermore, according to the article: "There are 3 types of military EMP based on pulse sources: the first is the HEMP produced by the detonation of a low yield nuclear bomb in the atmosphere at high-altitude; the second is…produced by high explosives and related devices; the third is the HPM…produced by HPM devices such as magnetrons and vircators." Nuclear EMP weapons are, or include, Enhanced-HEMP or so-called Super-EMP weapons designed to produce gamma rays and high-frequency E1 HEMP: "HEMP weapons are a type of weak nuclear explosive EMP bomb that produces EMP through the detonation of low-yield nuclear bombs at high-altitudes (70 to 100 km above ground)." The E1 HEMP field "produced by nuclear EMP is about 10 to 100 kV/m and can penetrate and melt any electronic components."

Another article "Special Means of Warfare in the Information Age" notes that Information Warfare includes computer viruses and nuclear HEMP attack, and can be used to collapse an enemy's electric grid and other national critical infrastructures:

"The methods used to achieve destruction or manipulation of the 'byte' can be 'atomic'—such as electromagnetic pulse bombs and so on—or can be 'byte' type—such as computer viruses….The so-called strategic information warfare is the use of destruction or manipulation of the flow of information on a computer network to destroy the enemy's telephone network, fuel pipelines, electric grid, transportation control system, national funds transfer system, various bank clearance systems, and health and sanitation systems, in order to achieve a strategic goal."[438]

---

[436] Zhao Meng, Da Xinyu, and Zhang Yapu, "Overview of Electromagnetic Pulse Weapons and Protection Techniques Against Them" Winged Missiles (PRC Air Force Engineering University: May 1, 2014).
[437] Ibid.
[438] Wang Xiaodong, "Special Means of Warfare in the Information Age," Jianchuan Zhishi, June 30, 1999 translated in FBIS FTS19990727000426.

A January 2016 article "General Trend of the Worldwide Revolution in Military Affairs" by China's National Security Policy Committee sees "electromagnetic pulse bombs" among the new "disruptive technologies" that "can change the 'rules of the game'" by disrupting U.S. military "precision warfare capabilities centered on information technology" thereby sounding "the horn of a new round of revolution in military affairs."[439]

An article in the newspaper of the People's Liberation Army notes that "The United States is more vulnerable than any other country in the world" to attacks by HEMP and Combined-Arms Cyber Warfare:

"Some people might think that things similar to the 'Pearl Harbor Incident' are unlikely to take place during the information age. Yet it could be regarded as the 'Pearl Harbor Incident' of the 21st century if a surprise attack is conducted against the enemy's crucial information systems of command, control, and communications by such means as the electronic warfare, electromagnetic pulse weapons, telecommunications interference and suppression, computer viruses, and if the enemy is deprived of the information it needs as a result. Even a super military power like the United States, which possesses nuclear missiles and powerful armed forces, cannot guarantee its immunity...In their own words, a highly computerized open society like the United States is extremely vulnerable to electronic attacks from all sides. This is because the U.S. economy, from banks to telephone systems and from power plants to iron and steel works, relies entirely on computer networks....When a country grows increasingly powerful economically and technologically...it will become increasingly dependent on modern information systems....The United States is more vulnerable to attacks than any other country in the world..."[440]

North Korea

North Korea appears to have practiced the military doctrines described above against the United States—including by simulating a nuclear HEMP attack against the U.S. mainland.[441]

Following North Korea's third illegal nuclear test in February 2013, North Korean dictator Kim Jong-Un repeatedly threatened to make nuclear missile strikes against the U.S. and its allies. In what was then the worst ever nuclear crisis with North Korea, that lasted months, the U.S. responded by beefing-up National Missile Defenses and flying B-2 bombers in exercises just outside the Demilitarized Zone to deter North Korea.[442]

North Korea's first satellite, the KMS-3, was launched successfully on December 12, 2013, exactly two months before, and probably in anticipation of, North Korea's illegal nuclear test on February 12, 2013. On April 2, 2013, a study by the U.S. Department of Homeland Security warned that North Korea might be able to deliver on its nuclear threats against the United States by making an HEMP attack by satellite.[443]

---

[439] Li Bingyan, "General Trend of the Worldwide Revolution in Military Affairs" PRC National Security Policy Committee (January 2016).

[440] Zhang Shouqi and Sun Xuegui, Jiefangjun Bao, 14 May 1996.

[441] "EMP Threat From North Korea, 2013" Family Security Matters, April 27, 2014.

[442] "U.S. Warns North Korea With Stealth Bomber Flights" Wall Street Journal, March 29, 2013.

[443] U.S. Department of Homeland Security, "North Korean Nuclear Threats (April 2, 2013 FOUO).

However, the study was suppressed as "politically incorrect" because it contradicted public statements by President Obama and his administration that North Korea could not make a nuclear missile strike on the U.S.[444]

On April 9, 2013, North Korea's KMS-3 satellite orbited over the U.S. moving from south to north on a polar trajectory that evades U.S. early warning radars and National Missile Defenses, at the near optimum altitude and location to place an HEMP field over all 48 contiguous United States.[445]

On April 16, 2013, the KMS-3 again orbited over the Washington, D.C.-New York City corridor where, if the satellite contained a nuclear warhead, it could project the peak HEMP field over the U.S. political and economic capitals and collapse the Eastern Grid, which generates 75 percent of U.S. electricity. On the same day, parties unknown used AK-47s to attack the Metcalf transformer substation that services San Francisco, the Silicon Valley, and is an important part of the Western Grid. Blackout of the Western Grid, or of just San Francisco, would impede U.S. power projection capabilities against North Korea.[446]

In July 2013, a North Korean freighter (the Chong Chon Gang) transited the Gulf of Mexico with SA-2 missiles in its hold, mounted on their launchers hidden under bags of sugar, discovered only after the freighter tried to return to North Korea through the Panama Canal.[447] Although the missiles were not nuclear-armed, they are designed to carry a 10 kiloton warhead, and could execute the Congressional EMP Commission's nightmare scenario of an anonymous HEMP attack launched offshore from a freighter. All during this period, the U.S. electric grid and other critical infrastructures experienced various kinds of cyber-attacks, as they do continuously every day.

On January 6, 2016, North Korea provoked another nuclear crisis with its fourth illegal nuclear test of what it claimed was an H-Bomb. On February 7th, again amidst threats to make a nuclear missile strike on the United States, Pyongyang orbited another satellite, the KMS-4, on the same polar trajectory as the KMS-3.[448]

North Korea now has two satellites orbiting over North America on trajectories optimized to evade U.S. Ballistic Missile Early Warning radars and missile defenses and make a surprise HEMP attack, if the satellites are nuclear-armed. The satellites could be nuclear-armed and constitute a constant HEMP threat, the 21st Century equivalent of "battleship diplomacy."

Kim Jong-Un has threatened to reduce the United States to "ashes" with "nuclear thunderbolts" and threatened to retaliate for U.S. diplomatic and military pressure by "ordering officials and scientists to complete preparations for a satellite launch as soon as possible" amid "the enemies' harsh sanc-

---

[444] F. Michael Maloof, "DHS Study: North Korea Capable Of EMP Attack On U.S." World Net Daily (April 9, 2014).

[445] KMS-3 is NORAD's acronym for North Korea's satellite Kwangmyongsong-3 (Lodestar-3 or Guiding Star-3), a name richly symbolic for Korean mythology and the deification of Kim Jong-Un who according to official propaganda was born on Mt. Paeku under a newly appeared bright guiding star, signifying the birth of a great general.

[446] Rebecca Smith, "Assault On California Power Station Raises Alarm On Potential For Terrorism" Wall Street Journal, February 5, 2014.

[447] "North Korean Ship Yields Worrisome Cargo" Wall Street Journal, July 17, 2013; "North Korea's Cuban Missile Crisis" 38 North, August 1, 2013.

[448] "North Korea May Have Tested Components Of A Hydrogen Bomb" CNN, January 29, 2016; "North Korea Launches 'Satellite,' Sparks Fears About Long-Range Missile Program" Washington Post, February 6, 2016.

tions and moves to stifle" the North.[449] North Korean press (for example in Rodong Sinmun; March 7, 2016) asserts readiness for "any form of war" and includes their satellite with "strengthening of the nuclear deterrent and legitimate artificial satellite launch, which are our fair and square self-defensive choice." Moreover: "The nuclear [weapons] we possess are, precisely, the country's sovereignty, right to live, and dignity. Our satellite that cleaves through space is the proud sign that unfolds the future of the most powerful state in the world." The same article, like many others, warns North Korea makes "constant preparations so that we can fire the nuclear warheads, which have been deployed for actual warfare for the sake of national defense, at any moment!"[450]

On April 30, 2017, South Korean officials told The Korea Times and YTN TV that North Korea's test of a medium-range missile on April 29 was not a failure, as widely reported in the world press, because it was deliberately detonated at 72 kilometers altitude. According to South Korean officials, "It's believed the explosion was a test to develop a nuclear weapon different from existing ones." Japan's Tetsuro Kosaka wrote in Nikkei, "Pyongyang could be saying, 'We could launch an electromagnetic pulse (EMP) attack if things get really ugly.'"[451]

On September 3, 2017, North Korea conducted its sixth underground nuclear test. The test produced a seismic signal of 6.3 on the Richter scale, indicating a yield of over 100 kilotons: an H-bomb. Shortly after that test, North Korea released an article titled "Kim Jong-Un Gives Guidance to Nuclear Weaponization" which contained the following paragraph: **"The H-bomb, the explosive power of which is adjustable from tens of kilotons to hundreds kiloton, is a multifunctional thermonuclear nuke with great destructive power which can be detonated even at high altitudes for super-powerful EMP attack according to strategic goals."** On September 4, 2017, Pyongyang published a technical report "The EMP Might of Nuclear Weapons" accurately describing what Russia and China call a Super-EMP nuclear weapon.[452]

Are North Korea's Satellites an EMP Threat?

"North Korea's KMS-3 and KMS-4 satellites orbit over the U.S. daily...Their trajectory is similar to that planned for a Soviet-era secret weapon called the Fractional Orbital Bombardment System (FOBS) deployed by the USSR to make a surprise nuclear attack on the United States. In 2004, two retired Russian generals, then teaching at Russia's Voroshilov General Staff Academy, told the EMP Commission that the design for Russia's Super-EMP nuclear weapon was accidentally transferred by Russian scientists and engineers working on North Korea's missile and nuclear weapons program. They said North Korea could test a Super-EMP weapon 'in a few years.' The 2006 and subsequent low-yield tests do not appear to have been failures because North Korea proceeded with weaponization. In 1997, Andrey Kokoshin, then Russia's First Deputy Defense Minister, stated Russia was

[449] Alex Lockie, "North Korea Threatens 'Nuclear Thunderbolts' As U.S. And China Finally Work Together" American Military News (April 14, 2017); Fox News, "U.S. General: North Korea 'Will' Develop Nuclear Capabilities To Hit America" (September 20, 2016) www.foxnews.com/world/2016/09/20/north-korea-says-successfully-ground-tests-new-rocket-engine.html

[450] Rodong Sinmun (March 7, 2016).

[451] Tetsuro Kosaka, "North Korea's 'Failed' Missile Test May Have Been A Thinly Disguised Threat" Nikkei (May 2, 2017).

[452] Kim Song-won, "The EMP Might of Nuclear Weapons" Rodong Sinmun (Pyongyang: September 4, 2017).

deploying a new generation of advanced nuclear warheads 'that have no counterparts in the world' including EMP weapons and 'ultra-small warheads weighing less than 90 kilograms.' Such weapons would be small enough for North Korea's satellites. General Vladimir Slipchenko and General Vladimir Belous, who warned the EMP Commission about North Korean development of Super-EMP weapons, are among Russia's most prominent military scientists and experts on EMP and advanced technology warfare. General Slipchenko's advocacy of EMP and Combined-Arms Cyber Warfare is recognized in Iran's military textbook Passive Defense *that advocates development of capabilities for nuclear EMP attack."*

Source: EMP Commission, *Chairman's Report* (July 2017) p. 24

Iran

Iran in more than 20 passages of a military textbook ironically titled *Passive Defense* (2010) endorses the theories of Russian General Slipchenko and the potential defeat the United States decisively by nuclear HEMP attack. Ambassador R. James Woolsey, former Director of Central Intelligence, writes:

"'Death to America' is more than merely an Iranian chant—Tehran's military is planning to be able to make a nuclear EMP attack....Rep. Trent Franks quoted from an Iranian military textbook recently translated by the Defense Intelligence Agency's National Intelligence University...The official Iranian military textbook advocates a revolutionary new way of warfare that combines coordinated attacks by nuclear and non-nuclear EMP weapons, physical and cyber-attacks against electric grids to blackout and collapse entire nations. Iranian military doctrine makes no distinction between nuclear EMP weapons, non-nuclear radio-frequency weapons and cyber-operations—it regards nuclear EMP attack as the ultimate cyber weapon."[453]

HEMP is most effective at blacking-out critical infrastructures, while it does not directly damage the environment or harm human life, according to Iran's *Passive Defense*:

"As a result of not having the other destructive effects that nuclear weapons possess, among them the loss of human life, weapons derived from electromagnetic pulses have attracted attention with regard to their use in future wars...The superficiality of secondary damage sustained as well as the avoidance of human casualties, serves as a motivation to transform this technology into an advanced and useful weapon in modern warfare."[454]

Former CIA Director Woolsey notes: "Because EMP destroys electronics directly, but people indirectly, it is regarded by some as Shariah-compliant use of a nuclear weapon. *Passive Defense* and other Iranian military writings are well aware that nuclear EMP attack is the most efficient way of killing people, through secondary effects, over the long run. The rationale appears to be that people starve to death, not because of EMP, but because they live in materialistic societies dependent upon modern technology."[455]

---

[453] "A Shariah-Approved Nuclear Attack" Washington Times, September 15, 2015.

[454] Ibid. Army of the Islamic Republic of Iran, *Passive Defense: Approach to the Threat Center* (Tehran: Martyr Lt. General Sayad Shirazi Center for Education and Research, Spring 2010).

[455] Ibid

An Iranian political-military journal, in an article entitled "Electronics To Determine Fate Of Future Wars," states that the key to defeating the United States is HEMP attack and that, "If the world's industrial countries fail to devise effective ways to defend themselves against dangerous electronic assaults, then they will disintegrate within a few years.":

"Advanced information technology equipment exists which has a very high degree of efficiency in warfare. Among these we can refer to communication and information gathering satellites, pilotless planes, and the digital system....Once you confuse the enemy communication network you can also disrupt the work of the enemy command and decision-making center. Even worse, today when you disable a country's military high command through disruption of communications you will, in effect, disrupt all the affairs of that country....If the world's industrial countries fail to devise effective ways to defend themselves against dangerous electronic assaults, then they will disintegrate within a few years....American soldiers would not be able to find food to eat nor would they be able to fire a single shot."[456]

Iran reportedly has attempted to purchase radiofrequency weapons from Russia, displaying interest in the kind of capability that nuclear HEMP would better provide.[457]

Ironically, while electric power lobbyists are fighting against HEMP protection of the U.S. grid in Washington, the Iranian news agency MEHR reported that Iran is violating international sanctions and going full bore to protect itself from nuclear HEMP attack, that the article equates with "cyber attack":

"Iranian researchers...have built an Electromagnetic Pulse (EMP) filter that protects country's vital organizations against cyber attack. Director of Kosar Information and Communication Technology Institute Saeid Rahimi told MNA correspondent that the EMP (Electromagnetic Pulse) filter is one of the country's boycotted products and until now procuring it required considerable costs and various strategies. 'But recently Kosar ICT...has managed to domestically manufacture the EMP filter for the very first time in this country,' said Rahimi. Noting that the domestic EMP filter has been approved by security authorities, Rahimi added 'the EMP filter protects sensitive devices and organizations against electromagnetic pulse and electromagnetic terrorism.' He also said the domestic EMP filter has been implemented in a number of vital centers in Iran."[458]

Artwork for this Iranian article depicts a satellite orbiting above the Earth apparently making a nuclear HEMP attack. Ambassador Henry Cooper, former Director of the Strategic Defense Initiative, has warned repeatedly that some Iranian satellite launches appear to be practice for making a nuclear HEMP attack on the United States.[459]

---

[456] Tehran, Nashriyeh-e Siasi Nezami, December 1998 -January 1999.

[457] Roger Fontaine, "Iran Said to be Developing New Class of Weapons," Washington Times (14 July 1997), p. A10. Iran Brief (Middle East Data Project: 3 July 1997).

[458] "Iran Builds EMP Filter For 1st Time" MEHR News Agency, June 13, 2015.

[459] Ambassador Henry F. Cooper, "Another Satellite Launch By Iran" High Frontier, February 23, 2016; "Quick Fixes to Counter the Existential EMP Threat" High Frontier, July 29, 2014.

HEMP Attack Basic Facts

We as a nation are not "connecting the dots" through a profound failure of strategic imagination. Like the Allies before the Blitzkrieg of World War II, we are blind to the unprecedented existential threat from HEMP attack that could befall our civilization—figuratively and literally, from the sky, like lightning.

High-altitude electromagnetic pulse (HEMP) attack is technically and operationally the easiest, least risky, and most effective use of a nuclear weapon available to a nuclear-armed state or non-state actor.

Any nuclear weapon, even a primitive first-generation weapon like the A-bombs that destroyed Hiroshima and Nagasaki, will produce gamma rays and fireballs that generate the high-frequency (E1 HEMP), medium-frequency (E2 HEMP), and low-frequency (E3 HEMP) electromagnetic pulses. HEMP attack delivers a three-fold punch to electronics small and large, ranging from personal computers to national electric grids and everything in-between:

—Nuclear HEMP attack entails detonating the weapon at such high altitude that no blast, thermal, fallout or effects other than HEMP are experienced on the ground.
—HEMP is like "super-lightning" in that it delivers a shock much more powerful than lightning against, not a point, but against electronics over a vast area.
—A single nuclear weapon can potentially make an HEMP attack against a target the size of North America.
—E1 HEMP is much faster (lasting nanoseconds) and much more powerful than lightning, cannot be stopped by devices designed for lightning protection, can damage and destroy small electronics and control systems necessary for the operation of everything from automobiles to airplanes, including electric grids, communications, and all other critical infrastructures.
—E2 HEMP is as fast (lasting milliseconds) and as powerful as lightning and can be stopped by lightning protection, but many commercial enterprises and homes lack lightning protection.
—E3 HEMP is much slower (lasting seconds) but has much more net energy than lightning, is potentially more powerful than the electromagnetic fields that could be generated by a solar super-storm that can melt transformers designed to carry hundreds of thousands of volts.[460]
—Because HEMP propagates in three "waves" their damaging effects will be dynamic and mutually reinforcing, the E1 HEMP damaging and destroying systems (including possibly lightning protection) that opens the door for wider and deeper damage by E2 and E3 HEMP.

---

[460] For example, the 1989 Hydro-Quebec solar storm melted the coils of an EHV transformer at the Salem Nuclear Power Plant in New Jersey, designed to carry 1,000 MVA (Mega-Volt Amps). The storm generated field strengths equivalent to 8 volts/kilometer E3 HEMP, yet a nuclear weapon can generate field strengths over 10 times higher, 85 volts/kilometer or more. See EMP Commission, *Recommended E3 HEMP Heave Electric Field Waveform for the Critical Infrastructures* (July 2017).

Any nuclear weapon detonated at an altitude of 30 kilometers or higher will generate a potentially catastrophic HEMP. A nuclear detonation at 30 kilometers altitude will generate an HEMP field with a radius on the ground of about 600 kilometers. Detonated at 400 kilometers altitude, the radius of the HEMP field will be about 2,200 kilometers.[461]

HEMP Attack Is Easy

Accuracy is not necessary for an HEMP attack because the target altitude (30-400 kilometers) is so wide, and the radius and the coverage of the HEMP field is so vast.

HEMP attack does not require a re-entry vehicle, heat shield, shock absorbers and other paraphernalia associated with a nuclear missile warhead designed for blasting a city. These are unnecessary for an HEMP attack, which detonates the warhead above the atmosphere, in outer space.

HEMP attack can be executed by a wide variety of delivery vehicles, anything that can loft a nuclear weapon to 30 kilometers or higher. Possible delivery vehicles against the United States include a satellite, a long-range missile, a medium- or short-range missile launched off a freighter, some kinds of cruise missiles and anti-ship missiles (like Russia's Club-K exported to Iran), a jet fighter or some kinds of jet airliner doing a zoom climb, even a meteorological balloon.

HEMP Fields and Effectiveness

The size of the HEMP field on the ground is determined by the altitude of detonation, HEMP propagating from the point of detonation to the horizon. The higher the altitude of detonation, the bigger the HEMP field on the ground.

In general, HEMP field strengths on the ground are stronger when the weapon is detonated at lower altitudes, where the effects are more concentrated within a smaller radius, and weaker when the weapon is detonated at higher altitudes, where the effects are within a larger radius and cover a bigger area. HEMP effects are dangerous at all altitudes. Varying the altitude of the HEMP attack can be used to adjust the size of the HEMP field to better fit the target. Since the radius of the HEMP field is not highly sensitive to altitude, relative to any delivery system (even the Houthis or Taliban could use commercial off-the-shelf technology to rig a fusing system that will detonate within less than one kilometer of the desired altitude) again accurate delivery is not an issue.

---

[461] For the best background on nuclear HEMP attack and effects see: Congressional EMP Commission, *Report of the Commission to Assess the Threat to the United States from Electromagnetic Pulse (EMP) Attack: Executive Report* (2004); *Report of the Commission to Assess the Threat to the United States from Electromagnetic Pulse (EMP) Attack: National Critical Infrastructures* (2008) and the unclassified 2017 EMP Commission reports at www.firstempcommission.org.

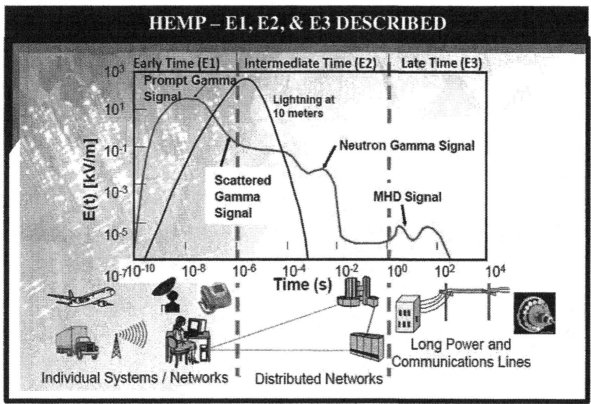

(Source: EMP Commission Briefing.)

HEMP fields are strongest at the center, where the peak field is located, and reduce in strength toward the margins. As a general rule, HEMP field strength at the outer edge of the field will be about one-half of the peak field strength. Even for a primitive first-generation nuclear weapon, the entire field is dangerous, not just the peak field.

Damage to electric grids and other critical infrastructures will not be limited to the HEMP field. Cascading failures will propagate far beyond the HEMP field through an unprotected electric grid, assuming the HEMP field is smaller than the electric grid being attacked.

For example, a 10 kiloton weapon detonated at 30 kilometers over the U.S. Eastern Grid would generate an HEMP field about 600 kilometers in radius, much smaller than the Eastern Grid. But the national electric grid being aged, over-taxed with demand, always operating on the verge of failure, capable of blackouts that put 50 million people into the dark because of cascading failures from a tree branch (like the Great Northeast Blackout of 2003), the entire Eastern Grid would certainly be plunged into a protracted blackout from such an EMP attack. The U.S. cannot survive without the Eastern Grid which generates 75 percent of the nation's electricity and supports most of the national population.[462]

---

[462] For a more in depth description of technical characteristics of nuclear HEMP attack, various HEMP attack scenarios and impact on the U.S. power grid see the Metatech studies Meta-R-320 and Meta-R-321 fully referenced later.

Any Nuke Will Do

For nuclear weapons of normal design, a high-yield weapon will generate a more powerful HEMP field than a low-yield weapon, but the difference in field strength is not nearly as great as the difference in yield. For example, a 1,000 kiloton nuclear weapon will not generate an HEMP field 100 times greater than a 10 kiloton nuclear weapon. Indeed, a 10 kiloton weapon will generate an E3 HEMP field nearly as powerful as the 1,000 kiloton weapon, but over a smaller area.[463]

Even a primitive first-generation nuclear weapon such as terrorists might build, like the first nuclear weapon ever built, the 10 kiloton bomb that destroyed Hiroshima, detonated at 30 kilometers altitude, will generate an HEMP field that at the weakest, on the margins, will be several thousand volts per meter. This is enough to put at risk all unprotected civilian and military systems within the field.[464]

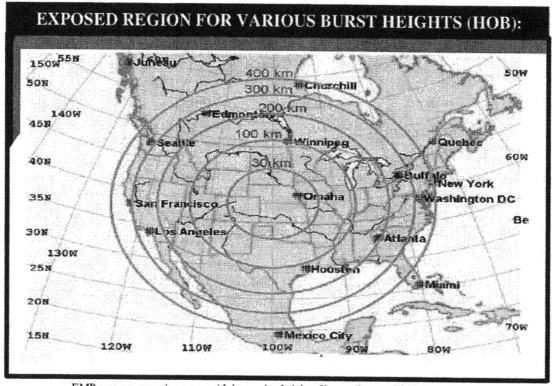

EMP area coverage increases with increasing height of burst. (Source: EMP Commission Briefing.)

---

[463] Ibid.

[464] Ibid.

ELECTROMAGNETIC PULSE (EMP) FIELD RADIUS ON EARTH'S SURFACE

ELECTROMAGNETIC PULSE (EMP) FIELD RADIUS ON EARTH'S SURFACE FROM NUCLEAR WEAPON DETONATED AT GIVEN HEIGHT OF BURST (Kilometers)

HOB	EMP Radius	HOB	EMP Radius	HOB	EMP Radius
30*	602**	160	1,391	290	1,873
40	696	170	1,434	300	1,905
50	778	180	1,476	310	1,937
60	852	190	1,516	320	1,968
70	920	200	1,556	330	1,998
80	984	210	1,594	340	2,028
90	1,044	220	1,632	350	2,058
100	1,100	230	1,668	360	2,087
110	1,153	240	1,704	370	2,116
120	1,205	250	1,739	380	2,144
130	1,254	260	1,774	390	2,172
140	1,301	270	1,807	400	2,200***
150	1,347	280	1,841		

Calculated from Radius = 110 ($\sqrt{HOB}$) in kilometers.

*High-altitude EMP (HEMP) begins at 30 kilometers height. No HEMP effect below 30 kilometers.

**Radius exceeds distance from New York to Washington.

***Radius covers all of continental United States.

(Source: Dr. Peter Vincent Pry, *Worldwide Military Ballistic Missiles Capable of Electromagnetic Pulse Attack*, EMP Commission Staff Paper, p. 10.)

Worldwide, most civilian electronic systems, and most military general purpose forces—including those of the United States—are not hardened against HEMP. According to the Congressional EMP Commission *Executive Report* (2004):

"The end of the Cold War relaxed the discipline for achieving EMP survivability within the Department of Defense, and gave rise to the perception that an erosion of EMP survivability of military forces was an acceptable risk. EMP simulation and test facilities have been mothballed or dismantled, and research concerning EMP phenomena, hardening design, testing, and maintenance has been substantially decreased. However, the emerging threat environment, characterized by a wide spectrum of actors that include near-peers, established nuclear powers, rogue nations, sub-national groups, and terrorist organizations that either now have access to nuclear weapons and ballistic missiles or may have such access over the next 15 years have combined to place the risk of EMP attack and adverse consequences on the US to a level that is not acceptable."[465]

Military planners correctly assume, and civilian emergency managers and engineers should assume, that electronic systems not protected against HEMP are vulnerable.

Super-EMP Weapons

"Super-EMP" weapons, as they are termed by Russia and China, are nuclear weapons specially designed to generate an extraordinarily powerful E1 HEMP field. Super-EMP warheads are designed to produce gamma rays, which generate the E1 HEMP effect, not a big explosion, and typically have very low explosive yields, only 1-10 kilotons. According to Russian open sources, a Super-EMP weapon can generate a peak E1 HEMP field of 100-200,000 volts per meter, which would be 50-100 kilovolts/meter at the margins. Even HEMP hardened U.S. strategic forces and C3I are potentially vulnerable to such a threat.[466]

The Congressional EMP Commission warns that Russia, China, and probably North Korea have Super-EMP warheads. Moreover, according to the EMP Commission *Executive Report* (2004):

"Certain types of low-yield nuclear weapons can be employed to generate potentially catastrophic EMP effects over wide geographic areas, and designs for variants of such weapons may have been illicitly trafficked for a quarter-century."[467]

EMP Commission Chairman, Dr. William Graham, acknowledged the potential vulnerability of the U.S. nuclear deterrent to HEMP attack in 2008 testimony to Congress: **"We designed both the missiles and their bases and the strategic communications systems during the Cold War to be able to survive and operate through EMP fields on the order of 50 kilovolts per meter, which was our**

---

[465] EMP Commission, *Executive Report* (2004) p. 47.

[466] "Russia: Nuclear Response To America Is Possible Using Super-EMP Factor" CEP20061108358006, Aleksey Vaschenko, "A Nuclear Response To America Is Possible," Zavtra, November 1, 2006.

[467] EMP Commission, *Executive Report* (2004) p. 2.

concern at the time, before we realized that weapons could be designed that had larger EMP fields."[468]

The U.S. has no Super-EMP weapons in its nuclear deterrent.

Questions and Answers to Common Myths and Misconceptions

Why would a military planner use HEMP attack when its exact effects on any specific target, like a particular EHV transformer or an individual computer, are highly unpredictable?

Although it is very difficult to predict exactly which electronic systems would be upset, damaged, or destroyed by an HEMP attack, with certainty massive disruption and damage will be inflicted on unprotected electronics within the HEMP field and, because of cascading failures, far beyond. HEMP is analogous to carpet bombing or an artillery barrage that causes massive random damage that is specifically difficult to predict, but reliably catastrophic in its macro-effects.

Cyber-attacks and physical sabotage against electric grids would rely far more heavily than HEMP on highly unpredictable cascading failures resulting from random damage to cause a protracted black-out. Yet cyber threats and sabotage despite their randomness of effect, unlike HEMP, are deservedly top priorities for the U.S. Department of Homeland Security and the electric power industry.

HEMP should be a top priority threat for DHS and industry too, but currently is not.

Are the effects of HEMP attack merely theoretical? **No.** The empirical basis for the threat of an HEMP attack to electric grids and other critical infrastructures is far deeper and broader than the data for cyber-attacks or sabotage. The notion that a cyber-attack or sabotage can plunge the U.S. into a protracted blackout—while very real threats that warrant deep concern—are far more theoretical constructs than HEMP attack.

We know for certain that HEMP will cause widespread damage of electronics and protracted black-out of unprotected electric grids and other critical infrastructures from such hard data as:

—The U.S. STARFISH PRIME high-altitude nuclear test in 1962 over Johnston Island that generated an HEMP field over the Hawaiian Islands, over 1,300 kilometers away, causing widespread damage to electronic systems.[469]
—Six Russian HEMP tests 1961-1962 over Kazakhstan, an area larger than Western Europe, that proved a single weapon can cause widespread destruction of the electric grid.[470]

---

[468] "Threat Posed By Electromagnetic Pulse Attack" Hearing before the House Armed Services Committee (Washington, D.C.: July 10, 2008). EMP Commission, *Nuclear EMP Attack Scenarios and Combined-Arms Cyber Warfare* (July 2017) pp. 50-51.

[469] Phil Plait, "The 50th Anniversary of Starfish Prime: The Nuke That Shook The World" Discover, July 9, 2012.

[470] Jerry Emanuelson, "Soviet Test 184: The 1962 Soviet Nuclear EMP Tests Over Kazakhstan" Future Science, Undated; Vladimir M. Loborev, "Up to Date State of the NEMP Problems and Topical Research Directions" Electromagnetic Environments and Consequences: Proceedings of the European International Symposium on Electromagnetic Environments, EUROEM Conference, Bordeaux, France, 1994; V. N. Mikhailov, *The Nuclear Tests of the USSR*, Vol. 2, Institute of Strategic Stability, Rosatom.

—30 years (1962-1992) of U.S. underground nuclear testing that included collecting data on HEMP effects.

—Over 50 years of testing by HEMP simulators, still ongoing, including by the Congressional EMP Commission (2001-2008) that proved modern electronics are over 1 million times more vulnerable to HEMP than the electronics of 1962.[471]

Moreover, hard data proving the threat from nuclear HEMP is available from natural EMP generated by geomagnetic storms, accidental damage caused by electromagnetic transients, and Non-Nuclear EMP (NNEMP) weapons (more commonly called Radio-Frequency Weapons). All of these produce field strengths much less powerful than nuclear HEMP, and in the case of accidental electromagnetic transients and Radio-Frequency Weapons, much more localized. There are many thousands of such cases, millions of localized unreported cases, indicating that: transformers, SCADAS, control systems, computers, navigation systems—everything from elevators, to TVs, to automobile automatic-braking systems—are potentially vulnerable to HEMP.

Instead of nuclear HEMP attack, why not rely on cyber-attack and physical sabotage to blackout the electric grid and other critical infrastructures? An adversary could black-out the United States for a protracted period of weeks, months, or longer by means of cyber-attack alone, sabotage employing small arms and explosives alone, or Non-Nuclear EMP attack alone.

However, compared to HEMP attack, cyber-attack, sabotage, and NNEMP are less proven and more problematical as means to effect a protracted nationwide blackout, especially against a nation like the United States that has 3,000 different electric utilities using a wide array of different hardware and software. Such technological diversity poses a significant challenge to other attack vectors, but not to HEMP attack. Anything that is not hardened against HEMP is potentially vulnerable.

A prudent military planner prosecuting a Blackout War against the United States or its allies would not likely gamble victory or defeat on cyber and sabotage operations alone, if he has the capability to make an HEMP attack. HEMP is the "big stick" and "ace in the hole" and is rightly regarded by Russia, China, North Korea, and Iran as "the ultimate cyber weapon."

Even those cyber warriors and commandos who may insist cyber and sabotage operations are just as great a threat to electric grids as HEMP cannot deny that the historically proven efficacy of combined-arms operations argues for including HEMP attack. Military history and common sense suggests that a threefold attack—using cyber, sabotage, and HEMP—will be better than an attack using just one of these.

Indeed, Lanchester's Square Law, a long-established war-gaming tool familiar to military theorists of all nations, can be used as a heuristic device to demonstrate the above point mathematically. Lanchester's Square Law—proven by calculations, war-gaming, and actual warfare since before World War I—is that the advantages of increasing firepower are not merely additive, but multiplicative. So if the value of cyber-attack =1 and the value of sabotage = 1, then their net firepower value is not merely 2 but the square of two = 4. Doubling firepower results in a fourfold advantage.

---

[471] "Electromagnetic Pulse: Threat to Critical Infrastructures" Hearing before the Subcommittee on Cybersecurity, Infrastructure Protection, and Security Technologies, House Committee on Homeland Security, Washington, D.C.: May 8, 2014.

Thus, if the value of cyber-attack = 1 and the value of sabotage = 1 and the value of EMP attack = 1, then their net firepower is 3 squared = 9. Even if one assumes EMP attack is no better than cyber or sabotage, its inclusion more than doubles the effectiveness of a combined-arms attack.

More realistically, since HEMP brings far more firepower to bear than cyber or sabotage, the equation should look more like cyber =1, sabotage =1, HEMP = 3, for net firepower of 5 squared = 25. In this case, inclusion of HEMP attack would increase attack effectiveness by more than sixfold.

Why won't the threat of U.S. nuclear retaliation assuredly deter a nuclear HEMP attack, just as the USSR was deterred from nuclear aggression throughout the Cold War? Deterrence depends on knowing who launched the HEMP attack so they can be punished by retaliation. But a HEMP attack can be delivered anonymously. Launched off a freighter, a submarine, by jet, or by satellite (hundreds of satellites are in low Earth orbit), the perpetrator of HEMP attack might never be identified.

HEMP attack can destroy radars, satellites and their downlinks and other national technical means necessary to identify the attacker. Bomb debris from a weapon detonated at high-altitude for HEMP attack is not collectible, unlike debris from a nuclear weapon detonated in a city, so forensic analysis cannot identify the perpetrator. HEMP attack leaves no fingerprints.

HEMP attack, especially from a Super-EMP weapon, might paralyze strategic forces and C3I (Command, Control, Communications and Intelligence), making retaliation impossible. In the aftermath of a nuclear HEMP attack that threatens the survival of millions of Americans, it seems likely that any president would order the U.S. military to give highest priority to helping the Department of Homeland Security rescue the nation, instead of prosecuting a war.

Instead of HEMP attack, why not just blast a city? A nation or terrorists having only one or a few nuclear weapons would not necessarily calculate that, instead of making a HEMP attack, it is technically and operationally less risky and likely to produce a bigger payoff by blasting a city.

Missile delivery of a nuclear warhead to blast a city requires an accurate guidance system, a reentry vehicle to penetrate the atmosphere and protect the physics package from the shock and heat of re-entry, and a fusing system capable of surviving re-entry and detonating the warhead at low-altitude or on impact. All of these requirements add significant technological and operational risk, compared to HEMP attack.

Moreover, blasting a North American city by missile would require penetrating U.S. National Missile Defenses—no mean feat for one or a few primitive nuclear missiles, the very kind of threat NMD is designed to intercept. For HEMP attack, the warhead can be rigged to "salvage fuse" so it will detonate if intercepted, thereby still successfully delivering HEMP.

Smuggling a nuclear weapon into a city by ship or truck would be riskier than HEMP attack. As soon as the weapon enters U.S. waters or territory, risks escalate dramatically that the operation may be detected by the Coast Guard or police or by sensors now deployed in harbors and metropolitan areas to detect nuclear threats.

What if the bomb smuggling operation is penetrated by the CIA or FBI, and they are waiting to seize the weapon as soon as it crosses into U.S. territory? What if a member of the smuggling team decides to betray the operation and sell the bomb to the CIA or FBI? What if something breaks on the bomb when it is stowed in the hold of a ship, or when off loaded from a freighter at sea, motor boated through choppy surf to shore, hauled up a beach, driven over bumpy roads by truck? Would the smuggling team, necessarily a small group, have the expertise necessary to make repairs, or would they be stuck inside U.S. territory with an inert nuclear bomb?

The worst possible outcome for a rogue state or terrorists would be for the U.S. to capture their nuclear weapon. Trying to smuggle a bomb into a U.S. city maximizes that risk.

And if a hostile nation succeeds in blasting a U.S. city, what have they accomplished but their own doom? A 10-kiloton weapon detonated in a city might kill and injure 300,000 through blast, thermal, and radiation effects, but the United States will not be destroyed, and the demand for revenge will be immediate and overwhelming.[472] Blasting a city is the ideal scenario for forensic analysis of bomb debris, and virtually guarantees that the U.S. can identify the culprit for annihilation.

In contrast, what could be accomplished by HEMP attack?

A HEMP attack could be made by satellite or launched from a ship outside U.S. territory. Shipboard there could be plenty of technicians to ensure nothing goes wrong, and plenty of security to ensure the operation is not betrayed.

HEMP attack detonates in outer space, leaving no collectible bomb debris. No fingerprints. HEMP attack might be executed anonymously, to escape retaliation.

The consequences of HEMP attack would be catastrophic and debilitating upon the United States, crippling U.S. military power projection capabilities and endangering national existence. According to the Congressional EMP Commission *Executive Report* (2004):

"EMP is one of a small number of threats that can hold our society at risk of catastrophic consequences....It has the capability to produce significant damage to critical infrastructures and thus to the very fabric of U.S. society, as well as to the ability of the United States and Western nations to project influence and military power....The recovery of any one of the key national infrastructures is dependent on the recovery of others. The longer the outage, the more problematic and uncertain the recovery will be. It is possible for the functional outages to become mutually reinforcing until at some point the degradation of infrastructure could have irreversible effects on the country's ability to support its population. "[473]

The Congressional EMP Commission estimates that a HEMP attack causing a protracted nationwide blackout lasting one year could kill up to 90 percent of the American people through starvation and societal collapse.[474]

---

[472] Alex Wellerstein's NUKEMAP model calculates a 10 kiloton weapon ground-burst in New York City, on Manhattan, would kill 103,000 and injure 213,430.

[473] EMP Commission, *Executive Report* (2004) pp. 1-2.

[474] Staff Paper, *Congressional EMP Commission Examples From Testimony And Reports That Fatalities Could Be High Numbering Millions And 90 Percent Of Population*, EMP Task Force On National And Homeland Security.

During the height of the Cold War, close upon the 1962 Cuban missile crisis when nuclear conflict with the USSR was a very real possibility, then Defense Secretary Robert McNamara estimated the Soviet Union could be deterred if U.S. nuclear retaliation could kill 25 percent of the Soviet population and destroy 75 percent of the USSR's industry. McNamara calculated this "Assured Destruction" of the USSR would require delivering 400 "equivalent megatons"—a force equivalent to hundreds or thousands of nuclear weapons.

Yet a nuclear rogue state or terrorists could by HEMP attack threaten or deliver upon the United States catastrophic destruction greater than McNamara's "Assured Destruction"—and do so employing just one or a few nuclear weapons. The Congressional EMP Commission warns (*Executive Report* 2004):

"Therefore, terrorists or state actors that possess relatively unsophisticated missiles armed with nuclear weapons may well calculate that, instead of destroying a city or military base, they may obtain the greatest political-military utility from one or a few such weapons by using them—or threatening their use—in an EMP attack. The current vulnerability of U.S. critical infrastructures can both invite and reward attack if not corrected..."[475]

In 2017, the EMP Commission warned again: "The critical national infrastructure in the United States faces a present and continuing existential threat from combined-arms warfare, including cyber and manmade electromagnetic pulse (EMP) attack, as well as from natural EMP from a solar superstorm. During the Cold War, the U.S. was primarily concerned about an EMP attack generated by a high-altitude nuclear weapon as a tactic by which the Soviet Union could suppress the U.S. national command authority and the ability to respond to a nuclear attack—and thus negate the deterrence value of assured nuclear retaliation. Within the last decade, newly-armed adversaries, including North Korea, have been developing the ability and threatening to carry out an EMP attack against the United States. Such an attack would give countries that have only a small number of nuclear weapons the ability to cause widespread, long-lasting damage to critical national infrastructures, to the United States itself as a viable country, and to the survival of a majority of its population."

HEMP attack is the only realistic scenario where a rogue state or terrorists having one or a few nuclear weapons could prevail by annihilating the U.S., or by credibly threatening Assured Destruction of the United States.

What about the international taboo against nuclear warfare? Russia, China, North Korea, and Iran in their military doctrines and training regard HEMP attack as part of all-out cyber warfare or radio-electronic warfare, not necessarily as nuclear warfare. China in military writings and exercises, despite its nuclear No First Use pledge, employs HEMP attacks, even though there is no evidence of U.S. nuclear first use.[476]

The EMP Commission warns: "Combined-arms cyber warfare, as described in the military doctrines of Russia, China, North Korea, and Iran, may use combinations of cyber-, sabotage-, and ultimately nuclear EMP attack to impair the United States quickly and decisively by blacking-out large portions of its electric grid and other critical infrastructures. Foreign adversaries may aptly consider nuclear

---

[475] EMP Commission, *Executive Report* (2004) p. 2.
[476] Dr. Peter Vincent Pry, "Foreign Views of Electromagnetic Pulse (EMP) Attack" Testimony before the U.S. Senate Subcommittee on Terrorism, Technology and Homeland Security, March 9, 2005.

EMP attack a weapon that can gravely damage the U.S. by striking at its technological Achilles Heel, without having to confront the U.S. military. The synergism of such combined arms is described in the military doctrines of all these potential adversaries as the greatest revolution in military affairs in history—one which projects rendering obsolete many, if not all, traditional instruments of military power."[477]

Even some analysts in Germany and Japan, among the most anti-nuclear nations, because HEMP destroys electronics instead of blasting cities, is regarded by them as acceptable use of a nuclear weapon.[478]

HEMP attack would be perfect for implementing Russia's strategy of "de-escalation"—that also appears to have been adopted by China and North Korea—where a conflict with the U.S. and its allies would be won by limited nuclear use, their version of "shock and awe" to cow the U.S. into submission.[479] An HEMP attack would be the most militarily effective use of one or a few nuclear weapons, while also being the most acceptable nuclear option in world opinion, the option most likely to be construed in the U.S. and internationally as "restrained" and a "warning shot."

In the West, generations of leaders and citizens have been educated that use of nuclear weapons is "unthinkable" and the ultimate horror. Not so in Russia, China, and North Korea where their nuclear capabilities are publicly paraded, missile launches and exercises are televised as a show of strength, an important part of national pride. Whereas the U.S. nuclear deterrent is kept low-profile, almost invisible, and its utility and legitimacy much debated, Russia and China run TV documentaries describing how they would win a nuclear war with the United States.[480]

The "international taboo" on nuclear warfare is one-sided and far more likely to have a psychologically paralyzing effect on the U.S., NATO and their allies than on Russia, China, North Korea, or Iran. A HEMP attack or demonstration made to "de-escalate" a crisis or conflict could raise a chorus of voices in the West against nuclear escalation and send some Western leaders in a panicked search for the first "off ramp."

Some analysts think the world is on the threshold of a "new nuclear age" where Cold War rules and assumptions about deterrence no longer apply and the likelihood of nuclear use is greatly increasing.[481] The first nation to use nuclear weapons today—even a rogue state like North Korea or Iran—will immediately become the most feared and most credible nuclear power in the world, a formidable force to be reckoned with, and perhaps the dominant actor in a new world order.

---

[477] EMP Commission, *Assessing the Threat from EMP Attack* (July 2017) p. 5.

[478] See for example Sun Tzu-yun in Jadi June 1, 2000 FBIS JPP 20000901000004 and Wolfgang Haas in "Infowarfare and the Military Strategy of the Bundeswehr," Telepolis November 3, 1998 FBIS EUP 20000413000200.

[479] Dr. Mark Schneider, *The Nuclear Forces And Doctrine Of The Russian Federation* Nation Institute Press for United States Nuclear Strategy Forum, 2006.

[480] "LIGNET: Why China Televised 'Nuclear War' Against The U.S." Newsmax, November 21, 2013.

[481] Paul Bracken, *The Second Nuclear* Age, Macmillan 2013.

Nationwide Blackout

One of the biggest and most dangerous myths about HEMP attack is that the consequences would be confined to a relatively small region comprising a few states, similar in extant and severity to the electric blackouts experienced during hurricanes. In fact, HEMP attack by a single nuclear weapon, such as those now possessed by North Korea, would almost certainly result in a protracted nation-wide blackout.

Gross underestimation of the HEMP threat originates from:

—Non-expert journalists and academics, posturing as experts, who falsely claim the EMP Commission threat assessments are "overblown."[482]
—"Junk science" studies from so-called "think tanks" for the electric power industry—especially the Electric Power Research Institute (EPRI)—authored by non-experts who never worked on HEMP for the defense or intelligence communities, never had access to classified data, and who flagrantly "cook the books" to make the existential HEMP threat disappear, becoming comparable to a hurricane.[483]
—Obama Administration non-experts in the intelligence community produced a classified "junk science" study grossly underestimating the HEMP threat to justify ignoring the recommendations of the EMP Commission. In 2016 the EMP Commission discovered this bogus classified study, that the Obama Administration tried to hide from scrutiny, provided a classified rebuttal, and recommended the recall of this erroneous report as injurious to U.S. national security.[484] Unaccountably, the Trump Administration failed to recall the erroneous JAEIC EMP classified report, despite issuing the "Executive Order on Coordinating National Resilience to Electromagnetic Pulses" (March 26, 2019) that is still undergoing implementation by the Biden Administration.

Unfortunately, the EMP Commission never had a megaphone as large as the mainstream media or as well-funded as lobbies for the electric power industry, such as NERC, EPRI, and EEI, that can spend hundreds of millions of dollars annually. Consequently, the myth that HEMP is not an existential threat, is not capable of inflicting a protracted nationwide blackout, is comparable to a hurricane, continues to persist even in some documents crucial to advancing national EMP preparedness, such as the Department of Homeland Security's *Strategy for Protecting and Preparing the Homeland Against Threats of Electromagnetic Pulse and Geomagnetic Disturbances* (October 9, 2018).[485]

The entire purpose of congressional commissions, like the Congressional EMP Commission, is to provide the best possible threat assessment and recommendations, using the best science and facts available to the U.S. Government, performed by the nation's foremost experts, to provide, as near as

---

[482] See for example the deeply erroneous articles by Yousaff Butt, "The EMP Threat: Fact, Fiction, and Response" Space Review (Part 1 January 25, 2010; Part 2 February 1, 2010). See also Dr. William Radasky and Dr. Peter Vincent Pry, "Rebuttal to 'The EMP Threat: Fact, Fiction, and Response" Space Review (July 6, 2010).

[483] See for example the deeply erroneous report by Electric Power Research Institute, *High-Altitude Electromagnetic Pulse and the Bulk Power System* (April 30, 2019) and Randy Horton, "Impact of High-Altitude Electromagnetic Pulse on Transmission Systems" T&D World (August 16, 2019).

[484] EMP Commission, *Assessing the Threat from EMP Attack* (July 2017) p. 18 "The Commission recommends the Director of National Intelligence circulate to all recipients of the 2014 JAEIC report the EMP Commission critique and direct a new assessment be prepared that supersedes the 2014 JAEIC EMP report."

[485] For a critique see Dr. Peter Vincent Pry, *The Power And The Light: The Congressional EMP Commission's War To Save America 2001-2020* (EMP Task Force on National and Homeland Security, 2020) Chapter 10.

possible, definitive guidance for making public policy. This process of using presidential and congressional commissions to address complex issues of science and technology to make sound public policy has worked well over the years, for example providing early warning about Cyber Warfare, Biological Warfare, and resulting in the National Missile Defense.

Thus, the Congressional EMP Commission threat assessments and recommendations should serve as the baseline for building national EMP preparedness. A rigorous study by the USAF Electromagnetic Defense Task Force agrees: *"EDTF recommends that the EPRI report, heavily dependent on theoretical analysis and optimistic scenarios, not be used as the basis for grid reliability standards, protection decisions, and other government/industry policies. EDTF instead recommends that the Congressional EMP Commission Reports, supported by real-world data, be used by government and industry as the most accurate assessment of the high-altitude EMP threat. EDTF recommends that the Congressional EMP Commission's recommendations be implemented."*

U.S. AIR FORCE

ELECTROMAGNETIC DEFENSE TASK FORCE

ASSESSMENT OF

EPRI HEMP REPORT:

Abstract

"In spring 2019, a group of nearly 200 military, government, academic, and private industry experts in various areas of electromagnetic defense gathered for the second Electromagnetic Defense Task Force (EDTF) summit. During this time a full analytical and technical review was initiated on the recently released report titled "High-Altitude Electromagnetic Pulse and the Bulk Power System: Potential Impacts and Mitigation Strategies" authored by the Electric Power Research Institute (EPRI)..."

Executive Summary

"The Electric Power Research Institute (EPRI) authored an April 2019 report titled: "High-Altitude Electromagnetic Pulse and the Bulk Power System: Potential Impacts and Mitigation Strategies." If US Government policymakers rely upon the methodology and conclusions of the EPRI report, effective high-altitude EMP protections will not be implemented, jeopardizing security of the US electric grid and other interdependent infrastructures."

"Participants in the Electromagnetic Defense Task Force 2.0 (EDTF 2.0) commend the work of EPRI and its supporting utilities for the testing of digital protective relays (DPRs) against ultrafast E1 high-altitude electromagnetic pulses (HEMP). Readers should understand however, that if EPRI's report recommendations are to be followed, the ultimate result would be a US power grid with remaining vulnerabilities impacting large power transformers, generating equipment, communication systems, data systems, and microgrid designed for emergency backup power."

"EPRI's effort draws conclusions about the survivability of the complete electric grid based on a limited assessment of the transmission grid only, omitting attention to the other two main grid sectors: generation and distribution. Furthermore, EPRI's assessment of the transmission grid focuses on transformers and digital protective relays and does not take into consideration the vulnerability of other essential electronic systems necessary for transmission grid communication and control."

"To be sure, the protective relays tested by EPRI are an important component of the electric grid since they take transmission lines out of service to prevent equipment damage during grid disturbances. Therefore, EPRI's testing does further the industry's understanding of HEMP effects on DPRs. However, while some test results among EPRI and recent Defense Threat Reduction Agency (DTRA) supported studies are consistent, the EPRI test results are inconsistent with those published by the Congressional Electromagnetic Pulse (EMP) Commission."

"When the Congressional EMP Commission tested protective relays, it found upsets and damage at 3-5 kV injected, indicating significantly more relay sensitivity to HEMP than tests conducted by EPRI. Those tests found relay malfunctions at 15 to 80 kV injected. EPRI did not disclose the relay manufacturers and models tested, nor did EPRI analyze relay populations by model used within the US electric grid. Because of the discrepancy between the EMP Commission's test results and EPRI's test results, EPRI may have significantly underestimated the number of malfunctioning or destroyed relays during a HEMP attack."*

"Notwithstanding these differences in test results, the EPRI-sponsored testing does indicate the need for cost-effective E1 HEMP protections for the electric grid and other infrastructures. Still, more relay testing and more research on relay populations is needed to accurately predict HEMP effects on the electric grid. EPRI did not adequately assess relay responses over the time period from the beginning of the E1 (early) pulse to the end of the E3 (late) pulse. Additionally, EPRI's report does not address interdependencies between E1 and E3 impacts on essential generation, transmission and distribution equipment. EPRI also incompletely assessed the risks of cascading grid collapse due to widespread relay malfunctions..."

"EPRI used a wide range of optimistic assumptions that downplay the threat of high-altitude EMP from the detonation of nuclear weapons over the United States. Despite having access to defense-conservative Department of Defense threat scenarios, EPRI used alternative Department of Energy scenarios that assume adversaries would detonate nuclear weapons at non-optimal altitudes, when the optimal altitudes are available in the open literature."

"For example, rather than modeling an optimal burst height of 75 km for peak E1 field strengths, EPRI chose a non-optimal burst height of 200 km, lowering the peak E1 field strength by approximately 65 percent. Rather than modeling the optimal burst height of 150 km for peak E3B field strengths, EPRI used an Oak Ridge National Laboratory scenario to assume a burst height of 400 km, significantly lowering the peak E3B field strength. EPRI used a Los Alamos National Laboratory (LANL) scenario to assume a non-optimal burst height of 200 km, again significantly lowering the maximum E3B field strength. EPRI also assumed latitudes and longitudes for its detonation scenarios that are non-optimal for producing maximum HEMP fields in the Northern Hemisphere."

"Additionally, the EPRI report implies that megaton class weapons are needed to cause serious HEMP effects, which is technically incorrect. Multiple high-altitude nuclear detonation scenarios

will amplify high-altitude EMP effects, but EPRI assumes that adversaries will conduct a HEMP attack with only one nuclear weapon."

"EPRI scientists did not use the data and modeling most accurate for assessing high altitude EMP impacts at northern latitudes, including the Soviet high-altitude nuclear tests over Kazakhstan. EPRI had available but chose not to use the HEMP model and waveforms of the Congressional EMP Commission Report of July 2017 which were derived from this real-world Soviet data. The Soviet data indicates that a peak E3 high-altitude HEMP threat of 85 V/km is possible over continental United States locations. The EPRI report relied instead on a DOE Laboratory (LANL) model that projected the late-time E3 peak field of approximately 35 V/m, which is just 41 percent of the peak field that the EMP Commission recommends for US critical infrastructures."

"By avoiding the use of data from declassified Soviet EMP tests on the realistic E3 threat level EPRI was able to minimize numerical estimates of damaged grid equipment, including hard-to-replace high voltage transformers."

"EPRI's optimistic assumptions and scenarios obtained from non-DOD sources allowed them to reach conclusions that do not accurately portray risks to the US electric grid."

"For example, EPRI's report states: 'Based on the assumptions made in the assessments, it was estimated that approximately 5% of the transmission line terminals in a given interconnection could potentially have a DPR that is damaged or disrupted by the nominal E1 EMP environment, whereas approximately 15% could potentially be affected by the scaled E1 EMP environment.'"

"The EDTF disputes EPRI's conclusion that potential loss of 5 percent of transmission line terminals is only a "moderate" concern. Protective relay damage and associated line terminal loss from realistic HEMP scenarios could be far greater, especially with a multiple-bomb EMP attack. Relay malfunction during a HEMP attack would likely cause other electric grid systems to fail, resulting in large-scale cascading blackouts and widespread equipment damage. Notably, E1 effects on protective relays are likely to interrupt substation self-protection processes needed to interrupt E3 current flow through transformers."

"According to EPRI's test results, a high-altitude EMP attack would cause relay malfunctions at thousands of points in the grid, simultaneously."

"Notably, large-scale grid blackouts have occurred in the past from single-point failures, such as the Northeast Blackout of 2003 which was caused by overgrown trees contacting electric transmission lines. According to the North American Electric Reliability Corporation (NERC) technical analysis of this blackout, it affected more than 70,000 megawatts (MW) of electrical load and left an estimated 50 million people without power. In contrast, EPRI's report concludes that a HEMP attack on the same Eastern Interconnection would cause limited regional voltage collapses and affect roughly 40 percent of the electrical load lost in the 2003 blackout. Experience with cascading collapse in the Eastern Interconnection shows EPRI's finding to be optimistic in the extreme."

"EDTF recommends that the EPRI report, heavily dependent on theoretical analysis and optimistic scenarios, not be used as the basis for grid reliability standards, protection decisions, and other government/industry policies. EDTF instead recommends that the Congressional EMP Commission

Reports, supported by real-world data, be used by government and industry as the most accurate assessment of the high-altitude EMP threat. EDTF recommends that the Congressional EMP Commission's recommendations be implemented."

*In the early 2000s NERC recommended that the EMP Commission test protective relays and other power electronics. Relay tests performed under contract to the EMP Commission showed the onset of serious upsets and some damage around 3-5 kV injected, a factor of three lower than the 15 kV reported level for failure onset by EPRI in April 2019. As a result, the EPRI tests indicate significantly lower failure rates for the more than one million protective relays in the electric grid. For the EMP Commission-sponsored testing of protective relays and other power system electronics, see E. Savage, W. Radasky, J. Kappenman, J. Gilbert, K. Smith and M. Madrid, HEMP Impulse Injection Testing of Power System Electronics and Electrical Components, Metatech Corporation, Meta-R225, December 2003.

SOURCE: USAF EDTF, "Electromagnetic Pulse Threats To America's Electric Grid: Counterpoints To Electric Power Research Institute Positions" OTH Journal (August 27, 2019).

HEMP Attack Impact on the U.S. Electric Power Grid

Still the best assessments of the HEMP threat to the U.S. power grid are in depth studies done by Metatech originally for the EMP Commission, and then in further depth for the Department of Defense's Oak Ridge National Laboratory and the U.S. Federal Energy Regulatory Commission:

—*The Early-Time (E1) High-Altitude Electromagnetic Pulse HEMP) and Its Impact on the U.S. Power Grid*[486]

—*The Late-Time (E3) High-Altitude Electromagnetic Pulse (HEMP) and Its Impact on the U.S. Power Grid*[487]

Metatech assessed the results from five HEMP attack scenarios, all scenarios postulating a single nuclear weapon detonated at high-altitude over the United States. The five scenarios assess the results of a HEMP attack using a single high-yield (100-1,000 kt) nuclear weapon at 500 kilometers HOB to generate peak HEMP fields centered over five different U.S. locations: New York, Chicago, Dallas/Fort Worth, Portland, and Las Vegas.

New York Scenario: "Every major state from the East Coast to the west coast states of Washington, Oregon and California, and from Maine to Florida and Texas, accumulated sufficient disturbance energy from this scenario to threaten collapse of the entire U.S. Power Grid."[488]

Chicago Scenario: "This disturbance is even more severe in total impacts than Case B16a [the New York Scenario]…The same impact concerns described for that event are even more of a concern for

---

[486] Edward Savage, James Gilbert, William Radasky, *The Early Time (E1) High-Altitude Electromagnetic Pulse (HEMP) and Its Impact on the U.S. Power Grid*, Meta-R-320 (Metatech: January 2010).

[487] James Gilbert, John Kappenman, William Radasky, Edward Savage, *The Late-Time (E3) High-Altitude Electromagnetic Pulse (HEMP) and Its Impact on the U.S. Power Grid*, Meta-R-321 (Metatech: January 2010).

[488] Ibid, p. 3-15.

this larger disturbance scenario. As in Case B16a, every major state from the East Coast to the west coast states of Washington, Oregon and California, and from Maine to Florida and Texas, accumulated sufficient disturbance energy from this scenario to threaten collapse of the entire U.S. Power Grid."[489]

Dallas/Fort Worth Scenario: "This disturbance is, in total, slightly less severe than Case B16a [the New York Scenario]…however the same impact concerns described for that scenario are also of concern for this slightly smaller disturbance scenario. As in Case B16a, every major state from the East Coast to the west coast states of Washington, Oregon and California, and from Maine to Florida and Texas, accumulated sufficient disturbance energy from this scenario to threaten the collapse of the entire U.S. Power Grid."[490]

Portland Scenario: "This disturbance is, in total, 35% less severe than Case B16a [the New York Scenario]…As a result, the estimated extent of power system collapse is not as extensive in as in B16a…the highest impact portions of the U.S. are the entire western grid and Texas grid, along with the portions of the Eastern grid from Minnesota to New York through Georgia…Considering the extent of the disturbance, it is conceivable that neighboring system may also collapse through a cascading process [resulting in collapse of the entire U.S. Power Grid]."[491]

Las Vegas Scenario: "This disturbance is, in total, 20% less severe than Case B16a [the New York Scenario]…As a result the estimated extent of power system collapse is not as extensive as in B16a… the highest impact portions of the U.S. are the entire Western grid and Texas grid, along with portions of the Eastern grid from Minnesota to New York through Florida. Considering the extent of the disturbance, it is conceivable that neighboring system may also collapse through a cascading process [resulting in collapse of the entire U.S. Power Grid]."[492]

In all five scenarios, HEMP attack threatens the entire U.S. Power Grid with collapse, directly everywhere in 3 of 5 scenarios, and indirectly through cascading collapse in 2 of 5 scenarios. In all five scenarios, HEMP attack from a single nuclear weapon threatens all or most of the U.S. Power Grid in all or most states, spanning the continent to the East and West coasts.

To liken a nuclear HEMP attack to a hurricane is grossly inaccurate and recklessly irresponsible.

A More Likely HEMP Scenario?

HEMP experts for many years and today typically describe a HEMP attack scenario using a single nuclear weapon to illustrate the existential threat that can be posed to an entire nation even by such a limited HEMP attack—using only one warhead. Non-experts and HEMP "naysayers" like EPRI, through ignorance or intellectual dishonesty or both, base their false claims that the HEMP threat is "overblown" on the "one warhead scenario."

---

[489] Ibid, p. 3-16.

[490] Ibid, p. 3-17.

[491] Ibid, p. 3-18.

[492] Ibid, p. 3-19.

Nuclear-armed terrorists or nations whose highest priority is blacking-out the U.S. power grid and other life-sustaining critical infrastructures can do so, as proven by the EMP Commission and Metatech, with a single warhead.

However, Russia, China, and North Korea waging "Blackout Warfare" against the United States may well give highest priority to using nuclear HEMP attack for disabling U.S. nuclear retaliatory forces and C3I, along with collapsing the U.S. power grid as a vital secondary objective. Counterforce HEMP attack against the U.S. nuclear deterrent could entail, optimally, multiple HEMP bursts at 30-100 kilometers HOB to maximize peak field strength over U.S. strategic targets.

Even North Korea could probably execute a disarming counterforce HEMP attack against the United States, targeting peak fields on:

—U.S. National Missile Defenses at Fort Greely, Alaska.
—U.S. National Missile Defenses at Vandenberg AFB, California.
—Washington, DC.
—North American Aerospace Defense Command (NORAD) Headquarters at Peterson AFB and Alternate Headquarters inside nearby Cheyenne Mountain, Colorado.
—91st ICBM Missile Wing and B-52 Bomber Wing at Minot AFB, North Dakota.
—90th ICBM Missile Wing at F.E. Warren AFB, Wyoming.
—341st ICBM Missile Wing at Malmstrom AFB, Montana.
—B-2 Bomber Wing at Whiteman AFB, Missouri.
—B-52 Bomber Wing at Barksdale AFB, Louisiana.
—Trident SSBN Base at Bangor, Washington.
—Trident SSBN Base at King's Bay, Georgia.
—C3I TACAMO Wing of E6B aircraft for emergency communications (to ICBMs, bombers, and patrolling submarines) at Tinker AFB, Oklahoma.

A single Super-EMP warhead detonated at 70 kilometers HOB over each of these 12 targets would generate HEMP peak field strengths of 100 kilovolts/meter or more, greatly exceeding the U.S. military HEMP hardening standard of 50 kilovolts/meter. The EMP Commission warned: "Current policy is to continue to provide EMP protection to strategic forces and their controls; however, the end of the Cold War has relaxed the discipline for achieving and maintaining that capability within these forces."[493]

In 2021, according to Colonel Erik Quigley, Director of the Minuteman III Systems Directorate: "Quigley said he couldn't share photos to show 'how much corrosion we have…on things like launch and closure doors, and the actual blast doors and the B-plug.' The corrosion 'prevents us from being able to close the blast doors and lock [them] appropriately. And you only scrape away the rust and take away layers so many times before you're putting the crews at risk for potential hardness concerns…[resulting from] an EMP blast and potential radiation."[494]

---

[493] EMP Commission, *Executive Report* (2004) p. 47.
[494] John Tirpak, "New GBSD Will Fly in 2023; No Margin Left for Minuteman" Air Force Magazine (June 14, 2021).

The HEMP counterforce attack postulated here, targeting 12 Super-EMP warheads on 12 U.S. strategic forces and C3I targets at 70 kilometers HOB over each target, would also generate 12 HEMP fields, each having a radius of 920 kilometers, covering virtually all the contiguous United States. The collective HEMP effects would surely collapse the national power grid and black-out other life-sustaining critical infrastructures. According to EMP Commission assessments, all the life-sustain critical infrastructures are seriously at risk, including:

Government
Military
Electric Power
Telecommunications
Water
Food
Transportation
Petroleum and Natural Gas
Emergency Services
Banking and Finance
Space Assets[495]

A U.S. President, in the aftermath of the postulated HEMP attack to paralyze the U.S. nuclear deterrent and inflict protracted nationwide blackout, would not have much left to work with, the sinews of U.S. military and economic power, and all the critical infrastructures that support modern electronic civilization, having been collapsed or severely disrupted at the speed of light.

Would a U.S. President even attempt to wage World War III, for revenge, or for example to preserve the sovereignty of South Korea, or of Taiwan, or of Ukraine and the Baltic states, under such disadvantageous circumstances? Or would the President's highest priority be mobilizing all remaining U.S. assets, including the Department of Defense, to recover the national electric power grid and other life-sustaining critical infrastructures, before millions of Americans die from starvation and societal collapse? The Constitution and common sense would vote for the latter.

---

[495] EMP Commission, *Critical National Infrastructures* (2008) passim.

3.3.2 Blast Wave Case B16a – New York

This case refers to a Blast Wave event whose peak electric fields are centered over the New York region; this location will spread a large footprint of the disturbance, particular over much of the eastern U.S.

Every major state from the East Coast to the west coast states of Washington, Oregon and California, and from Maine to Florida and Texas, accumulated sufficient disturbance energy from this scenario to threaten collapse of the entire U.S. Power Grid (Figure 311). The disturbance also generated very high levels of GIC in the Pennsylvania/New York/New Jersey and neighboring regions. These levels could be large enough to exceed the normal AC current loads, and, as a result, could have consequential impacts that may lead to permanent damage to circuit breakers and other apparatus on the high voltage networks in these regions, due to attempts to operate under these unusual conditions. Possible widespread failures of this type could lead to significant delays in power system restoration in these regions.

Figure 3-11. Summary of GIC flows in U.S. power grid for E3A Blast Wave Case B16a. The entire U.S. Power Grid is expected to collapse.

3.3.3 Blast Wave Case B16b - Chicago

This case refers to a Blast Wave whose peak electric fields are centered over the Chicago region; this location will spread a large footprint of the disturbance over much of the U.S.

This disturbance is even more severe in total impacts than Case B16a, which was previously described. The same impact concerns described for that event are even more of a concern for this larger disturbance scenario. As in Case B16a, every major state from the East Coast to the west coast states of Washington, Oregon and California, and from Maine to Florida and Texas, accumulated sufficient disturbance energy from this scenario to threaten collapse of the entire U.S. Power Grid (Figure 3-12). The disturbance also generated very high levels of GIC from Chicago to New Jersey and neighboring regions. These levels could be large enough to exceed the normal AC current loads, and, as a result, could have consequential impacts that may lead to permanent damage to circuit breakers and other apparatus on the high voltage networks in these regions. Possible widespread failures of this type could lead to significant delays in power system restoration in these regions.

Figure 3-12. Summary of GIC flows in U.S. power grid for E3A Blast Wave Case B16b. The entire U.S. Power Grid is expected to collapse.

3.3.4 Blast Wave Case B17a – Dallas / Ft. Worth

This case refers to a Blast Wave whose peak electric fields are centered over the Dallas/Ft Worth region; this location will spread a large footprint of the disturbance over much of the U.S.

This disturbance is, in total, slightly less severe than Case B16a, which was previously described, however the same impact concerns described for that event are also of concern for this slightly smaller disturbance scenario. As in Case B16a, every major state from the East Coast to the west coast states of Washington, Oregon and California, and from Maine to Florida and Texas, accumulated sufficient disturbance energy from this scenario to threaten collapse of the entire U.S. Power Grid (Figure 3-13). The disturbance also generated very high levels of GIC in much more widely scattered regions than Case B16a. These levels could be large enough to exceed the normal AC current loads, and, as a result, could have consequential impacts that may lead to permanent damage to circuit breakers and other apparatus on the high voltage networks in these regions. Possible widespread failures of this type could lead to significant delays in power system restoration in these regions.

Figure 3-13. Summary of GIC flows in U.S. power grid for E3A Blast Wave Case B17a. The entire U.S. Power Grid is expected to collapse.

3.3.5 Blast Wave Case B15a – Portland, Oregon

This case refers to a Blast Wave whose peak electric fields are centered over the Portland, Oregon region; this location will spread a large footprint of the disturbance over much of the U.S.

This disturbance is, in total, 35% less severe than Case B16a, which was previously described. As a result, the estimated extent of power system collapse is not as extensive as in B16a. In Case B15a, the highest impact portions of the U.S. are the entire western grid and Texas grid, along with the portions of the Eastern grid from Minnesota to New York through Georgia (Figure 3-14). Considering the extent of the disturbance, it is conceivable that neighboring system may also collapse through a cascading process. The disturbance also generated very high levels of GIC in much of the western U.S. These levels could be large enough to exceed the normal AC current loads, and, as a result, could have consequential impacts that may lead to permanent damage to circuit breakers and other apparatus on the high voltage networks in these regions. Possible widespread failures of this type could lead to significant delays in power system restoration in these regions.

Figure 3-14. Summary of GIC flows in U.S. power grid for E3A Blast Wave Case B15a.

3.3.6 Blast Wave Case B15b – Las Vegas, Nevada

This case refers to a Blast Wave whose peak electric fields are centered over the Las Vegas, Nevada region; this location will spread a large footprint of the disturbance over much of the U.S.

This disturbance is, in total, 20% less severe than Case B16a, which was previously described. As a result the estimated extent of power system collapse is not as extensive as in B16a. In Case B15b, the highest impact portions of the U.S. are the entire Western grid and Texas grid, along with the portions of the Eastern grid from Minnesota to New York through Florida (Figure 3-15). Considering the extent of the disturbance, it is conceivable that neighboring system may also collapse through a cascading process. The disturbance also generated very high levels of GIC in much of the western U.S. These levels could be large enough to exceed the normal AC current loads, and, as a result, could have consequential impacts that may lead to permanent damage to circuit breakers and other apparatus on the high voltage networks in these regions. Possible widespread failures of this type could lead to significant delays in power system restoration in these regions.

Figure 3-15. Summary of GIC flows in U.S. power grid for E3A Blast Wave Case B15b.

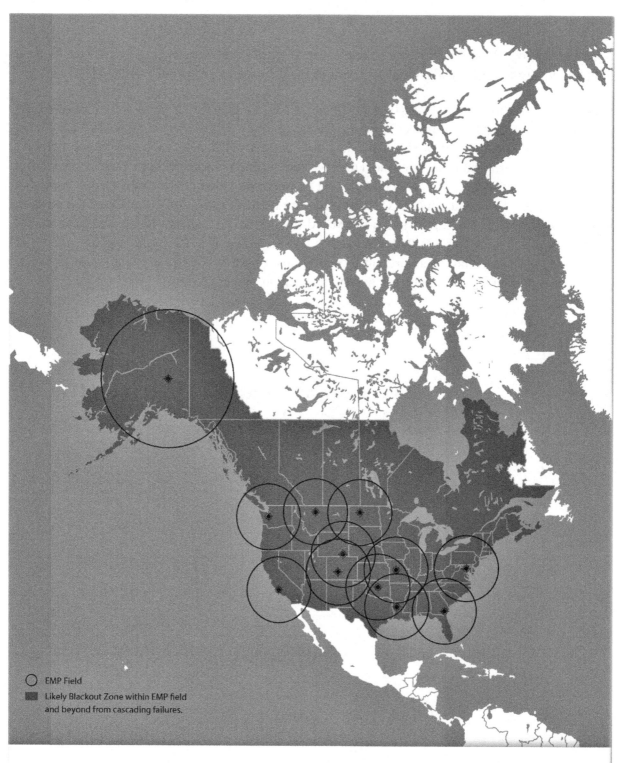

EMP Field

Likely Blackout Zone within EMP field
and beyond from cascading failures.

NUCLEAR EMP ATTACK SCENARIOS

HEMP Counterforce Attack

VULNERABILITIES TO EMP
Dr. William R. Graham, Chairman
Dr. Peter Vincent Pry, Chief of Staff
Commission to Assess the Threat to the United States from
Electromagnetic Pulse (EMP) Attack
Testimony Before Congress
(October 12, 2017)

When assessing the potential vulnerability of U.S. military forces and civilian critical infrastructures to EMP, it is necessary to be mindful of the complex interdependencies of these highly-networked systems, because EMP upset and damage of a very small fraction of the total system can cause total system failure.

Real world failures of electric grids from various causes indicate that a nuclear EMP attack would have catastrophic consequences. Significant and highly disruptive blackouts have been caused by single-point failures cascading into system-wide failures, originating from damage comprising far less than 1 percent of the total system. For example:

—The Great Northeast Blackout of 2003—that put 50 million people in the dark for a day, contributed to at least 11 deaths, and cost an estimated $6 billion—originated from a single failure point when a powerline contacted a tree branch, damaging less than 0.0000001 (0.00001%) of the system.
—The New York City Blackout of 1977, that resulted in the arrest of 4,500 looters and injury of 550 police officers, was caused by a lightning strike on a substation that tripped two circuit breakers.
—The Great Northeast Blackout of 1965, that effected 30 million people, happened because a protective relay on a transmission line was improperly set.
—India's nationwide blackout of July 30-31, 2012—the largest blackout in history, effecting 670 million people, 9% of the world population—was caused by overload of a single high-voltage powerline.
—India's blackout of January 2, 2001—effecting 226 million people—was caused by equipment failure at the Uttar Pradesh substation.
—Indonesia's blackout of August 18, 2005—effecting 100 million people—was caused by overload of a high-voltage powerline.
—Brazil's blackout of March 11, 1999—effecting 97 million people—was caused by a lightning strike on an EHV transformer substation.
—Italy's blackout of September 28, 2003—effecting 55 million people—was caused by overload of two high-voltage powerlines.
—Germany, France, Italy, and Spain experienced partial blackouts on November 4, 2006—effecting 10-15 million people—from accidental shutdown of a high-voltage powerline.
—The San Francisco blackout in April 2017 was caused by the failure of a single high voltage breaker.

In contrast to the above blackouts caused by single-point or small-scale failures, a nuclear EMP attack would inflict massive widespread damage to the electric grid causing millions of failure points. With few exceptions, the U.S. national electric grid is unhardened and untested against nuclear EMP attack.

In the event of a nuclear EMP attack on the United States, a widespread protracted blackout is inevitable.

Source: Excerpt from Statement for the Record by Dr. William R. Graham, Chairman, and Dr. Peter Vincent Pry, Chief of Staff, Congressional EMP Commission, "North Korea Nuclear EMP Attack: An Existential Threat" Hearing "Empty Threat Or Serious Danger: Assessing North Korea's Risk to the Homeland" before the House Committee on Homeland Security, Subcommittee on Oversight and Management Efficiency (October 12, 2017).

VI

ADVANCING NATIONAL PREPAREDNESS AGAINST BLACKOUT WARFARE

by Dr. Peter Vincent Pry

White House Leadership Needed

The Congressional EMP Commission in 2017 recommended a White House "EMP Czar" to lead the functional equivalent of a Manhattan Project to quickly protect the nation from existential threats posed by solar and manmade electromagnetic pulse (EMP). The new White House "Cybersecurity Czar" should also serve as an "EMP Czar" since EMP attack is part of adversary planning for Cyber Warfare:

"Combined-arms cyber warfare, as described in the military doctrines of Russia, China, North Korea, and Iran, may use combinations of cyber-, sabotage-, and ultimately nuclear EMP-attack to impair the United States quickly and decisively by blacking-out large portions of its electric grid and other critical infrastructures...The synergism of such combined arms is described in the military doctrines of all these potential adversaries as the greatest revolution in military affairs in history—one which projects rendering obsolete many, if not all, traditional instruments of military power."—EMP Commission[496]

Protecting from EMP/Cyber/Sabotage the national electric power grid—the keystone critical infrastructure that energizes operations of all other life-sustaining critical infrastructures—must have highest White House priority as these threats are more imminent than climate change, imperil the existence of modern electronic civilization, and could kill millions:

"A long-term outage owing to EMP could disable most critical supply chains, leaving the U.S. population living in conditions similar to centuries past, prior to the advent of electric power. In the 1800s, the U.S. population was less than 60 million, and those people had many skills and assets necessary for survival without today's infrastructure. An extended blackout today could result in the death of a large fraction of the American people through the effects of societal collapse, disease, and starvation."—EMP Commission[497]

Fortunately, the existential threats from EMP/Cyber/Sabotage all have some common solutions that can be part of an "all hazards" strategy for protecting electric grids and other life-sustaining critical infrastructures.

The White House should immediately undertake the steps and strategies outlined below, some of which can advance national EMP/Cyber/Sabotage preparedness at virtually no cost to the U.S. Government, and all at relatively low-cost relative to the magnitude of the threats:

---

[496] EMP Commission, *Assessing the Threat from EMP Attack* (July 2017) p. 5. See also: General Vladimir Slipchenko, *Non-Contact Wars* (Moscow: 2000); Shen Weiguang, *World War, the Third World War—Total Information Warfare;* Army of the Islamic Republic of Iran, *Passive Defense: Approach to the Threat Center* (Tehran: Martyr Lt. General Sayad Shirazi Center for Education and Research, 2010).

[497] Ibid, p. 4.

—The EMP Commission made over 100 recommendations to protect electric power grids and other critical infrastructures, including: telecommunications, transportation, petroleum and natural gas, emergency services, space systems, banking and finance, food and water infrastructures. Virtually all of these recommendations would improve resilience not only against EMP, but against all hazards, including against sabotage and the worst cyber-attacks. The White House should send copies of the EMP Commission report *Critical National Infrastructures* to all relevant Senate and House committees, asking them to launch legislative initiatives implementing the EMP Commission recommendations for the sectors over which the committees have jurisdiction.[498]

—The EMP Commission warned that the U.S. Federal Energy Regulatory Commission (FERC) and the North American Electric Reliability Corporation (NERC) are deeply dysfunctional, hence the need for a White House "Czar" to lead national EMP/Cyber/Sabotage preparedness. U.S. FERC should be reformed by replacing existing commissioners with persons whose highest priority is not the fiduciary interests of electric utilities, but national security: especially protecting national power grids from Blackout Warfare.[499]

—Add a provision to the National Defense Authorization Act authorizing the Secretary of Defense to reprogram monies to help utilities protect from Blackout Warfare local and regional electric grids that support CONUS military bases. For example:

*"**Energy Security For Military Bases And Critical Defense Industries.** Whereas 99 percent of the electricity used by CONUS military bases is supplied by the national electric grid; whereas the Department of Defense (DOD) has testified to Congress that DOD cannot project power overseas or perform its homeland security mission without electric power from the national grid; whereas the Congressional EMP Commission warned that up to 9 of 10 Americans could die from starvation and societal collapse from a nationwide blackout lasting one year; therefore the Secretary of Defense is directed to urge governors, state legislators, public utility commissions of the 50 states, the North American Electric Reliability Corporation (NERC) and the utilities that supply electricity to CONUS military bases and critical defense industries, to protect the electric grid from EMP/Cyber/Sabotage, including a high-altitude nuclear electromagnetic pulse (EMP) attack, from natural EMP generated by a solar super-storm, from other Cyber-EMP threats including radiofrequency weapons, and from special forces sabotage, and to help the States, NERC, public utilities commissions, and electric utilities by providing DOD expertise and other such support and resources as may be necessary to protect the national electric grid. The Secretary of Defense is authorized to spend up to $4 billion in FY2022 and every year thereafter to help protect the national electric grid."*

—Electric grid transformers, SCADAs, and other equipment hardened against EMP will also survive worst-case cyber-attacks that manipulate SCADAs to cause system-generated over-voltages (SGOVs). Cyber-induced SGOVs, like EMP, can overload and destroy critical equipment, cause cascading systemic collapse, resulting in protracted regional or nationwide blackout. Likewise, SGOVs induced by special forces sabotage of just a small number of EHV transformers can cause cascading failures blacking-out electric grids. Protecting the over 100 CONUS military bases and their supporting civilian electric grids would create "islands of survivability" that could support a quick national recovery.

---

[498] EMP Commission, *Critical National Infrastructures* (2008).

[499] EMP Commission, *Chairman's Report* (July 2017) pp. 39-42.

—$2 trillion is planned for infrastructure modernization, including $100 billion for electric power. The EMP Commission estimates $2-4 billion could protect the electric bulk power system which, with smart planning, would enable rapid recovery from a nationwide blackout, saving the lives of millions.[500] $20 billion could very significantly advance protection of all critical infrastructures, making recovery from Blackout Warfare more assured and faster.

Education

The President and Secretary of Homeland Security should send a letter, perhaps co-signed by other high-ranking U.S. Government officials, to the 50 State Governors and 100 biggest electric utilities spotlighting EMP/Cyber/Sabotage as highest-priority threats. The letter should urge action to protect electric grids, and alone might even be sufficient to motivate States and utilities to protect their electric grids without Federal intervention. For the U.S. Government this could be the easiest and most cost-effective strategy:

—Appended to the letter should be supplementary materials providing in depth education on EMP/Cyber/Sabotage threats and technical guidance on how to protect electric grids, including: the EMP Commission Reports, the Cybersecurity and Infrastructure Security Agency (CISA) *EMP Protection and Resilience Guidelines for Critical Infrastructures and Equipment*, the Department of Energy approved HEMP waveform, and the CenterPoint Energy briefing on protecting electric power substations.[501]

—The letter should include a list of defense contractors experienced in EMP protection. A chief impediment to national Blackout Warfare preparedness is that policymakers and utilities do not know how to protect against the threat.

—The letter should encourage electric utilities to share the EMP/Cyber/Sabotage educational materials with their employees, to have an educational program to raise situational awareness, to conduct exercises responding to EMP/Cyber/Sabotage events, and to solicit from employees "grassroots" ideas for preparing for a catastrophic Blackout War.[502] The best ideas do not always come from Washington.

—DHS should sponsor an aggressive public service messaging campaign encouraging electric utilities to protect themselves from EMP/Cyber/Sabotage, praising utilities like American Electric Power, CenterPoint Energy, and Duke Energy that are already taking action voluntarily.

EMP/Cyber National Manufacturing Standards

National manufacturing standards for equipment critical to electric grids, like transformers and SCADAs, could require such equipment to be designed and manufactured hardened against EMP and Cyber:

---

[500] EMP Commission, *Critical National Infrastructures* (2008) pp. 60-61.

[501] All the unclassified EMP Commission reports are located at www.firstempcommission.org. DHS and CISA, *Electromagnetic Pulse (EMP) Protection and Resilience Guidelines for Critical Infrastructure Equipment* (National Cybersecurity Integration Center: February 5, 2019) www.cisa.gov. Department of Energy, "Physical Characteristics of HEMP Waveform Benchmarks for Use in Assessing Susceptibilities of the Power Grid, Electrical Infrastructures, and Other Critical Infrastructure to HEMP Insults" (January 11, 2021) see also Dr. Peter Vincent Pry *Will America Be Protected?* Volumes I and II (EMP Task Force: March 2021) pp. 153-161. Eric Easton, "EMP Mitigation for Electric Substations" Briefing (CenterPoint Energy: November 11, 2020) see also *Will America Be Protected?* pp. 171-225.

[502] For scenarios see EMP Commission, *Nuclear EMP Attack Scenarios and Combined-Arms Cyber Warfare* (July 2017).

—Defense Department experience over 50 years manufacturing missiles, bombers, communications and other equipment that must survive EMP indicates that incorporating protection into the original design adds only 1-6% to system manufacturing costs.

—Lightning protection (equivalent to nuclear E2 EMP protection) is already routinely built-into most critical electric equipment as part of national manufacturing standards and best practices. So we as a society have, through manufacturing standards and best practices, already proven we can protect ourselves—at relatively low-cost and through a process that is so politically painless as to be unnoticeable—against the natural EMP threat from lightning. The same process can be used to protect against the threat from the "super-lighting" that is EMP and Cyber Warfare.

—The National Institute of Standards and Technology (NIST) could propose EMP/Cyber standards to electric utilities and manufacturers of transformers and SCADAs.

—NIST and DHS could sponsor a design competition. Offer an award and purchase of patents to those who invent the most cost-effective design for transformers, SCADAs and other equipment, incorporating EMP/Cyber protection in original designs, as well as for retroactive protection.[503]

—The Institute of Electrical and Electronic Engineers (IEEE) oversees the National Electrical Safety Code for equipment in the electrical bulk power system, including transformers and SCADAs.[504] The National Electrical Safety Code should include protection against EMP/Cyber/Sabotage.

—The National Fire Protection Association (NFPA) oversees the National Electric Code for electricity consumers, including industries and homes, which is codified into law by the States, and should include protection against EMP/Cyber/Sabotage.[505]

Critical Infrastructure Protection Act (CIPA)

CIPA requires the Department of Homeland Security to partner with utilities and the States in pilot projects demonstrating that electric grids and other critical infrastructures can be protected cost-effectively:

—Developing a plan to protect the electric grid of an entire State can be achieved very inexpensively, depending on the contractor, or even at no cost if the State Public Utilities Commission invites bids for developing EMP/Cyber/Sabotage protection of the State electric grid.

—The Louisiana Public Service Commission began a project to protect the Louisiana electric grid, received several free proposals, including a bid to develop a state-wide plan for $250,000. Unfortunately, the Louisiana EMP project terminated prematurely for political reasons. Perhaps the Louisiana EMP Project could be revived if encouraged by DHS.

—Several States have passed legislative initiatives or tried to move utilities to protect electric grids from EMP, including Arizona, California, Florida, Maine, Texas, Utah, and others, but been stymied by electric power industry lobbyists.[506] Federal political and material support could be the decisive factor reviving these efforts to achieve Blackout Warfare protection.

---

[503] The Royal Academy of Science, in the 18th century, offered an award for a clock that could operate accurately at sea to determine longitude, resulting in the invention of the chronometer.

[504] "Standards" www.ieee.org.

[505] "National Electrical Code" www.cpsc.gov.

[506] Dr. Peter Vincent Pry, *Blackout Wars: State Initiatives to Achieve Preparedness Against an Electromagnetic Pulse (EMP) Catastrophe* (EMP Task Force: 2012).

—Once a State has an EMP/Cyber/Sabotage protection plan describing necessary technical work and costs, especially when costs are found to be affordable, practical and political incentives to implement the plan will increase greatly.

—Once DHS has a "pilot" EMP/Cyber/Sabotage protection plan for any State, it can serve as a blueprint for other States. The political and technical process of achieving national preparedness against Blackout Warfare would be greatly simplified for States and utilities merely by invoking CIPA to get help from DHS.

EMP/Cyber Protected Nuclear Power Reactors

If the nation's 100 nuclear power reactors are protected from Cyber/EMP, it would eliminate the threat that they might "go Fukushima" and they would become "islands of survivability" for quickly recovering the national grid:

—Duke Energy's Lake Wylie project is a pilot program for protecting a nuclear reactor so that it can survive and continue operating through an EMP.[507]

—Nuclear reactors are inherently robust against EMP/Cyber/Sabotage, except their current standard operating procedure in an emergency would be to power down and rely on vulnerable emergency power to cool the reactor while it is "turned off." The goal is to change operational procedures so nuclear reactors would continue to generate power through any emergency, so they do not become part of the "Black Start" problem but a big part of the solution.

—Small Modular Reactors (SMRs) are under development or ready for manufacture that are designed with EMP protection. SMRs on 100 CONUS military bases would prevent blackout of U.S. military capabilities, and could become "islands of survivability" for recovering the nation from Blackout Warfare.

—New generation SMRs are "green" as they produce no nuclear waste and have virtually no "carbon footprint" and so are also a potential solution to climate change.

Toward An Electrical Revolution

In the long-term, the United States needs a revolution in the way electricity is generated and distributed, moving toward greatly increased generating power and more decentralized distribution, to meet the energy demands of an increasingly electrified civilization, while better protecting that civilization from a solar or manmade "blackout apocalypse."[508]

The "big grid" that provides electric power to the United States is inherently vulnerable to EMP/Cyber/Sabotage because of its size and antiquity. Constructed haphazardly over the course of a century, the national power grid was never designed with national security in mind. Nor has electrical power generation kept pace with increasing demand, so the grid always operates on the verge of failure, another major factor in its vulnerability.

---

[507] Ambassador Henry Cooper, "Lake Wylie Pilot Study: Marking Time!" High Frontier (October 5, 2020); "Lake Wylie Pilot Study Video" High Frontier (December 8, 2020); "Lake Wylie Study Status" (June 19, 2020).
[508] See my books *Will America Be Protected?* (2021), *The Power And The Light* (2020), *EMP Manhattan Project* (2018), *Apocalypse Unknown* (2013), and *Blackout Wars* (2012) available from Amazon.com.

New technologies for generating electrical power and decentralizing distribution can supplement, and perhaps someday replace, the "big grid" to meet a future where nearly everything, including automobiles, may be electrically powered. Solar and wind generation are the focus of most political and financial support for a "green energy revolution" despite their significant technological limitations, costly inefficiency, and unreliability. Examples of some better alternatives include:

—Small Modular Reactors, as noted earlier, are a technological "great leap forward" from existing large nuclear reactors. SMRs arguably are "greener" than windmill and solar generation, while offering a much wider range of applications, being able to service a major city, a military base, or a small town. For example, the MicroNuclear "battery" is essentially a micro-nuclear reactor that can fit inside a large room, power a military base or town with 10 megawatts, and is designed protected against EMP.[509] Perhaps someday every city and town can have its own SMR, manage its own electrical power, making FERC and NERC and their often lethal regulatory mismanagement extinct.[510]

—Hydro-electricity is an underexploited resource, environmentally "green" and inherently one of the sources of electricity least vulnerable to EMP/Cyber/Sabotage, especially if distribution is decentralized into microgrids. 91,457 dams exist in the U.S. but only 3% (2,744) are harnessed for electricity.[511] New technology micro-hydropower turbines could harness some 80,000 dams, thousands of rivers and streams, previously unusable for electric power, making microgrids possible almost everywhere.[512] But DOE seems uninterested in helping small companies and inventors who, as in the past, are the source of most, and often the most revolutionary, technological innovations.

—Battery technology is a revolution awaiting invention. Battery-power would be the ultimate in decentralizing distribution of electricity, and would maximize civilizational resilience to EMP/Cyber/Sabotage threats. At least one small inventor has a prototype design that theoretically could power cars and individual households, making the "big grid" extinct. Again, DOE is uninterested.

Small Modular Reactors and other innovations would make practical a "green energy revolution" that could kill with one stone three existential threats: EMP, Cyber Warfare, and climate change.

---

[509] MicroNuclear LLC "Nuclear Reactor Testing Device Opens Doors To Safe Energy In Idaho, Nation" https://www.uidaho.edu/news/news-articles/news-releases/2020-fall/111920-msnb.

[510] EMP Commission, *Chairman's Report* (July 2017) pp. 39-42.

[511] U.S. Army Corps of Engineers, "National Inventory of Dams" (2018) https://nid.sec.usace.army.mil/ords/f?p=105:113:3839158335878::NO::: Department of Energy, "Types of Hydropower Plants" www.energy.gov.

[512] John Hull, Eagleaf Enterprises jhull95247@yahoo.com. For another innovation, wireless transmission of electricity from remote dams to the power grid, see www.emrod.energy.

VII

CONCLUSIONS AND COMMENTARY

"Someday science shall have the existence of Mankind in its power,
and the human race commit suicide by blowing up the world."
—Henry Adams (1862)

DR. PETER VINCENT PRY
(Executive Director, EMP Task Force)

The A-bomb that destroyed Hiroshima killed 135,000. An H-bomb detonated over New York City could kill 10 million. A HEMP attack over North America could kill 300 million. So too could a cyber-attack, special forces sabotage, and/or Non-Nuclear EMP (NNEMP) attack that blacks-out electric grids and other life-sustaining critical infrastructures for a year, causing 90% of the population to perish from starvation eventually.[513]

Immediately, few or no fatalities may result from HEMP, cyber, sabotage and NNEMP attacks on electric grids, an attractive feature of this revolutionary new mode of warfare. Adversaries can, in effect, hold hostage the lives of the North American population (330 million), whose salvation will depend upon the U.S. government focusing all resources on their rescue, instead of fighting World War III.

Blackout Warfare, the term of art used here to describe a military strategy focused on attacking national electric grids and electronics that sustain military and civilian critical infrastructures, is called many things by many nations.

In the United States, the Congressional EMP Commission calls it Combined-Arms Cyber Warfare.

Russian military doctrine writes of No Contact Warfare, Electronic Warfare, and Network Centric Warfare. China calls it Total Information Warfare. Russia, China, North Korea, and Iran all call it Cyber Warfare. But their version of Cyber Warfare, and all these other labels for the same concept, include special forces sabotage, NNEMP, and nuclear HEMP attack.

Blackout Warfare seems the best name for a military strategy that attacks electric grids in order to blackout all national critical infrastructures. The EMP Commission warns that this new way of warfare is regarded by adversaries as the greatest Revolution in Military Affairs in history:

"Combined-arms cyber warfare, as described in the military doctrines of Russia, China, North Korea, and Iran, may use combinations of cyber-, sabotage, and ultimately nuclear EMP attack to impair the United States quickly and decisively by blacking-out large portions of its electric grid and other critical infrastructures. Foreign adversaries may aptly consider nuclear EMP attack a weapon

---

[513] The EMP Commission assessed HEMP attack causing nationwide blackout of life-sustaining critical infrastructures lasting one year could kill millions, up to 90% of the population. See: Dr. William R. Graham, Ambassador R. James Woolsey, Dr. Peter Vincent Pry "Prepare For The Worst" RealClearDefense (21 October 2019).

that can gravely damage the U.S. by striking at its technological Achilles Heel, without having to confront the U.S. military. The synergism of such combined arms is described in the military doctrines of all these potential adversaries as the greatest revolution in military affairs in history—one which projects rendering many, if not all, traditional instruments of military power obsolete."[514]

Russia, China, North Korea, and Iran are right—as demonstrated by the collective analysis of preceding chapters—that Blackout Warfare is the greatest Revolution in Military Affairs in history. The U.S. electric grid is a technological Achilles heel, vulnerable to attack by many different means. Blackout Warfare could quickly and relatively easily paralyze all U.S. critical infrastructures, including those analyzed for vulnerability by the EMP Commission:

Government
Military
Electric Power
Telecommunications
Transportation
Petroleum and Natural Gas
Banking and Finance
Food and Water
Emergency Services
Space[515]

Imagine the consequences of the collapse of all these critical infrastructures, as would happen by blacking-out the electric grid—electric power being the keystone critical infrastructure that sustains all the others—some failing immediately, others within hours, virtually all within 72 hours (after exhaustion of emergency power).

It would be the end of civilization.

Never before in history have little failed states like North Korea and Iran, or terrorists, been able to destroy the most advanced societies on Earth. For the first time in history, the dependency of nations upon the very electronic technologies that make possible modern civilization, also makes them vulnerable to malevolent modern barbarians and pygmy powers.

As demonstrated by preceding chapters, adversaries can blackout electric grids, and thereby other national critical infrastructures, by any one of several attack vectors:

—Cyber-attacks
—Special Forces Sabotage
—Non-Nuclear EMP (NNEMP) Attack
—Nuclear HEMP Attack

---

[514] EMP Commission, *Assessing the Threat from EMP Attack* (17 July 2017) p. 5. All the unclassified EMP Commission reports are located at www.firstempcommission.org.
[515] EMP Commission, *Critical National Infrastructures* (2008) passim.

Journalists, and some experts in the above black arts enamored of their specialty, assume an adversary would employ only one of these attack vectors, usually cyber-attack. But a prudent military planner is highly likely to use multiple attack vectors—if possible, all attack vectors. Since winning or losing World War III would depend upon this operation, they would likely "throw in the kitchen sink" and be glad of "overkill" instead of risking doing too little.

Very importantly, these multiple axes of attack are synergistic, compensating for short-comings of some attack vectors, and greatly multiplying the likely effectiveness of the overall attack. Moreover, the sequence of attacks as described above and below makes the most sense strategically:

Cyber-attack on electric grids and other critical infrastructures is the attack option that is stealthiest, most likely to go unrecognized as a military act of aggression for longest, most likely to be mistaken as highly unusual systemic failure caused by accident, especially if the cyber-attack is executed in the context of severe weather. Severe weather routinely causes utilities to lower their cyber-defenses and so increases vulnerability while providing cover. Yet cyber-attack is the most novel and problematical of the attack options against hundreds of U.S. utilities employing different software, different hardware, and different levels and kinds of cyber-security. Only Russia and China probably have the means and sophistication to blackout the whole North American electric power grid by cyber-attack.

Special Forces Sabotage of electric grids can be executed by very small numbers, in one scenario described here by 40 personnel—the numbers could be even fewer. Shooting or blasting EHV transformers is the surest way of ensuring their destruction, and the destruction of relatively few would cause protracted blackout of the national electric grid. But operations by saboteurs would probably of necessity be geographically limited to areas in the Eastern, Western, and Texas grids having the highest concentration of EHV transformers, to maximize their targeting and destruction in the shortest time. Severe weather—a hurricane, rain storm, or blizzard—could provide cover for the operation while making more difficult apprehension by law enforcement of the saboteurs. Virtually any state or terrorist group could sabotage the national electric power grid.

Non-Nuclear EMP Attack of electric grids could be executed simultaneously with kinetic-attack by saboteurs and by the same personnel, using NNEMP panel trucks as described in a previous chapter. They could blast EHV transformers with rifles or RPGs while simultaneously "frying" SCADAs with NNEMP, achieving a "double-whammy" on critical equipment. Eventual replacement of EHV transformers could be defeated if NNEMP damage to SCADAs goes unnoticed. A more sophisticated NNEMP attack using drones or cruise missiles could damage many more EHV transformer substations over a much wider geographic area than saboteurs. NNEMP drones or cruise missiles would likely attack different EHV transformer substations than saboteurs, to maximize damage to the grid. Virtually any state or terrorist group could attack the national electric power grid with NNEMP weapons.

HEMP Attack is the surest way of blacking-out electric grids and all other national critical infrastructures nearly simultaneously, potentially destructive and disruptive electromagnetic effects being delivered virtually everywhere against virtually everything at the speed of light. Theoretically, cyber-attacks could collapse more than one critical infrastructure, but probably not all, and the effectiveness would be far more problematical than HEMP attack. HEMP attack can be stealthy and anonymous: delivered by satellite; by missile launched from a submarine or freighter; by cruise missiles like the Club-K that can launch from a shipping container, fly under radar, and boost supersonically to high-altitude when near target. If precursor HEMP, NNEMP, sabotage or cyber-attacks blind early warning satellites and radars for minutes, a slightly later HEMP attack can be delivered anonymously even by ICBMs. Nuclear HEMP attack against the U.S. is presently possible by Russia, China, North Korea, possibly Iran—or by any state or terrorist group armed by one of these nations with a nuclear weapon. **HEMP is the only one of these several attack options that could paralyze U.S. nuclear retaliatory capabilities.**

Sequencing these attack options as above—cyber, sabotage and NNEMP, HEMP—could enable an aggressor to do damage assessment as the attacks unfold and terminate operations at the lowest level when national blackout of the U.S. is achieved, perhaps executing only the cyber-attack. This would maximize stealth and anonymity.

Blackout War against the United States could be executed for its own sake—to eliminate the U.S. as an actor on the world stage and establish a New World Order dominated by the aggressor, which could even be failed states like North Korea or Iran. Such a possible outcome is why Russia's General Vladimir Slipchenko and his colleagues in China, North Korea and Iran are right: Blackout Warfare is the greatest Military Revolution in history.

Blackout War against the United States could be performed to paralyze the U.S. while Russia, China, North Korea, Iran or all coordinating together attack U.S. allies to achieve, individually or collectively, their regional interests. For example, Russia's VOSTOK-18 massive military exercise in September 2018 was preceded by cyber-attacks on U.S. electric grids, prior to what was probably VOSTOK-18's practice for Russian invasion of NATO.

Blackout Warfare can indirectly kill millions in the long-run, by collapsing electric grids and other life-sustaining critical infrastructures for weeks, months, or forever, causing starvation and societal collapse. Threatening mega-deaths is always attractive to adversaries for purposes of diplomacy and blackmail against the United States.

Blackout Warfare could quickly cripple U.S. military power projection capabilities. CONUS military bases depend for 99% of their electricity from the national civilian electric grid, and would be literally powerless without it. Blackout Warfare would incentivize a U.S. President—instead of defending NATO, Taiwan, South Korea, Israel, or fighting World War III while severely crippled—to focus on using all remaining national assets, including the Defense Department, to recover U.S. critical infrastructures before millions of Americans die.

Some lessons learned from this study that deserve special emphasis:

—Severe weather should become for the U.S. government and utilities a possible early warning indicator of cyber-attacks and Blackout Warfare and inaugurate heightened, not lessened, vigilance.
—Severe weather occurring during an international confrontation with Russia, China, North Korea, or Iran should move the U.S. government and utilities toward especially heightened vigilance against Blackout Warfare.
—Extremely cold or hot weather nationwide or regionally maximally stresses electric grids and is ideal for Blackout Warfare.
—Cyber-attacks on electric utilities should no longer be regarded by the U.S. government as isolated incidents, but as an early warning indicator, potentially the "tip of the spear" for escalating attacks

including special forces sabotage, NNEMP, and HEMP, demanding greatly increased vigilance, including by U.S. nuclear retaliatory forces.
—HEMP attack is optimal during cold weather and at night.

The U.S. government should quickly implement the recommendations of the EMP Commission to protect electric grids and other critical infrastructures against HEMP, as protection against this worst-case threat can mitigate all lesser threats.

ADMIRAL WILLIAM O. STUDEMAN (Retired)
(Former Director NSA, Acting Director CIA, U.S. Navy Intelligence)

It has now been 30 years since the U.S. Congress, in 2001, called for the standup of the National EMP Commission which, via its distinguished leadership and members, reported to the Nation in 2008. Since that time, Peter Pry, and his highly informed colleagues, have continued to herald developments and make strategic recommendations related to this and related evolving and extant threats. Churchill was right in saying, in his own way, that Americans are slow to see real threats coming and even slower to comprehend, adapt and respond appropriately.

In the past 30 years, Cyber/Information-Control and Nuclear Warfare have exploded in far more inter-related and dangerous directions. These now highly evolved threats are characterized by their now combined and sheer continuous speed of development and evolution, and their mind-numbing complexity.

Today, as a professional intelligence officer for the past almost 60 years, I can say that this combined area of potential warfare is the most significant and real threat to the U.S. and our Allies that exists today at the high and strategic end of warfare, and in its worst case happening, would likely be existential. In its evolution, even small global powers constitute a Damoclean threat to the free world.

This situation notwithstanding, today's top responsible U.S. Executive and Congressional leadership mostly speak to these issues only in passing, or perhaps in back-rooms, and public serendipity and ignorance abounds. More likely, this juggernaut worst case strategic threat more likely befuddles most global government seniors, as well as our media.

Today, we are well beyond the 20th Century Industrial Age of the classic "heat, light and blast" effects of potential Cold War nuclear exchanges, strategic thinking, and doctrine, and have moved to a new and dangerous high plane of potential Information Age Cyber and Nuclear use cases and scenarios working together. These circumstances require immediate, imaginative and new out-of-the-box thinking, strategies, technologies, organizations and actions. The old paradigms and frameworks built around past "classic" strategic warfare are likely unworkable. Cold War deterrence models, stability management, escalation control, classic response/retaliation/reconstitution/recovery/rideout, warning and attack characterization, attribution, assured mutual destruction, arms control, etc., are now likely only prologue to understanding and dealing with these multi-variant modernized combined Cyber and Nuclear threat circumstances so aptly described in "Blackout Warfare" and other prolific Pry writings.

Obviously, new and more dynamic and compelling domestic, allied and international (including adversary) frameworks for highly adaptive strategic thinking and action need to be considered. Pragmatism may mean accepting that we don't know a lot; the need to work closely even with heinous adversaries, that proliferation of cyber and nuclear means, especially HEMP, is occurring and will likely accelerate, that things like arms control, pursuit of norms, might not be immediately possible, that defenses will be difficult and costly, as are offensive means, that geo-politics today are highly polarized and dangerous, and most of all, that today's top global leadership is not focused and may not know what they are dealing with. It is also now important for the U.S. and even all the "global" public, to demand consequence-based top leadership accountability, action and progress metrics on this topic. The Cyber/Info Warfare and Nuclear/EMP threat train is now roaring down the tracks to potentially dangerous, uncertain and even apocalyptic destinations, and it is now time to listen, learn, dialog, adapt and act as Peter Pry has so consistently reminded and recommended.

AMBASSADOR HENRY F. COOPER
(Former Director Strategic Defense Initiative and High Frontier)

Bureaucratic, Lethargic Washington Still Doesn't Get It on the Grid: I strongly recommend Dr. Peter Vincent Pry's excellent book *Blackout Warfare* that describes the military strategy our adversaries plan to use in attacking our increasingly vulnerable electronic military and critical civil infrastructure upon which our survival quite literally depends. Indeed, this revolutionary form of warfare is included in the military doctrines of Russia, China, North Korea and Iran—and it seems that we and our leaders are playing "catchup," when it comes to protecting our interests against this threat to everything we hold dear.

In a way, Pry's *Blackout Warfare* echoes Ted Koppel's *Lights Out- A Cyberattack, A Nation Unprepared; Surviving the Aftermath* that was a best seller six years ago, recently summarized in a 2020 review[516] that illustrates how little attention our "powers that be" have paid to Koppel's warnings and recommendations.

Hopefully, Dr. Pry will be better heeded by the government "powers that be"—and especially the private citizens of our nation who need to understand these threats to all we hold dear—and demand better at the ballot box.

Like Ted Koppel, I would also emphasize that average citizens and local authorities should get involved in what we used to call "civil defense," when it was a Defense Department mission and therefore, unlike today's Federal Emergency Management Agency (FEMA), military threat oriented.

And because of Washington's disaggregated dysfunctional bureaucracy, I believe these existential threat issues must be addressed from the "bottom up" beginning at the local level. All Americans must take seriously the existential threats to the electric power grid and demand that the "powers that be" address this existential threat "from the bottom-up." Then perhaps they can influence Washington to "provide for the common defense," as is their sworn duty.

---

[516] Lights Out by Ted Koppel: A Review with Reading Notes | Simple Green Living: Tips, Tales, Reviews, & Recipes

While Washington negotiates to provide trillions of dollars for infrastructure, they largely ignore our most vital and vulnerable infrastructure—*our nation's electric power grid.*

Editors of The American Legion Magazine were not far from this truth in titling my April 20, 2018 article: "The Threat We Fail To Address."

Little has changed since then, except that a study, the Lake Wylie Pilot Study has proven that protecting the grid at the same standards as our most important military systems is affordable—our main problems are bureaucratic and political.

Then Senate Homeland Security Committee Chairman Ron Johnson, R-Wis., accurately closed his important February 17, 2019 "Round Table" hearing by noting that we have known about «the existential threat posed by electromagnetic pulses (EMP) and geomagnetic disturbances (GMD)» for decades, but without "sufficient public pressure to take effective action to mitigate these threats."

Instead, we establish commissions and study panels, conduct research, and develop plans to develop strategies.

"It is way past time to stop admiring this problem, and actually begin to do something concrete to protect our vulnerable electrical grid, control systems, and the ever-increasing array of electronic devices our society has become dependent upon," Senator Johnson declared rightly.

Dr. George Baker's prepared testimony still challenges the government's lethargic practices. Senator Johnson urged the others testifying to respond to Dr. Baker's recommendations, many of which are included in his recent article, «Electromagnetic Pulse Resilience of United States Critical Infrastructure: Progress and Prognostic" in the Spring Summer 2021 Issue of the Journal of Critical Infrastructure Policy.

While serving on the National Security Council Staff, Dr. Baker sought to direct the federal bureaucracy to execute the March 26, 2019 Executive Order 13865, which was strengthened and became the law of the land, so to speak, via Sen. Johnson's Amendment to the December 20, 2019 National Defense Authorization Act for 2020.

It is still the law of the land but the federal bureaucracy has not responded effectively.

For example, a 13-page May 14, 2020 alleged "whole of government" report signed by the President's Science Adviser and Director of the White House Office of Science and Technology (OSTP), called for more studies—illustrating Sen. Johnson's concern. And the anemic six-month late, four-page August 17, 2020 report illustrated the "whole of government" bureaucracy still was "admiring the problem."

For my purposes, I again refer to Dr. Baker's key role in the Lake Wylie Pilot Study before he became a member of the National Security Council staff, e.g., as discussed in my April 10, 2021 Newsmax article.

Dr. Baker believes we need complementary "bottom-up" and "top-down" effort.

I would agree if I had confidence in Washington's ability to lead competently from the top down. Meeting Dr. Baker's objective might be possible, were he still playing a leadership role, but alas he is not. And while he was there fighting the good fight, his efforts were undermined by numerous bureaucratic obstacles.

Actually, I long ago concluded the federal bureaucracy was not likely to deal effectively with the existential natural and manmade EMP threat, unless Washington had to respond to demands from the local and state level. So, I focused on working from the bottom-up with local and a few state authorities, as discussed in my May 4, 2017 written testimony at a Senate Energy Committee Hearing on Protecting the Grid against EMP.

Former Speaker of the House Newt Gingrich and I explicitly warned about the existential EMP and GMD threat and the need for the government powers that be to address it urgently.

The others assured that all was well; and if not, then studies were underway that would assure an effective response to this existential threat. I think these claims were, and similar assurances over five years later continue to be, misplaced.

Based on our "Lake Wylie Pilot Study," I testified that we should address how best to protect the electric grid from the bottom-up—and am even more convinced today. Then Chair Senator Lisa Murkowski, R-Alaska, seemed to give my perspective the benefit of the doubt in her concluding comments:

"I appreciate the urging that we not let our guard down … recognizing that this [threat] is complicated and multifaceted … truly daunting … and that we need to start out locally … It is important that we in congress be reminded of the urgency and imperative of our task and I think we were given that message this morning."

Alas, this has not happened. Instead, a top down approach has focused on the bulk power grid—consisting of power plants and high voltage transmission lines, but omitting the Distribution Grid that makes up about 90% of the nation's grid and actually delivers electricity to America's citizens and their businesses, hospitals, emergency managers and other critical civil infrastructure.

There was hope that this situation might change based on former Michigan Governor Jennifer Granholm's January 27, 2021 confirmation hearing to become Secretary of Energy.

Her encouraging response to questions by Senator Murkowski indicated that she understands at least the importance of the distribution grid:

". . . We have 5 million miles of distribution wires, 200,000 miles of high-voltage electric wires. I haven't been fully briefed on the national security, and the confidential aspects of the SolarWinds cyber hack, but clearly that's one example and we are getting hacked all the time and attacked all the time. We will have, inside the DOE, a person at a very high level that is responsible for making sure the response to this is coordinated. <u>We have to harden our electric grid for protection of our energy system. I hope that this is a part of the infrastructure package that will be coming from the administration as well</u>." (Emphasis added)

But little if anything has happened to protect this absolutely vital infrastructure.

And while her response was in the context of cyber-attack threats, remember that EMP constitutes the most catastrophic cyber-attack strategy—as pointed out by the Congressional EMP Commission.

Such an EMP attack strategy is included in the military doctrine of Russia, China, North Korea and Iran—and possibly could be executed by terrorists.

The Department of Energy has a key role in protecting the electric grid against EMP/GMD threats, but is still failing to address this existential threat to all U.S. citizens.

Nowhere is this clearer that in its refusal to fund an assessment of the large transformers that are essential to viable operations of the electric grid, as discussed in my Newsmax articles of <u>July 16, 2021</u> and <u>July 22, 2021</u> respectively.

As discussed in the second, Duke Energy, a partner in the Lake Wylie Pilot Study from its beginning, over two years ago gave a large transformer, worth over a million dollars, to Savannah River National Laboratory for testing up to threat level EMP events—and it has sat idle and deteriorating in North Charleston for lack of DOE funding to ship it to the SRNL site and conduct threat level EMP and potentially Cyber threats.

And although the Lake Wylie Pilot Study demonstrated well over two years ago that we know how affordably to protect the grid from the bottom-up, our effort stalled due to the bureaucratic lethargy in Washington.

Too bad, so sad. . . Will the current infrastructure deliberations make any difference?[517]

COLONEL BOB LINDSETH (Retired)
(Former Faculty National Intelligence University)

There is little I can add that would enhance this superb analysis in Dr. Pry's book *Blackout Warfare*.

Perhaps a paradigm for indications and warning of an impending Blackout War could be adapted from the previously classified (SECRET/NOFORN) classic book by Cynthia M. Grabo *Anticipating Surprise: Analysis for Strategic Warning* (Defense Intelligence Agency, DECLASSIFIED 2002).

---

[517] Ambassador Henry F. Cooper, "Bureaucratic, Lethargic Washington Still Doesn't Get It On The Grid" Newsmax (28 July 2021).

I first met Cynthia Grabo in 1975 when I was attending the Defense Intelligence School at Bolling AFB. That institution is now the National Intelligence University (NIU) at ICC-B in Bethesda, Maryland. Cynthia's report went through the declassification process by a colleague of mine, Jan Goldman, and was signed-off by Lt. General Williams. Cynthia used Bayesian Analysis in her calculations.

Her work was so influential that they had a system built called the <u>Advanced Indications System (AIS)</u> and it's older brother the <u>Protype AIS</u> using an IBM-370 as a platform. Unfortunately, the results were very poor.

Cynthia's analytic technique was good, but the technology of the day was far behind her advanced analytic techniques.

The technique was looking at command-control-communications networks to find abnormal activity. Obviously when an adversary is about to engage in hostilities he communicates more, checking logistics, personnel, weapons, communications and etc. Of course, everything is encrypted, but it is still energy on the commlink. Cynthia's technique accurately predicted a vast number of Soviet attacks from Hungary to Czechoslovakia and others. It never missed one.

So when it comes to Blackout Wars there will be a number of indicators to look for prior to an adversary attacking:

—Hostile Rhetoric increase
—Blaming
—Incidents

Followed by:

—logistics growth
—weapons testing
—personnel training
—exercises and etc.

An adversary has a tall hill to climb before he begins a war risking their total destruction. There will be a frenzied attempt to build defensive forces to protect their society and weapons systems from U.S. attack. They will have a deterrence plan of offensive and defensive capabilities that would terrify DoD, Congress and the White House.

Now any proxy force would need top cover from their sponsor. The Cuban's thought they had that in 1962 but Nikita Khrushchev lied about Russia' superior nuclear capabilities. JFK had Curtis E. LeMay and SAC. CHECKMATE. Unfortunately that capability does not exist today. America has old tired Minutemen III ICBMs and a dysfunctional CYBERCOM/NSA.

Keep publishing your superb work and maybe, just maybe, our Congress and Executive branches will awaken to the threat you have so well described..

COLONEL KEVIN RIEDLER (Retired)
(Former Joint Chiefs Of Staff, Chief Homeland Division)

Either with a single nuclear device or coordinated, simultaneously timed, multiple missile High-altitude Electromagnetic Pulse (HEMP) attack; or equally coordinated, cyber-induced, high voltage surges capable of destroying transformers and other electrical production/distribution, directed at key nodes throughout the nation's electrical grid; combined with the current inability to quickly produce/replace large transformers here in the United States, the nation's grid is vulnerable to a long-term (6 months or greater) shutdown with the associated loss of all other services dependent upon electricity. To mitigate these threats requires hardening of key assets throughout the grid, strenuous counter-cyber warfare efforts coordinated throughout federal agencies associated both with national defense and electrical generation/distribution, and reenergized efforts to renew the U.S. industrial capability to produce key electronic grid components.

Background: The US Federal Government's agencies tasked with defending the nation's citizens (Military, Homeland Security, etc.) regularly wargame scenarios, both manmade and natural disaster events, in order to assess the threat to the nation, determine the likelihood of each scenario, ascertain potential risk associated with each, and develop means to minimize or eliminate the threat. With unlimited resources, and a likely trade-off of lost liberties enjoyed by the citizens, it would be possible to eliminate all threats. As the reality is limited resources (time, funding, personnel, equipment, industrial capability, opportunity cost, etc.), and a desire to balance individual freedom with security, an intricate comparison must be made to determine against which scenarios, considering likelihood, associated risk, and cost, those national resources should be directed.

Members of the National Security Council hold bi-weekly meetings in the Eisenhower Executive Office Building (EEOB) adjacent to the White House, attended by representatives of all major agencies (Joint Staff, Office of the Secretary of Defense, DHS, FEMA, FBI, Labor, Commerce, etc.) to discuss the identified threats and coordinate federal security efforts. The respective representatives present their agency's input and bring back shared intelligence to their agencies to help develop their portion of the nation's strategies.

The U.S. Military has a regular schedule of wargame assessment/development built into the national security cycle. Based upon the processes outlined in the National Security Act of 1947 and the 1986 Goldwater-Nichols Act, the Executive Branch establishes and shares overarching priorities in the National Security Strategy (NSS). Defense implementation elements of the NSS are outlined in the National Military Strategy (NMS), developed by the Chairman of the Joint Chiefs of Staff in consultation with the Service Chiefs, the Secretary of Defense, and Combatant Commanders, and then submitted to the Senate and House Armed Services Committees not later than 15 February of each even-numbered year. The Joint Staff and each of the military services review and re-develop their wargame scenarios based upon the NSS and NMS information.

Each of the services (Army, Navy, etc.) develop and exercise their portion of these wargame scenarios at various schools and commands within their respective service, while the Pentagon's Joint Staff coordinates combined efforts. Within the Army, a goodly portion of these exercises are developed and reviewed by Army War College's Center for Strategic Leadership (AWC-CSL) in Carlisle, Pennsylvania. Various other schools and commands throughout the Army develop their piece of these exercises, inherent in carrying out their portion of the Army's overarching mission. One extremely effective element of the Army's school system involved in this process is the John F. Kennedy Special Warfare Center and School, headquartered at Ft. Bragg, North Carolina.

The main portions of this chapter stem from discussions between the chapter author and subject matter experts of the Special Warfare Center (SWC). All agreed that topics must remain on an unclassified level. SWOT analysis (Strengths–Weaknesses–Opportunities–Threats) formed the framework for the dialogue.

Threat: In order to provide for the greatest common defense, analysts throughout the entire wargaming process often attempt to "think like the enemy," enabling them to determine likely scenarios. The overriding question initiating this process becomes, "What would I do in order to _____" (inserting an antagonist's desired outcome of choice, antithetical to national defense).

Respective to the US electrical grid, the question used to initiate this discussion was: "***From a military perspective, how would we go about attacking and bringing down the US grid, with long-term effect against the nation (i.e. max devastation with greatest time possible required to repair)?***"

The follow-on question, covered later in this chapter, was "***Having postured one or more cost-effective ways of doing so (attacking and bringing down the grid), what actions would we advocate to mitigate those potential threats?***"

Two scenarios seemed most likely to have the desired long-term effect: simultaneous, multiple-missile High-altitude Electromagnetic Pulse (HEMP); and repetitive cyber-attacks against key nodes to lock down the grid at large. A combination of these two could be even more debilitating and deadly. Each of the two will be discussed more in-depth.

HEMP Attack: While a HEMP attack is significantly more expensive than the second scenario outlined next (cyber), unclassified intelligence is available showing that Russia and China have run scenarios with the US as its target, and have developed specific HEMP attack strategies. Smaller actors (Iran, North Korea, and others) have similar plans to counter the West's overwhelming conventional and nuclear capabilities.

If an enemy chose to utilize a boat-hidden strategy, such ships would not need to approach US waters. Southwest, while remaining far out to sea, one could launch west of Baja California (Mexico). Northwest, shipping and fishing lanes traverse the west coast of British Columbia (Canada). Northeast, the fishing areas of the Labrador Sea and approaching Newfoundland or even Nova Scotia would suffice. Southeast, one could stage in the Caribbean near Cuba, or even further north and east of the Bahamas.

In addition to a ship-borne strategy, both the Russians and Chinese have sufficient means to deploy short-range missiles via submarine.

All of those nation-states, and many non-state actors, have sufficient funding available to finance such a strike, by any of these or similarly driven means. The subsequent loss of US economic prowess (not to mention life), would be many orders of magnitude greater than the smaller investment such an attack would require.

It should also be noted that both Russia and China have already employed methods to ensure their national electrical infrastructure is protected from an EMP event, whether manmade or naturally occurring. In a rare mutual military exercise, both countries also simulated how they would carry out a HEMP attack. Given that both nations are highlighted in U.S. military doctrine as potential adversaries, if they have taken both defensive and offensive EMP steps, we need to pay attention.

If a leader or party of one of these adversaries had both the means and sufficient provocation to do so, this would be the most preferable way to bring the U.S. to its knees, watching its people destroy themselves in the aftermath, while keeping the natural resources unscathed by a more popularly anticipated direct nuclear attack.

Cyber-Attack: Several of the military Subject Matter Experts (SMEs) with whom I spoke have had significant recent experience in cyber-security, and it came as no surprise that they suggested, short of the funding required to carry-out the HEMP attack described above, that a properly planned cyber-attack could effectively damage or neutralize the US power grid, and would be their preferred method of doing so. Indeed, the fact that the US Army has created a separate Cyber Branch with officer, enlisted, and civilian personnel assigned with specific expertise in this area, outlines how serious they believe this threat is to the U.S. (defensive cyber), and the potential it has as a weapon (offensive) if utilized against the nation's enemies.

Several possibilities came to the fore during this portion of the discussions: Directed Denial of Service (DDoS) attacks; weaponized artificial intelligence; artificially-induced power surges capable of damaging key grid nodes such as transformers–each of which will be covered further.

Directed Denial of Service: Perhaps the most common type of cyber attack is the DDoS, where the attacker sends an overload (bombardment) of "messages" to a specific controlling computer with the intent of denying actual/proper messages from getting through. If not configured to handle such, an electrical grid controlling computer could lose its capability to send signals to grid distribution nodes, effectively shutting down the portion of the grid controlled by that computer. Typically, such an attack is short-term in duration (minutes to hours), and while extremely inconvenient, it is likely that power would be restored throughout the system in a relatively short period of time … at least that should be the case in isolated cyber-attacks.

Taking such DDoS efforts to the next level, however (and particularly as discussed in the next section–*Weaponized AI*), a coordinated, repeated "*volumetric*" DDoS effort, if unchecked, could bring down the grid for an extended period of time, with all the long-term effects of a HEMP attack, though in all likelihood minus the physical damage to transformers, power production capabilities, and users' electronic equipment.

Weaponized Artificial Intelligence (AI): Realizing that human efforts alone are too slow, would-be attackers develop software to detect weak links within a system susceptible to attack, and then to carry out coordinated attacks from hundreds or thousands of locations. Such AI can be utilized in isolated attacks, or much more effectively, hide itself within an infected computer, only to pop-up at a designated time to execute mini-programs to shut down the grid, and/or to propagate itself on other servers to which that computer is connected. Until discovered and removed from the system, these actions can be repeated any number of times, thus shutting down electricity distribution over extended periods.

Power Surge Generation: One particular AI cyber deviation that could have greater effect than simple denial of service, would be to send commands to the computer that would cause a power spike directed at specific nodes, sufficient to damage or destroy the physical components at that location. While software has been developed to deal with such overloads, if an attacker had sufficient expertise to detect such software and then disable it, when coupled with a malicious ability to create such a surge, the consequences could be devastating, and rival that of a HEMP event, at least for power distribution capabilities.

It does not take great imagination to carry it even further, sending such spikes down power lines in an attempt to damage user equipment attached to the grid. Again, while measures have been taken to control such surges, a sufficiently trained state or terrorist organization-sponsored cyber warrior may be able to overcome such procedures.

Combination: Depending on the cyber-attackers' level of sophistication and means of generation, it is theoretically possible to combine any or all of the attacks mentioned thus far … or others not yet imagined. Therein lies the difficulty of countering cyber-attacks– onstantly monitoring different types of potential attacks, implementing new defense and detection measures with every software update, isolating computer-controlled nodes insofar as possible, and proactively protecting the very fragile US power grid.

One scenario that could prove even more disturbing would be combining cyber with HEMP. If malicious software could be surreptitiously imbedded so that it could begin such cyber-attacks after a computer is returned to service following a HEMP attack, the chaos created by the former could be exacerbated.

Recommended Mitigation Efforts: Suggested means of preventing or defeating any of the attacks above range from actions individuals, families, neighborhoods, or social groups can take to deal with situations should long-term power outages take place, to those the nation must take at large to harden the grid.

There are many sources of technical expertise for "how to" harden the grid, and it does not fall within my purview to reiterate such. National responsibility lies with those holding political and appointed positions dealing with the nation's power utilities. Suffice it to say, military experts strongly encourage such actions to be engaged at the national level. It should be noted, however, that many current and former military members are encouraging efforts, at least for larger military installations, to create hardened "*microgrids*" at each of those locations that as needed, could be detached from the larger regional and national grids. If the larger grids fail, such microgrids would permit the services to carry-on their defense missions, such defense being arguably one of the primary functions assigned to the federal government, as outlined directly within the Constitution.

Individuals, households, local organizations, neighborhoods, Community Emergency Response Teams (CERT), local governments, businesses small and large, should all review what they would need to do to survive and maintain health given the very real possibility of long-term power loss. Such measures should take into consideration loss of ability to store food requiring refrigeration, long-term loss of water (including sewage), lack of food and medical distribution, loss of communication requiring electricity (cell phones, internet, TVs / radios except for "hand-cranked/powered" equipment), and the greatly inhibited ability for law enforcement to respond– even if they could be notified of situations requiring their services. Most military installations have plans for such in place, and many actually exercise them. Most communities, households, and businesses do not.

At the local and regional power generation level, mitigation must include both hardening the grid and redoubling efforts to prevent cyber-interruptions of the automated systems that run distribution. While it may sound counter-intuitive given the ever-increasing reliance on computers attached to the internet to automatically adjust electrical distribution, determining means of isolating these systems and placing hands-on human activity back in the loop, may in fact make the system at large more robust and dependable, at least when it comes to keeping would-be cyber attackers at bay.

Finally, as both a function of national security and quickly restoring power should distribution equipment be damaged either by HEMP or cyber (or any other means), the nation must reenergize domestic production of power-related items such as large-scale transformers. That industry now exists primarily in Germany and China. The US must be able to rely on its own means to produce, stockpile, and replace these items, and not those of foreign governments, at least one of which, does not appear to have U.S. interests foremost in their planning and production cycles.

After-Action Review: Within military realms there are several axioms held sacrosanct when it comes to operational planning. The first is, *"No plan survives first contact with the enemy."* In other words, the enemy always gets a vote as to how battles will be engaged, and with rare exception do they take the exact action anticipated by military strategists. Thus military plans tend to clearly outline the desired outcome and lay out at least one specific means of attaining the objective. However, they also recognize that the leader must be able to improvise.

The second is a close take-off from the Marine motto – *"Semper Gumby"* – translated, "always flexible". Thus, military schools attempt to teach officers and senior NCOs "how to think", assess, and analyze fluid situations, rather than "what to think." This process and authority to adjust (within prescribed parameters and always keeping in mind the outlined objective) is somewhat unique within major militaries throughout the world.

When it comes to the two scenarios outlined above (HEMP and/or cyber attacks on the grid), both axioms should be taken into account. The preparation for them, with the ability to adjust on the fly, give the nation the greatest chance of countering adversaries' efforts to bring down the grid.

It is extremely unlikely that an enemy will take the exact measures described above, though some action similar, utilizing one or other general measure, is anticipated. The measures to be taken to counter such actions, at least in the planning, training, and resourcing phases, should certainly be derived from these scenarios, always keeping in mind the need to remain flexible and adjust immediately when whatever enemy does "vote."

In conclusion, it should also be noted that the conversations with the military experts at the Special Warfare Center that generated the scenarios outlined in this chapter, took place during the month of April 2021, ***prior*** to the ransomware cyber-attack that brought down the Colonial Pipeline, depriving much of the southeast portion of the nation of gasoline, which commenced on Friday, 7 May. Little did any of us know that the second scenario to which we devoted considerable time, would play out in another portion of the nation's energy infrastructure. And sadly, the alleged action by Colonial (paying of $5-million to the hackers to provide the codes required to remove the software hack), only serves to encourage similar actions on part of other adversaries, whether state sponsored or otherwise.

There is considerable work to be done, though again, the efforts to counter such action given the staggering devastation that would take place if the electrical grid goes down long-term, are more than worthwhile.

MICHAEL MABEE, CSM USA (Retired)
(Expert On Electric Grid Physical Security and Combat Tactics)

The electric utility industry, Congress and the regulators (such as the Department of Energy (DOE), the Federal Energy Regulatory Commission (FERC) and state public utility commissions have failed for over four decades to address the known threats to the electric grid. I am frequently asked "why can't they fix grid security?"

The question is not so much "why *can't* they fix grid security" because they *can*. Congress has considered legislation that would have improved the security of the electric grid but this legislation always dies in committee. The regulators could improve standards for grid protection but they don't.

So, the more appropriate question is "why *won't* they fix it?" There are *1.2 billion reasons* why Congress and the regulators won't fix electric grid security.

The electric utility industry has exerted a great deal of influence over the United States Government. In fact, according to The Center for Responsive Politics, the electric utilities in the 2020 cycle:

- Spent $108,468,019 on lobbying the U.S. Congress.
- Made total contributions to the U.S. Congress of $28,562,003.
    —Made $11,626,034 in political contributions to members of the U.S House.
    —Made $5,140,906 in political contributions to members of the U.S. Senate.
- Total lobbying and contributions in the 2020 cycle: over $137 million.

In the last decade the electric utility industry has spent *$1.2 billion lobbying* the U.S. Congress and another $150 million in "contributions." (Not including lobbying and contributions at the state level.) Imagine if this $1.2 billion, which largely originated from the bills of ratepayers, was put towards electric grid security rather than lobbying against further regulation.

The industry's lobbyists have embedded themselves over the years, as "partners" in DOE and FERC via the Electric Subsector Coordinating Council ("ESCC") and trade organizations such as the Edison Electric Institute ("EEI"), the American Public Power Association ("APPA"), the National Rural Electric Cooperative Association ("NRECA"), the Large Public Power Council ("LPPC"), the Transmission Access Policy Study Group ("TAPS"), the Electric Power Supply Association ("EPSA"), WIRES, and the Electricity Consumers Resource Council ("ELCON").

These industry groups have actively *fought against* grid security regulation, mandatory critical infrastructure protection standards and public transparency.

The industry *does not* represent the public interest. They *do not* represent the U.S. Government (although it does appear they have largely coopted the U.S. Government).

Here are a few facts about the electric industry's posture on grid security:

- After the Great Northeast Blackout of 2003, the industry was forced to write a mandatory vegetation management standard. (Yes, the industry writes its own standards.) The standard took a decade to finally be implemented in 2013.[518] Problem solved? Ask the people of Paradise, California, where 85 people died in the 2018 Camp Fire and PG&E subsequently plead guilty to 85 felony counts for its role in that catastrophe.[519]

- After the spectacular physical attack against a transformer in Metcalf, California in 2013[520] the industry advised *against* a mandatory physical security standard.[521] They were forced to write the standard. The resulting weak physical security standard exempts most facilities from compliance (generation facilities are specifically exempted.) As a result, there have been hundreds of physical attacks against the grid since the "physical security standard" was implemented.[522]

- Despite the well-documented physical security problem in the critical electric infrastructure[523], the industry continues for fight *against* stronger physical security regulations. The inadequacy of the physical security standards was highlighted in a complaint filed with the Federal Energy Regulatory Commission (FERC) on January 29, 2020 alleging that grid physical security was inadequate.[524] At the urging of the industry, on June 9, 2020 FERC dismissed the complaint.[525]

---

[518] See: https://www.ferc.gov/industries-data/resources/tree-trimming-and-vegetation-management

[519] San Francisco Chronicle. "PG&E, a 'killer company,' admits to 85 felony counts. Now what?" March 29, 2020. https://www.sfchronicle.com/business/article/PG-E-a-killer-company-admits-to-85-felony-15163078.php

[520] Smith, Rebecca. The Wall Street Journal. *"Assault on California Power Station Raises Alarm on Potential for Terrorism."* February 5, 2014. https://www.wsj.com/articles/assault-on-california-power-station-raises-alarm-on-potential-for-terrorism-1391570879 and Smith, Rebecca. Wall Street Journal. "U.S. Risks National Blackout From Small-Scale Attack." March 12, 2014. https://www.wsj.com/articles/SB10001424052702304020104579433670284061220

[521] NERC's then CEO Gerry Cauley told Congress in a February 12, 2014 letter: "I do not believe it makes sense to move to mandatory standards at this time. There are more than 55,000 substations of 100 Kv or higher across North America, and not all those assets can be 100% protected against all threats. I am concerned that a rule-based approach for physical security would not provide the flexibility needed to deal with the widely varying risk profiles and circumstances across the North American grid and would instead create unnecessary and inefficient regulatory burdens and compliance obligations." Letter available at: https://michaelmabee.info/wp-content/uploads/2021/05/NERC-Response-to-Senators-Letter-Reid-2-11-14-v4.pdf

[522] See: https://michaelmabee.info/oe-417-database/

[523] See for example: Smith, Rebecca. Wall Street Journal. "How America Could Go Dark." July 14, 2016. https://www.wsj.com/articles/how-america-could-go-dark-1468423254

[524] See Exhibit A.

[525] See 171 FERC ¶ 61,205. https://elibrary.ferc.gov/eLibrary/idmws/file_list.asp?document_id=14867700

- The industry vehemently fought FERC's Notice of Proposed Rulemaking to establish a mandatory standard for Geomagnetic Disturbances.[526] Once forced to write a standard (TPL-007-1) the effectiveness of this industry-written standard is still the subject of considerable debate.[527]

- The industry has consistently fought *against* stronger supply chain cybersecurity standards. The inadequacies of the cybersecurity standards were highlighted in a complaint filed with the Federal Energy Regulatory Commission (FERC) on May 11, 2020 about the need for increased supply chain cybersecurity.[528] At the urging of the industry, on October 2, 2020 FERC dismissed the complaint.[529] A month and a half later, the SolarWinds hack came to light and the regulators – NERC and FERC – were caught flat-footed.

- The irony of the SolarWinds hack is that since 2017, the industry vehemently fought against modifying CIP standards to require detection, mitigation and removal of malware from the electric grid.[530] While fighting this common-sense petition for rulemaking, the head of NERC testified in 2019 that he didn't know whether there was Russian or Chinese equipment or software already installed in the grid.[531] SolarWinds was first detected in 2020 but to this day, thanks to the industry's diligent efforts, there is no requirement that malware be detected, mitigated or removed.

- The Texas grid collapse in February of 2021, which was responsible for over 150 deaths[532] and between $80 billion–$130 billion in economic loss[533], was a repeat offense. Similar outages for identical reasons occurred in 1989 and 2011. The government and the industry have failed to fix the underlying critical electric infrastructure issues that caused all three incidents. Yet the industry urged FERC to take no action to investigate whether the existing standards were followed or if improvements are needed.[534] At the urging of the industry, FERC dismissed a complaint on this issue on May 26, 2021.[535]

- There is currently no mandatory standard for protecting the grid against an electromagnetic pulse (EMP) attack—a standard that the industry opposes and FERC declines to order. The industry enlisted its Electric Power Research Institute (EPRI) to "study" the electromagnetic pulse (EMP) threat to the electric grid. EPRI disregarded the findings of the Congressional EMP Com-

---

[526] See FERC Order No. 779, issued May 16, 2013 at 143 FERC ¶ 61,147 https://elibrary.ferc.gov/eLibrary/filelist?document_id=14115712&optimized=false

[527] See FERC Docket RM15-11-000. Multiple experts outside the electric industry argue that the standard is not sufficient to protect the grid from a GMD event.

[528] See Exhibit B.

[529] See 173 FERC ¶ 61,010. https://elibrary.ferc.gov/eLibrary/filelist?accession_num=20201002-3033

[530] See FERC Docket AD17-9-000 Petition for Rulemaking by the Foundation for Resilient Societies in a New Docket: For the Commission to Require an Enhanced Reliability Standard to Detect, Report, Mitigate and Remove Malware from the Bulk Power System.

[531] See February 14, 2019 Senate Committee on Energy and Natural Resources hearing: "Hearing to Consider the Status and Outlook for Cybersecurity Efforts in the Energy Industry" (at 1 hour and 30 minutes). Available at: https://michaelmabee.info/senate-cybersecurity-hearing/

[532] See: https://dshs.texas.gov/news/updates.shtm#wn

[533] See: https://www.dallasfed.org/research/economics/2021/0415.aspx

[534] Attached as Exhibit C is the complaint on the inadequacy of the reliability standards and their failure to prevent the Texas grid collapse of February 2021 filed with FERC on February 28, 2021.

[535] See 175 FERC ¶ 61,163. https://elibrary.ferc.gov/eLibrary/filelist?accession_num=20210526-3061

mission[536] and severely understated the EMP threat. The resulting disingenuous report by EPRI (which was lauded by the industry) has placed the United States in great danger.[537] EPRI's report is contradicted by multiple experts of the Electromagnetic Defense Task Force (EDTF) [538] and by a January 11, 2021 Department of Energy memo.[539] However, the industry continues to propound that the EPRI report is the benchmark report for EMP protection of the critical electric infrastructures. Regardless, there is no movement towards developing an EMP standard to protect the electric grid.

- Edison Electric Institute (EEI) is the trade organization that purports to represent "all U.S. investor-owned electric companies." EEI is a frequent intervenor and commenter in FERC dockets and Congressional hearings related to Critical Infrastructure Protection (CIP) standards and issues. EEI spends millions of dollars annually lobbying the U.S. Congress on matters pertaining to the U.S. critical electric infrastructure. EEI also makes contributions to key members of Congress involved in critical infrastructure security legislation and oversight. EEI counts among its members State Grid Corporation of China, which is a state-owned corporation, owned by the government of the People's Republic of China. EEI also counts as a member Power Assets Holdings, a company based in Hong Kong (which China calls "Hong Kong Special Administrative Region of the People's Republic of China").[540]

The U.S. Government has been concerned about the cybersecurity of the critical electric infrastructure since at least 2003,[541] the security of the electric grid from physical threats since at least 1981[542] and electromagnetic pulse (EMP) threats since at least 1975.[543] In other words, we have been talking about securing our critical electric infrastructure for over four decades from the very threats we still face today.

The electric utility industry has lobbied and fought against grid protection regulations every step of the way. After the Great Northeast Blackout of 2003, Congress passed the Energy Policy Act of 2005 which added Section 215 to the Federal Power Act. However, this moved the needle very little on the security of the critical electric infrastructure. The impact was we moved from "voluntary" self-regulation to "mandatory" self-regulation—but only for a small portion of the whole critical electric

---

[536] Commission to Assess the Threat to the United States from Electromagnetic Pulse (EMP) Attack. Reports are available here: https://michaelmabee.info/unclassified-emp-commission-reports/

[537] See: https://michaelmabee.info/epri-emp-report/

[538] Electromagnetic Defense Task Force (EDTF) Review of EPRI EMP Report August 23, 2109. http://bit.ly/2OglqYl

[539] Department of Energy. "Physical Characteristics of HEMP Waveform Benchmarks for Use in Assessing Susceptibilities of the Power Grid, Electrical Infrastructures, and Other Critical Infrastructure to HEMP Insults." January 11, 2021. https://bit.ly/3rLmztL

[540] See: https://michaelmabee.info/electric-industry-lobbyists-china-ties-questioned/

[541] See: "Implications of Power Blackouts For The Nation's Cybersecurity and Critical Infrastructure Protection," Before the US House, Joint Hearing of the Subcommittee on Cybersecurity, Science, and Research and Development, and the Subcommittee on Infrastructure and Border Security of the Select Committee On Homeland Security, (108th Congress) September 4 & 23, 2003. http://bit.ly/2qV9La3

[542] General Accounting Office (GAO). Federal Electrical Emergency Preparedness Is Inadequate. EMD-81-50. May 12, 1981. http://bit.ly/354ZN4i

[543] See: Defense Civil Preparedness Agency (DCPA). Vulnerability of Regional and Local Electric Power Systems— Nuclear Weapons Effects and Civil Defense Actions. July 1975. http://bit.ly/2QogiVj

infrastructure. Perhaps the problem we face today was best summarized in 2003 in Congressional testimony when the bill was being debated:

"We must not rely on industry self-regulation. The proposal to move from voluntary self-regulation to mandatory self-regulation misses the point. The difficulty is not the voluntary versus the mandatory. It is the 'self' part. We need clear accountability to public authorities."[544]

While public-private partnerships have their place, the industry has lobbied, promoted and ultimately hornswoggled the federal government into a system of "all carrots and no stick." They laud the public-private partnerships and have fought for decades against regulation and mandatory standards to secure the critical electric infrastructure. Everything they do is calculated to kick the grid security can down the road and commission more "studies." When finally forced to write a mandatory standard, the resulting weak standards should not be surprising. This hands-off regulatory approach has not worked and today our national security is jeopardized.

In short, the electric utility industry has had their chance—and for many more years than this regulatory boondoggle should have been allowed to go on. Enough is enough. The present dismal state of our critical electric infrastructure security is *because* the federal government listened to the electric utility industry and applied a light regulatory touch at the urging of industry lobbyists.

The tail has been wagging the regulatory dog for decades on grid security—which is the primary reason we are in a national security crisis today.

Unfortunately, the United States has occasionally been a bad judge of character. A rogues' gallery including Osama bin Laden, Saddam Hussein and Manuel Noriega count themselves as former U.S. allies. Here, we have placed our trust and our national security in the hands of an industry with a checkered past[545]: Samuel Insull, Enron, PG&E's multiple felony convictions, the recent Ohio and Illinois bribery scandals to name only a few. In fact, R Street Institute pointed out[546]:

"Policymakers should not dismiss these developments as merely the work of a few bad actors, but as the latest evidence of an established behavioral pattern tied to perverse incentives from flawed institutions."

We should not trust the electric utility industry. If after all the industry's efforts and counsel over the past decades, our critical electric infrastructure is not secure, perhaps their agenda is not the same as that of the United States Government.

---

[544] Testimony of Mark N. Cooper, Director of Research, Consumer Federation of America. Page 25. "Keeping The Lights On: The Federal Role In Managing The Nation's Electricity." Before the Committee on Governmental Affairs, Oversight of Government Management, the Federal Workforce and the District of Columbia Subcommittee. (108th Congress) September 10, 2003. http://bit.ly/357GCHh

[545] ProPublica. "Four Types of Scandals Utility Companies Get Into With Money From Your Electric Bills." October 10, 2020. https://www.propublica.org/article/four-types-of-scandals-utility-companies-get-into-with-money-from-your-electric-bills

[546] Hartman, Devin and Haugh, Mike. R Street Institute. "Electric Competition: The Antidote For Bad Behavior." September 2020. https://www.rstreet.org/wp-content/uploads/2020/09/Final-No-205-electric-competition-updated.pdf

When some of the thousands of entities who own, operate or supply the electric grid do the right things, we should incentivize them. But we must hold those who endanger the critical electric infrastructure accountable. And we must ensure that the public, Congress and state regulatory authorities have the transparency necessary to scrutinize the results.

Ultimately, to secure the electric grid, we need mandatory enforceable standards that apply to the entire electric grid: the generation, transmission and distribution systems. Violators must be held publicly accountable and the government must vigorously enforce the standards to protect our nation's most critical infrastructure.

The preamble of the U.S. Constitution gives the federal government the responsibility to "provide for the common defense." The federal government needs to do its constitutionally mandated duty and secure the grid.

DR. EDWARD M. ROCHE
(Cyber Warfare Expert, United Nations and Columbia University)

Deterrence As A Strategic Model Has Failed: If the effectiveness of national defense against a blackout attack were measured by the amount of money spent, the United States would be the most secure country in the world. But it is not.

At great expense, the U.S. has developed powerful offensive cyber capabilities, although they are kept secret. Defensive investments also are extensive. Of the world's top three cybersecurity industry clusters, numbers 1 and 2 are in Silicon Valley and Washington, D.C. The U.S. also has built up extensive cyber intelligence capabilities, monitoring systems, and response procedures at both the Federal and State levels. A cornucopia of specialized teams are working on national cyber and infrastructure security: The AF Research Laboratory (AFRL)/Rome Lab; AFCYBERWORX; LevelUP; the 16th Air Force; the U.S. Army Futures Command Research Laboratory; the Army Cyber Command; Army North; the powerful U.S. Cyber Command; the Joint Information Operations Warfare Center; the Defense Innovation Unit (DIU); the Defense Advanced Research Projects Agency; the Defense Intelligence Agency; the National Security Agency; and DHS's Cyber Infrastructure and Security Agency. In the Department of Energy we find the Cyber, Energy Security and Emergency Response team, and the line-up of national laboratories at Idaho, Los Alamos, Oakridge, the Pacific Northwest and Sandia.

With all of this Herculean effort, what is the result?

Deterrence as a strategic model has failed. Critical infrastructure has been put at risk. It was developed for management of nuclear weapons. It assumes a fear of retaliation or a debilitating first strike. If today's attackers have a fear of retaliation, it does not show. As shown in the previous chapters, the United States on an hourly basis is attacked with impunity with cyber.

Why does deterrence not do its job?

There can be only three reasons:

—First, the attacks are not coming from nation states, in which case the bulk of diplomacy is meaningless.
—Second, nation state attackers do not perceive them as being risky enough to avoid.
—Third, they are provoked by attacks from the United States.

If the attacks are not coming from nation states, but from non-state actors working independently of government, then diplomacy can respond by improving the mechanisms of international police force coordination and enforcement. This would lead to international standardization of rules for evidence and probable cause, as well as expedited pathways for extradition and prosecution. Here, the agreements already in place could be improved on a bilateral basis, or for the long-term an international authority could be tasked with some of the work.

But the most likely explanation for today's out-of-control situation is that the United States is in the middle of fighting an undeclared cyberwar. Each side, indeed all nations, are fighting around the clock both offensively and defensively. Each is trying to give as well as it gets. Our government complains bitterly about foreign attacks against the nation's infrastructure, but does not acknowledge what it is doing to others overseas. We see the effects but never the cause. This lack of transparency to civil society obviates any political pressure to bring this tit-for-tat to an end. There is no accountability. This has led to an ongoing "soft" war, but one that continues to get worse.

If the United States starts dropping bombs somewhere, it will show up on the news. Questions will be asked. Congress will wish to interfere. Cyber is different. Operations take place behind a wall of classification. If the U.S. launches an attack against an opponent, it is invisible. No one sees. It does not make the news. Civil society is kept in the dark, never to know what is done in its name. It assumes the attacks are coming unprovoked out of the blue. So if the current tsunami of attacks against infrastructure are in response to U.S. attacks, then it means there is an undeclared cyber war in full swing. The answer is to revise the War Powers Act to include cyber.[547]

Blackout Warfare is the logical end of this undeclared and invisible war. If today's pattern continues, attacks will continue to get more severe, and more frequent. The level of damage will increase. Nation states will become more accustomed to using cyber-attacks as forms of diplomatic signaling or "warning shots." We always should remember that the Great War (First World War) was one that no nation wanted. An undeclared Cyber War can lead to an unintended global disaster that no one wants.

What we see here is a complete and utter failure of diplomacy. At best, the U.S. has been resorting to public jaw-boning and threats: "If cyber attacks continue, the U.S. will retaliate." In the most recent statements, the 46th President made allusions to a "shooting war" that could result from cyber escalation. Both the 44th and 45th Presidents mentioned cyber problems at leadership summits. In all cases, they have returned with vague promises the attacks will stop. Instead, attacks escalated.

In the end, the fundamental problem is the false assumption that Cyber War or EMP-type attacks are not real "war." After all, it is said that if one cuts off power or disrupts information systems, there is no permanent damage, and no one is hurt physically. But from the previous chapters, we can see this is a dangerous myth. It is a mistake to under-estimate the power or determination of one's enemy, but

---

[547] War Powers Resolution of 1973, 50 U.S.C. 1541–1548

it is even more foolhardy to play loose with the possible effects of a "soft" war because no matter how much has been spent, the United States is not prepared to cope with a dead grid.

In sum, in order to lower the risk of catastrophic damage to its economy and society, the United States should supplement its massive expenditures on domestic infrastructure security with a new diplomacy aimed at building an international mechanism for monitoring and defending against cyber-attacks. This will require much more investment in technical intelligence, but also enhanced internationalization of homeland security initiatives. International Humanitarian Law should be emphasized, because it outlaws military action against civil society or against its supporting infrastructure. Cyber peacekeeping capabilities should be built. Diplomats should be ordered to work on multilateral conventions to tie things together. The United States needs to spend much more on civil defense, but also double its efforts on using diplomacy to throttle the threat in the first place. Only an effective mobilization in both directions will mitigate the threat of a Blackout War.

DAVID T. PYNE
(National Deputy Director, EMP Task Force)

What U.S. Leaders Must do to Ensure America's National Survival: Since the end of the Cold War three decades ago, America has "slept," with its leaders either unaware or unconcerned about the increasingly bellicose and militarily superior "New Axis" Powers aligning against it. This alliance by America's two most powerful adversaries is not a recent development. It was in July 2001, that the Russian Federation and the People's Republic of China (PRC) joined together to form the Shanghai Cooperation Organization (SCO), which President Putin has since described as "a reborn Second Warsaw Pact."[548] They now lead a military alliance which includes over 68% of the landmass of the Eurasian super continent, nearly 42% of the world's population, nearly 30% of the world's GDP, and approximately 75% of the world's operational nuclear weapons, with over two-thirds of them deployed by Russia alone.[549]

Russia, China and North Korea have been assessed as likely having the capability to use Super-EMP and cyberwarfare attacks to shut down America's electrical power grid, other critical infrastructure, internet, financial system, transportation system, food and water distribution system, communications system and emergency services in a matter of minutes.[550] They might even be capable of disabling U.S. Global Positioning System (GPS) and military early warning satellites, potentially blinding us to subsequent attacks against the U.S. and its allies.[551] Such an attack could also serve to cut off our military forces from being able to communicate with their commanders or coordinate their attacks, making them much easier to defeat. The U.S. has yet to develop any Super-EMP weapons to help deter the use of such powerful weapons against us.

---

[548] Douglas E. Schoen and Melik Kaylan, "The Russia-China Axis—the New Cold War and America's Crisis of Leadership." (9 September 2014)

[549] Rick Rowden, "The Shanghai Cooperation Organization is the Biggest Organization You've Never Heard of." speri.dept. shef.ac.uk (3 September 2017)

[550] Jamie Crawford, "The U.S. Government Thinks China Could Take Down the Power Grid." www.cnn.com 21 November 2014

[551] Zak Doffman, "U.S. Military Satellites Likely Cyberattacked by China or Russia or Both." www.forbes.com, (5 July 2019)

President Joe Biden was elected, in part, on a platform of protecting the environment from global climate change. However, many do not realize that the threat of a nuclear/EMP/cyberattack on the U.S. homeland would likely be far more catastrophic for U.S. citizens, as well as for the environment, due to several reasons such as the fact that it would cause all 94 U.S. nuclear reactors to meltdown, spreading radioactive contamination and fallout to nearby U.S. cities. If such a nationwide EMP/cyberattack were to occur, it is quite possible that U.S. leaders might not be certain which country attacked us or who to retaliate against. In 2008, the Congressional EMP Commission estimated that such a cataclysmic attack on a national scale could cause up to ninety percent of Americans to die within twelve months due to starvation, disease and societal breakdown.[552] Despite this fact, U.S. leaders have done virtually nothing to protect the American people from EMP and cyberattack just as they have failed to deploy a national missile defense system to protect us from nuclear missile attack. In the event of a catastrophic Sino-Russian attack against the U.S. homeland, there is a good chance that none of its allies would come to our defense out of fear that if they were to do so they might share our fate.

How did U.S. leaders allow America to become so vulnerable? After the end of the Cold War in 1991 under the mistaken assumption that the existential threat of nuclear attack had disappeared virtually overnight, U.S. leaders engaged in a policy of rapid unilateral nuclear disarmament at a pace far exceeding Russia's, exposing the U.S. to unnecessary and increasingly unacceptable risks. The U.S. nuclear arsenal was reduced from 30,000 nuclear weapons to a mere 1,750 operational warheads deployed on aging delivery systems of increasingly questionable reliability, some of which are over half a century old. Only 720 of our warheads are ready to launch at any given time, of which fifty percent would likely survive a full-scale nuclear first strike.[553] The reliability of the U.S. nuclear stockpile is also a major concern due to a failure of successive U.S. administrations to ensure they will function as designed in the event of a crisis. Over the past decade, the U.S. has allowed itself to be overtaken/overmatched by the Sino-Russian alliance in virtually every recognized measure of strategic military power including offensive nuclear weapon systems, national missile defenses, hypersonic weapons, Super-EMP weapons, Cyber Warfare capabilities, economic and industrial manufacturing might, the ability to produce major weapon systems without foreign components, critical infrastructure hardening against EMP/cyberattack, civil defenses and overall nuclear war survivability.[554]

Recent satellite imagery reveals that the PRC is constructing 250 nuclear DF-41 ICBM silos at an extremely rapid pace, which could enable them to increase their deployed strategic nuclear arsenal by as many as 2,500 additional warheads as early as next year.[555] In 2017, the U.S. Department of Defense estimated that the Russian Federation is in the process of building up its own nuclear arsenal to total 8,000 deployed warheads, which is over four and a half times more operational nuclear warheads than the U.S. possesses.[556] Despite this increasing Sino-Russian nuclear superiority, the U.S. government currently has no plans to increase the size of the U.S. nuclear arsenal at all, let

---

[552] James Woolsey and Peter Pry, "The Growing Threat from an EMP Attack" www.wallstreetjournal.com (12 August 2014)

[553] Hans M. Kristensen and Matt Korda, "United States Nuclear Forces, 2020." www.tandfonline.com (13 January 2020)

[554] Jamie Seidel, "China and Russia Have Formed Axis of Power, NATO's Top General Warns." www.news.com.au (6 February 2021

[555] Thomas Newdick, "China Increasing its Intercontinental Ballistic Missile Silos by a Factor of Ten." www.thedrive.com (27 July 2021)

[556] Mark Schneider, "The Terrifying Way Russia Would Start a Nuclear War," www.19fortyfive.com (29 April 2021)

alone restore "rough nuclear parity" with Russia and China along with our ability to credibly deter a nuclear/cyber/EMP attack on the U.S. homeland. Russia has also been deploying a number of nuclear "superweapons," which the U.S. does not even possess that are not limited by any existing arms control treaty.[557] As a result, the chances of an unconventional nuclear/EMP/cyberattack on the U.S. homeland have, arguably, never been greater in U.S history.

Disturbingly, the commander of U.S. Strategic Command, Admiral Richard, testified to Congress in April 2021 that the U.S. might well face a two-front or even a three-front war if Russia were to invade Ukraine and/or other Eastern Europe nations, China attacked Taiwan and North Korea were to attack South Korea at about the same time in coordination with one another.[558] Admiral Richard testified that the U.S. currently has no contingency plans for how to confront two allied nuclear superpowers in a future war.[559] Accordingly, the ability of the U.S. and its allies to survive, let alone win, a war fought with such powerful, unconventional weapons against our enemies remains very much in doubt. Their growing military strategic superiority has provided Russia and China with the self-confidence to engage in increasingly brazen aggressions abroad including Russia's invasion of Ukraine, China's occupation of disputed islands in the South China Sea and what appears to be an increasingly imminent Chinese invasion of Taiwan.

As a result of its increasing strategic military inferiority, America faces increasingly stark and uncomfortable choices. Some of the most prudent national security policy options we can undertake might be criticized by some as amounting to accommodation or even "appeasement" of our enemies. However, history is replete with examples when limited, strategically targeted concessions to adversaries helped ensure, not merely "peace in our time" and the protection of vital national interests, but also ensured long-term national survival. If the U.S. continues its risky, provocative policy of military brinkmanship with Russia and China, attempting to challenge and contain them along their borders and coastal seas, without engaging in some limited accommodations of Russia and China's vital interests either by diplomacy or unilateral declarations and actions, the outcome, however unthinkable, might be the end of our nation.

The answer to this unprecedented national security dilemma we face today is two-fold. First, U.S. leaders must wage a "peace offensive" and negotiate a global sphere of influence agreement, which safeguards vital U.S. interests, to avert the increasing likelihood of stumbling into an unnecessary and cataclysmic war with Russia and China.[560] Second, we must return to more realist Cold War ways of thinking in the realization that a cyber/EMP/nuclear war with our nuclear superpower adversaries is not only possible, but increasingly probable. This realization should compel U.S. leaders to engage in a near-herculean, bi-partisan effort to rebuild our strategic defenses in accordance with the specific policy recommendations at the end of this essay as swiftly as possible, re-purposing funding from less important programs for that purpose, much as we did just before and shortly after the outbreak of the Second World War.

---

557 Mark B. Schneider, "Putin's Nuclear Superweapons." www.realcleardefense.com (7 May 2018)

558 "U.S. Armed Services Hearings on U.S. Strategic Command and U.S. Space Command." www.senate.gov (20 April 2021)

559 Ibid.

560 David T. Pyne, "Trump Could Win Peace Prize with this Tri-polar Deal." www.wnd.com (15 October 2019)

The last sphere of influence agreement negotiated by President Franklin Delano Roosevelt, Prime Minister Winston Churchill and Soviet dictator Josef Stalin at Yalta was successful in keeping the great power peace in Europe for over a half-century thanks, in large part, to the U.S. retention of "rough" nuclear parity with the Soviet Union during the entirety of the Cold War. Under such an agreement, the U.S. would retain the largest sphere of influence including the entire Western Hemisphere, Western Europe, Japan, Australia and New Zealand. The Russian sphere of influence would include the former Soviet republics, Iran, Iraq, Syria and Libya. China's sphere of influence might consist of North Korea, Taiwan, the South China Sea, Pakistan, Afghanistan, four Marxist/Communist nations in southeast Asia and around half a dozen African nations led by Marxist/Communist dictators.

As the ancient Chinese general, Sun Tzu, wisely stated in his book *The Art of War*: "Thus, what is of supreme importance in war is to attack the enemy's strategy. Next best is to disrupt his alliances by diplomacy." In furtherance of this axiom, the U.S. might even agree to withdraw from NATO, which would continue to function as a European-led rather than U.S.-led alliance, in exchange for a Russian withdrawal from their alliance with China and an end to all Sino-Russian military cooperation and mutual assistance. The purpose of this comprehensive agreement would be to recognize and respect the vital interests of all three nuclear superpowers and resolve all major outstanding disputes while minimizing potential risks of military conflict in the interests of preserving the great power peace.

Another potentially more viable and politically palatable alternative to concluding a comprehensive agreement with Russia and China, would be for the Biden Administration to take unilateral actions to pull back forward-deployed U.S. military forces from Eastern Europe, Central Asia, the Middle East, the South China Sea and the Korean Peninsula. The Biden Administration should follow the shrewd recommendation of former U.S. Assistant Secretary of Defense Graham Allison in his groundbreaking article, "The New Spheres of Influence—Sharing the Globe with Other Great Powers" by subjecting all U.S. alliances with other nations to a zero-sum cost-benefit analysis to determine which ones serve to enhance U.S. national security and which ones put us more at greater risk of being dragged into wars with Russia and China that do not concern vital U.S. interests.[561] Then America could shed all of our security commitments that do not pass the test.

Most importantly, U.S. leaders should inform Moscow and Beijing that the America will not intervene militarily in any potential wars over Taiwan or the former Soviet republics (all of which are indefensible anyway), essentially renouncing future U.S military interventions in their spheres of influence. Such actions would serve to strengthen U.S. national security and greatly reduce the chances of an attack by Russia, China and North Korea on the U.S. homeland by reducing our perceived threat to Moscow, Beijing and Pyongyang while increasing the likelihood of fissures and dissention between them, potentially dividing and disrupting their alliance over time. This is because nothing has united Russia and China more than America's short-sighted attempts to project its power into Eastern Europe and East Asia along with its attempt to become the dominant world power, without which their historical adversarial relationship might have resumed long ago.

---

[561] "Graham Allison, "The New Spheres of Influence-Sharing the Globe with Other Great Powers," Foreign Affairs (March/April 2020)

As Secretary Allison notes in his seminal essay, Russia and China already have their own spheres of influence whether U.S. policymakers are willing to admit they do or not.[562] It has been repeated U.S. military incursions into their spheres of influence since the end of the Cold War (most notably the expansion of NATO into Eastern Europe including three former Soviet republics) that have provoked them to ally more closely together militarily. Russia and China have reportedly even formed a joint missile defense system consisting of several thousand ABM interceptors potentially capable of shooting down eighty percent of America's nuclear second-strike retaliatory warheads following a hypothetical Sino-Russian nuclear first strike.[563] According to top China expert, Gordon Chang, Russia and China are likely coordinating, not just their joint defensive planning, but their joint offensive plans as well, to push the U.S. out of their respective spheres of influence by force.[564] They might even be planning to neutralize the U.S. with one or more unconventional means of existential attack at the onset of any conflict to eliminate the chances of any future U.S. interference in their respective spheres of influence entirely.

There are several important measures which the Biden Administration and the U.S. Congress should implement as soon as possible to safeguard America against these existential threats. First, President Biden should declare a presidential cyber/EMP/missile defense emergency to re-allocate $30 billion dollars in funding to fully harden our electronic power grid and other critical infrastructure, particularly our nuclear C3 system as well as future U.S. military satellites, against cyber/EMP attack. In addition, he should use this emergency declaration to re-allocate $90 billion more to build 3,000 SM-3 Block IIA ABM interceptors to deploy on sixty of our Aegis cruisers and destroyers whose primary role should be "boost phase" national missile defense, not conventional military power projection. Hundreds of these missiles have already been purchased by the U.S. Navy. The Biden Administration should also consider deploying space-based non-nuclear missile defenses which would be even more effective in deterring enemy nuclear attack and shooting down rogue, accidental or deliberate nuclear missile attacks. Furthermore, as part of this emergency declaration, President Biden should invoke the Defense Production Act to order U.S. companies to increase U.S. tritium gas production to ensure we can produce enough of it to make sure our aging strategic nuclear warheads will work in a crisis. Full-funding for these measures could be readily obtained by ending America's two-decades long Global War on Terror, closing the vast majority of America's nearly 800 overseas military bases and bringing most of our nearly 200,000 forward-deployed military personnel home to their families, which has been estimated could save up to $160-200 billion per year.[565]

Second, President Biden should act swiftly to increase the Operations Tempo (OPTEMPO) of America's Ohio-class nuclear missile submarines from one-third to two-thirds, increasing the number of nuclear missile submarines at sea at any given time from four to eight. This critically important and relatively inexpensive measure would effectively increase the number of "ready to fire" land- and sea-based nuclear warheads to 1,040 while doubling the number of survivable, second-strike retaliatory strategic warheads. That would serve to ensure that America's nuclear adversaries would not be able to destroy the bulk of our nuclear missile submarine fleet in port in the event of a nuclear first strike. This is one of the most critical near-term steps U.S. leaders can take to rapidly restore the

---

[562] Ibid.

[563] David Reid, "Russia is Helping China to Build a Missile Defense System, Putin Says." www.cnbc.com (4 October 2019)

[564] Gordon Chang, "China and Russia are Setting a Collision Course with the United States." www.thedailybeast.com (4 September 2018)

[565] David Vine, Where in the World Is the U.S. Military? www.politico.com (July/August 2015)

credibility of America's nuclear deterrent to discourage potential nuclear aggression by our nuclear-armed adversaries. Important related steps would be to return our fifty-eight B-52H and twenty B-2 nuclear bombers to twenty-four hour "strip alert" to help ensure a significant number of them survive a potential nuclear first strike as well as restoring the nuclear capabilities of our sixty B-1B bombers, which are the only supersonic strategic bombers the U.S. currently has in service.

Third, since both the Russians and the Chinese appear to be in the process of rapidly surging their strategic nuclear arsenals to more than 2,500, if not 3,000, warheads each, and in view of China's refusal to agree to limit the size and scope of its nuclear arsenal in any way, the Administration should immediately rescind the New START Treaty which limits the U.S. to only 1,550 Treaty-accountable strategic warheads. President Biden should then take urgent action to issue an executive order to begin to restore rough nuclear parity with Russia and China by returning the 2,000 strategic nuclear warheads we have in reserve, "as a hedge" against precisely the kind of geopolitical contingency which we see unfolding today, to active service atop our Minuteman III ICBMs and Trident II SLBMs. This would serve to expand our strategic nuclear weapons from 1,600 today to as many as 3,600 over a period of six to twenty-four months without the need to build additional warheads in the near-term. As part of this undertaking, the Administration should also increase the number of Trident II SLBMs on each Ohio nuclear missile submarine from 20 to 24 while increasing the number of warheads on each SLBM from four to eight and increasing the number of warheads on each of our Minuteman III ICBMs from one to three. This would increase the number of operational SLBM warheads from 900 to approximately 2,200 and the number of ICBM warheads from 400 to 1,100. In addition, rather than developing hypersonic missiles with conventional warheads, the U.S. should build and deploy hypersonic missiles that are armed with nuclear warheads to deter the use of the Russian and Chinese hypersonic missiles, all of which are armed with nuclear warheads, against us. Furthermore, the U.S. should consider employing full-spectrum deterrence by developing and deploying Super-EMP weapons similar to Russia and China's to hold their nations at risk in order to more effectively discourage the use of these devastating weapons against the U.S.

Should Chinese leaders withdraw their objections, the administration could negotiate a new arms control treaty with both Russia and China that limit each signatory to no more than 3,600 warheads. Such a treaty should include much stronger verification measures than the New START Treaty, encompass all of the various Russian nuclear superweapons including Russian and Chinese hypersonic missiles, as well as rail-mobile ICBMs not currently covered by New START, perhaps by limiting the aggregate megatonnage of each superpower's nuclear arsenal.

Fourth, President Biden should rescind Presidential Decision Directive (PDD-60) which, according to some reports, makes it official U.S. policy to "launch on impact" (following confirmation of the first nuclear impact on U.S. soil) and return to a policy of "launch on warning." This would serve to better deter potential nuclear aggressors like Russia, the People's Republic of China and North Korea who may believe they can take advantage of our "launch on impact" posture to render a decisive "knockout" blow against us before we can retaliate against them. Opponents of returning to a "launch on warning" posture argue that it could lead to an accidental launch leading to a nuclear exchange. However, given the fact that all U.S. nuclear missiles are pre-targeted at empty oceans, the risks of that happening are extremely low.

Fifth, in the realization that nuclear weapons constitute only a small fraction of the U.S. defense budget but are by far the most critical program to defend and deter against catastrophic and existential attack, the U.S. should fully fund the Columbia-class nuclear submarines to replace the Ohio nuclear missile submarine fleet, which will have to start being retired due to their aging hulls in 2030. In addition, the U.S. should fully fund the Ground Based Strategic Deterrent (GBSD) program to replace the 400 Minuteman III ICBMs, many of which were built a half-century ago (as opposed to Russia and Chinese strategic nuclear weapons system which are much newer and more modern) beginning in 2027.

In conclusion, the time has come to put aside America's partisan political differences and unite our country, as we did during the Second World War, to quickly implement these critical pro-active diplomatic and national security measures which are so desperately needed to safeguard the United States against the unprecedented dangers which threaten our continued existence as a nation. If President Biden and congressional leaders are willing to provide the courageous leadership needed to do so, while helping to educate other U.S. policymakers and our citizens about the threats we face and what we need to do to overcome them, we can and we will.

JEFFREY R. YAGO, P.E.
(Physical Engineer, Expert On Emergency Power)

Having inspected literally thousands of government and military facilities at hundreds of locations throughout the United States during my 50 plus years as a professional engineering consultant, I have grave concerns that these facilities will function as expected after a national grid down event. Regardless if caused by an EMP, solar storm, sabotage, or just plain incompetence, when the resulting grid down event finally occurs this country's ability to respond both militarily to an adversary, and to provide humanitarian assistance to the civilian population will be far more down-graded than anyone seems to realize.

Our country's Continuity of Government (COG) emergency preparedness has significantly improved since 911. This included upgrading Liberty Crossings, which is the National Counterintelligence Center located in McLean, Virginia; Camp Peary (the Farm) which is the CIA facilities located near Williamsburg, Virginia; the National Security Agency Headquarters (Puzzle Palace) in Fort Mead, Maryland; the FEMA Emergency Operations Center (Mount Weather) in Bluemont, Virginia; the Pentagon's Raven Rock Mountain Complex (Site "R") located in Adams County, Pennsylvania; the Cheyenne Mountain Complex (NORAD) located in El Paso County, Colorado; the Federal Register and FEMA's main backup data computer systems at the Allegany Ballistic Laboratory (ABL) located in Ridgeley, West Virginia; plus many smaller underground facilities scattered mostly on the east coast. All of these emergency backup facilities include underground bunkers having extensive back-up power, emergency food and water supplies, and living accommodations that combined can house thousands of top government and military leaders for months. While this may provide comfort to the President, congress, the heads of all federal agencies, and Pentagon brass, what can they accomplish if everyone else is without power and communication?

For example, every Army, Navy, Marine, and Air Force base obtains all of their electrical power, water, and phone communications from the same public utilities we all do. While it is true the most critical mission facilities located on these bases do have emergency backup power, in almost every case these are the same types of commercial emergency generators you will see providing emergency power at any airport or hospital. A military base is actually a small city that includes multiple roads, schools, gas stations, shopping centers, fast food restaurants, banks, dining facilities, barracks, training facilities, medical facilities, recreational facilities, airport, fire department, and police station needed to house and train thousands of soldiers, plus their families and lots of support personnel.

This means most of the normal day-to-day activities taking place on these military bases will experience the same complete shutdown and grid lock that will take place in every civilian population center when, not if, a major grid down event occurs.

In addition, most emergency backup generators rarely include more than a few days' supply of fuel. It's even questionable if these unprotected generators and emergency backup power systems will even operate after a real EMP or solar storm event. It is also doubtful refueling trucks, parts deliveries, and maintenance personnel from the civilian side of the fence will even be available to keep these generators operating, assuming they were not damaged by the event.

Our military and air defense bases need all of their facilities operating during a grid down event, and that will require central backup power plants and a base wide micro-grid distribution system that can isolate when the rest of the interconnected national electric grid fails. This will also allow any large solar and wind farms, including their backup battery banks, to continue to feed power into each micro-grid when they would normally shut down upon the loss of the commercial electric grid.

If the political and military leaders locked safely in their underground bunkers expect to have all these bases still functioning to carry out their instructions, they need to rethink the entire concept of providing emergency backup power for these bases and not just think in terms of keeping a few critical buildings operating.

PROFESSOR ZHANNA MALEKOS SMITH, ESQUIRE[566]
(Faculty West Point and USAF Air War College)

Summary: Both naturally occurring and manmade EMPs represent existential threats to the United States. In particular, the electric grid is a vulnerable attack vector and an attractive target for malign actors to disrupt a nation's command and control centers and ability to function in the Information Age. Building off of the momentum of President Joe Biden's July 2021 National Security Memorandum (NSM) on Improving Cybersecurity for Critical Infrastructure Control Systems,[567] the administration should next support legislation to harden electric infrastructure from both natural and man-made

---

[566] Zhanna Malekos Smith, J.D., is an assistant professor in the Department of Systems Engineering at the U.S. Military Academy at West Point and a senior associate with the Strategic Technologies Program at the Center for Strategic and International Studies in Washington DC. The views expressed are those of the authors and do not necessarily reflect the official policy or position of the Department of Defense, the U.S. government, or the Center for Strategic and International Studies (CSIS). CSIS is a private, tax-exempt institution focusing on international public policy issues. Its research is nonpartisan and nonproprietary. CSIS does not take specific policy positions. Accordingly, all views, positions, and conclusions expressed in this publication should be understood to be solely those of the author(s).

[567] https://www.whitehouse.gov/briefing-room/statements-releases/2021/07/28/fact-sheet-biden-administration-announces-further-actions-to-protect-u-s-critical-infrastructure/

EMP incidents and develop contingency plans for such scenarios.[568] Lastly, from an international law perspective, an EMP attack by a state would likely rise to the level of an 'armed attack' under Article 51 of the United Nations Charter, and a use of force under Article 2(4) because destroying critical life-sustaining infrastructure would yield violent effects and indiscriminately harm innocent civilians, resulting in high-level destruction and death. Furthermore, given that a nuclear EMP attack would be experienced indiscriminately — not distinguishing between harm to military combatants and innocent civilians — it would violate the *jus in bello* (*i.e.*, the law in waging war) principles of proportionality and distinction under the Law of Armed Conflict (LOAC), along with the Convention on Certain Conventional Weapons.[569] For these reasons, the use of EMPs weapon would likely violate international law and customary international law on the use of indiscriminate weapons.

Both naturally occurring and manmade EMPs represent existential threats to the United States: Nuclear electromagnetic pulses (EMP) and naturally occurring EMPs both constitute existential threats to the United States' critical infrastructure and the military.[570] An EMP weapon is an energy weapon that can either be activated by a nuclear detonation, or a coordinated directed-energy strike. Determining the qualities of an existential, versus a great, or moderate threat, might very well appear like trying to hold sand in one's hand. Nick Bostrom and Milan Cirkovic explain:

*"[t]he distinction between objective and subjective (epistemic) risk is often hard to make out. The possibility of an asteroid colliding with Earth looks like a clear-cut example of objective risk. But suppose that in fact no sizeable asteroid is on collision course with our planet within a certain, sufficiently large interval of time. We might then say that there is no objective risk of an asteroid-caused catastrophe within that interval of time. Of course, we will not know that this is so until we have mapped out the trajectories of all potentially threatening asteroids and are able to calculate all perturbations. . . . In the meantime, **we must recognize a risk from asteroids even though the risk might be purely subjective, merely reflecting our present state of ignorance**."*[571]

Applying that same reasoning here, the U.S. should prioritize protecting electronic infrastructure from EMP threats, even if the risk is "subjective," reflecting our current state of "ignorance."[572] In 2018 the Department of Homeland Security described EMP threats as "hard problems," and "low probability/high consequence scenarios that challenge effective policymaking."[573] A shortcoming of DHS' analysis is that it misapprehends the relationship between existential threats and probability. While probability can help inform how we evaluate national security threats in general, it is not as helpful for existential threats. To that point, the strategist Colin Gray reasons that although we possess "zero empirical knowledge concerning the dread event [bilateral nuclear war] . . . we know enough to know it would certainly be grim and that we should work hard for conflict prevention."[574] For instance, DHS could assign a low probability score (*i.e.*, a characteristic of risk) to the threat

---

[568] Dowdy *et al.*, *U.S. Army Law of Armed Conflict Deskbook*, p. 13.

[569] Ryan Dowdy *et al.*, *U.S. Army Law of Armed Conflict Deskbook*, (Fifth edition, 2015), p. 13, *available at* http://www.loc.gov/rr/frd/Military_Law/pdf/LOAC-Deskbook-2015.pdf

[570] *U.S. Report from the Commission to Assess the Threat to the United States from Electromagnetic Pulse Attack*, (2017), *available at* https://apps.dtic.mil/dtic/tr/fulltext/u2/1051492.pdf (13 December 2018).

[571] Nick Bostrom and Milan Cirkovic, *Global Catastrophic Risks*, (Oxford University Press, 2008), p. 5 (emphasis added).

[572] *Ibid.*

[573] DHS (2018) https://www.dhs.gov/sites/default/files/publications/18_1009_EMP_GMD_Strategy-Non-Embargoed.pdf

[574] Colin Gray, *Theory of Strategy*, (Oxford University Press, 2018), p. 39.

of a nuclear EMP war between the U.S. and Russia, however, it should not diminish the existential concerns inherent in any type of nuclear conflict—it undermines the nation's existence.[575] Precision of concept in risk modeling helps reinforce precision of thought in understanding how to mitigate subjective biases.

Whether we can precisely determine the probability of an EMP attack or not, the fact remains that the U.S. electronic infrastructure is not hardened against an EMP event—the advent of which would produce catastrophic harm to the U.S. well-being and security.

In contrast to DHS 2018 report, the Congressional EMP Commission regarded both natural and nuclear EMPs as existential threats[576] and in 2017 released its formal report exhorting Congress to take legislative action:

*"The critical national infrastructure in the United States faces a present and continuing **existential threat** from combined-arms warfare, including cyber and manmade electromagnetic pulse (EMP) attack, as well as from natural EMP from a solar superstorm . . . . With the development of small nuclear arsenals and long-range missiles by new, radical U.S. adversaries, **the threat of a nuclear EMP attack against the U.S. becomes one of the few ways that such a country could inflict devastating damage to the United States.** It is critical, therefore, that the U.S. national leadership address the EMP threat as a critical and **existential issue[.]"**[577]

Despite this major contretemps, however, a common thread in the discourse is that both sides are concerned about harm inflicted on critical infrastructure like the electric grid.

Speaking generally to the threats posed by malicious actors on U.S. critical infrastructure, the former Director of National Intelligence, Dan Coats, warned in 2018 that "the warning lights are blinking red again. Today, the digital infrastructure that serves this country is literally under attack."[578] Director Coats cited the top offenders attempting to infiltrate and manipulate U.S. industrial control systems and critical infrastructure as Russia, North Korea and Iran.[579] Further, U.S. Army General David Petraeus (ret.) writes that Russia has continuously attempted to "install malware in our electrical grid" and breach utility-control rooms.[580]

But are all attacks the same? According to Professor Thomas Rid of Johns Hopkins University, there are three categories of attacks on industrial control systems: "simple attacks that merely crash sys-

---

[575]   https://ksr.hkspublications.org/2019/12/27/borrowing-a-column-from-thomas-jefferson-the-architecture-of-national-security-risks/

[576] Personal Interview with Dr. Peter V. Pry.

[577] *U.S. Report from the Commission to Assess the Threat to the United States from Electromagnetic Pulse Attack*, (2017), *available at* https://apps.dtic.mil/dtic/tr/fulltext/u2/1051492.pdf (13 December 2018) (emphasis added).

[578] 'Transcript: Dan Coats Warns the Lights Are 'Blinking Red' on Russian Cyberattacks', *NPR*, (18 July 2018) https://www.npr.org/2018/07/18/630164914/transcript-dan-coats-warns-of-continuing-russian-cyberattacks (22 January 2019).

[579] *Ibid.*

[580] David H. Petraeus and Kiran Sridhar, 'The Case for a National Cybersecurity Agency', *POLITICO*, (5 September 2018), https://www.politico.com/agenda/story/2018/09/05/cybersecurity-agency-homeland-security-000686 (23 January 2019).

tems or interrupt their correct operation, for instance by exploiting a widespread lack of authentication in those systems; moderate attacks where attackers have intelligence on a process and learn how to damage a physical component or subsystem; and complex attacks, where attackers modify a process in a stealthy manner over an extended period of time."[581] A nuclear EMP event meets the definition of a "simple attack" because its designed to knock systems offline in a single stream event. [582]

What would be the financial impact if the Eastern Interconnection power grid were taken offline for a significant period of time from an attack? General Petraeus cited a study that if a coordinated operation took out the East Coast power grid, thereby rendering the region without power for months, it could "cause thousands of deaths due to the failure of health and safety systems, and cost the U.S. almost $250 billion."[583] Going one step further in surveying the scope of harm, if the Western Interconnection were taken off offline as well, given the roughly equal size of the geographic area it services, it is reasonable to estimate that it could cost the U.S. almost $250 billion. Thus, as a general estimate, the financial damage from an EMP waged "Blackout War"[584] could amount to $500 billion— and this estimate does not even include a 'blackout attack' on the third U.S. interconnection; the Texas Interconnection.[585] The term blackout war, refers to "Lightning War strikes against the societal Achilles Heel of our civilization, going around our armed forces to attack civilians in the utilities and our families that depend upon them for survival. Our civilian critical infrastructures are outside of our national security culture and are the least prepared[.]"[586] The U.S. electric grid is a vulnerable attack vector and an attractive target for malign actors to disrupt a nation's command and control centers, and ability to function in the Information Age. [587] Thus, building off of the momentum of President Joe Biden's July 2021 National Security Memorandum (NSM) on Improving Cybersecurity for Critical Infrastructure Control Systems,[588] the administration should next support legislation to harden electric infrastructure from both natural and man-made EMP incidents and develop contingency plans for such scenarios.[589]

EMPs pose a threat to U.S. Military Readiness and War-fighting Capabilities: Dr. Lowell Wood of the Lawrence Livermore National Laboratory describes the EMP threat as the "Achilles heel" for global superpowers because their reliance on information is at the mercy of "electronic data flows

[581] Thomas Rid, *Cyber War Will Not Take Place*, (Hurst and Company London, 2013) pp. 51-52.

[582] *Ibid.*

[583] Petraeus and Sridhar, 'The Case for a National Cybersecurity Agency'.

[584] Peter V. Pry, *Blackout Wars: State Initiatives To Achieve Preparedness Against an Electromagnetic Pulse Catastrophe*, (EMP Task Force on National and Homeland Security, 2015), p. 52.

[585] 'Learn More About Interconnections', *Energy.gov,* https://www.energy.gov/oe/services/electricity-policy-coordination-and-implementation/transmission-planning/recovery-act-0 (23 January 2019).

[586] *Ibid.*

[587] Pry, *Blackout Wars*, pp. 51-52.

[588] https://www.whitehouse.gov/briefing-room/statements-releases/2021/07/28/fact-sheet-biden-administration-announces-further-actions-to-protect-u-s-critical-infrastructure/

[589] Dowdy *et al., U.S. Army Law of Armed Conflict Deskbook*, p. 13.

on EMP-fragile integrated circuits."[590] Modern warfighting techniques rely heavily on global navigation systems to deliver calibrated effects, and achieve precision targeting with minimal collateral damage.[591]

Thus, if an adversary were to initiate an EMP attack against the U.S. interconnected communication and defense systems, the U.S. would be in a highly vulnerable position, unable to communicate defense plans.[592] To that end, scholars Paul Barnes and Alexandra Stickings aver that "[t]he three most significant threats to global navigation satellite systems come from jamming, spoofing, and counter-space capabilities."[593] EMP weapons fall into the counter-space threat category.

A more mediated perspective on the threat posed by a deliberate EMP attack is offered by Schneider and Burke, who posit that an EMP attack "could cause significant loss of life and catastrophic economic consequences, given the thorough dependence of modern American life on electricity."[594] They also reason that "[a]n EMP attack resulting from a high-altitude nuclear detonation seems a possible but not very plausible scenario. An adversary looking to carry out such an attack on the United States would need ballistic missiles and nuclear weapons."[595] Rather, it is the threat of naturally occurring space weather event which poses a greater security risk because of the increasing probability of another severe space weather event like Carrington in the future.[596]

International Law and EMP Warfare: There are several international legal frameworks to consider when assessing the legality of EMP warfare. First, under the United Nations Charter Article 2(4), states are prohibited for employing a "use of force."[597] This prohibition is subject to several exceptions, however, such as the inherent right of self-defense from an armed attack under Article 51.[598]

Another exception is Article 39, which describes the UN Security Council's authority to "determine the existence of any threat to the peace, breach of the peace, or act of aggression and shall make recommendations, or decide what measures shall be taken in accordance with Articles 41 and 42, to maintain or restore international peace and security."[599]

---

[590] Electromagnetic Pulse (EMP): Should This Be a Problem of National Concern to Private Enterprise, Businesses Small, and Large, as well as Government?, Hearing before the Subcommittee on Government Programs and Oversight, U.S House of Representatives, 116th Congress, First Session (1 June 1999), *available at* https://www.gpo.gov/fdsys/pkg/CHRG-106hhrg59747/pdf/CHRG-106hhrg59747.pdf, p. 8, (22 January 2019).

[591] Paul Barnes and Alexandra Stickings 'The Death of Precision in Warfare', *War On the Rocks,* (27 November 2018), https://warontherocks.com/2018/11/the-death-of-precision-in-warfare/?utm_source=WOTR+Newsletter&utm_campaign=fede5dff39-EMAIL_CAMPAIGN_10_30_2018_11_23_COPY_01&utm_medium=email&utm_term=0_8375be81e9-fede5dff39-62602985 (14 December 2018).

[592] Hearing, Electromagnetic Pulse (EMP): Should This Be a Problem of National Concern to Private Enterprise, Businesses Small, and Large, as well as Government?, p. 8.

[593] *Ibid.*

[594] Sharon Burke and Emily Schneider, 'Enemy Number One for the Electric Grid: Mother Nature', *SAIS Review of International Affairs* 35(1), (Johns Hopkins University Press, 2015), p. 77.

[595] Burke and Schneider, 'Who's Afraid'.

[596] *Ibid.*

[597] UN Charter Article 2(4).

[598] UN Charter Article 51.

[599] UN Charter Article 39.

From an international law perspective, pursuant to Chapter VII of the UN Charter, the Security Council is endowed with certain powers to act in the face of an emergency.[600] Specifically, Article 39 grants the Security Council the power to assess a threat, or "breach of the peace,"[601] and Article 41 gives teeth to this by providing:

"The Security Council may decide what measures not involving the use of armed force are to be employed to give effect to its decisions, and it may call upon the Members of the United Nations to apply such measures."[602]

Overall, Chapter VII of the Charter outlines the "special powers granted to governments and officials to respond to emergencies, grave dangers or existential threats."[603]

From an international law perspective, an EMP attack by a state would likely rise to the level of an "armed attack" under Article 51 of the United Nations Charter, and a use of force under Article 2(4) because destroying critical life-sustaining infrastructure would yield violent effects and indiscriminately harm innocent civilians, resulting in high-level destruction and death.[604] Additionally, given that an EMP attack would be indiscriminately felt, not distinguishing between harm to military combatants and innocent civilians, at a minimum this act would violate the *jus in bello* (*i.e.,* the law in waging war) principles of proportionality and distinction under the Law of Armed Conflict (LOAC), along with the Convention on Certain Conventional Weapons.[605] Further, an EMP attack by a state would likely rise to the level of an "armed attack" under Article 51 of the UN Charter, and a use of force under Article 2(4) because destroying critical life-sustaining infrastructure would yield violent effects and indiscriminately harm innocent civilians.[606] For these reasons, the use of EMP weapons would likely violate both international law and customary international law on the use of indiscriminate weapons.

PROFESSOR CYNTHIA E. AYERS
(Deputy Director EMP Task Force, Former U.S. Army War College and NSA)

Internet Kill-Switch: Cyber Sabotage and the End of Sovereignty. "A few blows from a sledge hammer in the right place, can stop a power station working."—George Orwell. George Orwell, in his 1942 essay entitled "The Meaning of Sabotage," discussed the ability of a few within Europe to significantly inhibit the workings of Hitler's military industrial base. His description of active, physical sabotage was instructive; but he also explained the concept of "passive sabotage"—a form of willful demolition that is much less recognizable as such. This type of vandalism can be accomplished by

---

[600] Devon Whittle, 'The Limits of Legality and the United Nations Security Council: Applying the Extra-Legal Measures Model to Chapter VII Action', 26:3 *European Journal of International Law*, (1 August 2015,) *available at* https://doi.org/10.1093/ejil/chv042 (12 February 2019).

[601] UN Charter, Chapter VII.

[602] *Ibid.*

[603] Whittle, 'The Limits of Legality'.

[604] UN Charter Article 2(4).

[605] Ryan Dowdy *et al., U.S. Army Law of Armed Conflict Deskbook*, (Fifth edition, 2015), p. 13, *available at* http://www.loc.gov/rr/frd/Military_Law/pdf/LOAC-Deskbook-2015.pdf

[606] UN Charter Article 2(4).

slowing processes; encouraging confusion, complexity and chaos; and eventually "preventing it [e.g. the system, organization, etc.] from working smoothly."

How would "passive sabotage" most likely present itself today? Cyberwarfare. It would probably be implanted within the computer systems that run modern civilization and could come in many forms. Although cyber sabotage could just as easily come from domestic sources as foreign/adversarial entities, the threat posed by cyberwarfare is one of the reasons the concept of cyber sovereignty became so important over the past two decades. Our laws, regulations, policies, and treaties are all based on territorial and conceptual boundaries within the context of the Westphalian form of national sovereignty. Cyberspace, however, with its worldwide interconnected technical infrastructure and global, almost ubiquitous and instantaneous wireless access, challenges traditional concepts of sovereignty.

Many—especially "tech gurus"—believe that sovereignty in cyberspace is irrelevant. Still others—possibly with the assistance of the same tech gurus—have found a way to impose a form of sovereignty in the cyber realm, specifically for use of what has come to be known as an Internet "kill-switch." Unfortunately, the cyber kill-switch comes with its own multidimensional problems.

At first glance, a kill-switch might appear to be a solution for use against quick-spreading malware inserted by bad actors. In fact, action taken to halt operations can prove efficacious when used by companies trying to limit malware damage to their systems. Even regional use by public utilities may be acceptable (perhaps even desirable) under those conditions, especially since damage to critical infrastructure equipment and facilities could cost billions of dollars, and potentially a significant number of lives (as in a collapse of a dam and/or long-term loss of electricity).

Ostensibly for purposes of defense as noted above, a kill-switch such as that described in a proposed version of the U.S. Cybersecurity Act of 2009, would provide a U.S. President authority to initiate emergency control over government *and* private sector networks in order to shut down or "turn off" online activity. It was soon recognized, however, that a Presidential kill-switch, even if intended solely for defensive measures, could do more harm than good. In a masochistic twist, a kill-switch could become—or even be used specifically as—a form of passive sabotage.

Negative effects of limiting or denying Internet access have been recognized globally as government leaders attempt to control their populations and prevent intervention by other nations. Reports of recent Cuban dissent (July 2021) have included accusations that the Cuban dictatorship used technology provided by China to block Internet and cell phone access across the country. Indeed, Human Rights Watch, in their study "Shutting Down the Internet to Shut Up Critics" (2020), called out several governments (e.g. the Democratic Republic of Congo, Sudan, Iran, Iraq, India, Egypt, Myanmar, and others) for resorting to Internet communications lockdowns, justified by officials of these countries as "necessary for public safety or curbing the spread of misinformation."

Recognizing the potential for a kill-switch to be used as a means of population control even within the sovereign area of the United States, many politicians have sought to keep legislation permitting such a capability from being passed. Even so, in 2012, President Obama issued an Executive Order titled "Assignment of National Security and Emergency Preparedness Communications Functions," which gave the task of prioritizing communications requirements to the Department of Homeland Security upon declaration of a state of emergency. The vague nature of the wording within the Executive Order was cause for concern; but the ultimate realization was that the Communications Act of

1934 gave the President the power to "suspend . . . any or all stations or devices capable of emitting electromagnetic radiations within the jurisdiction of the United States."

Thus, a renewed attempt at legislation to "kill the kill-switch" addressed the intent of the Communications Act of 1934. Senate Bill 4646 "Unplug the Internet Kill Switch Act of 2020" was introduced by five Senators, led by Senator Rand Paul (116th Congress), and referred to the Committee on Commerce, Science, and Transportation for action.

At this point in time, a U.S. President could still opt to use the emergency powers provided under Section 706 of the Communications Act of 1934 to control, shutdown, or "kill" the internet, if that President should decide it was "in the interest of the national security and defense . . . [due to] a state or threat of war involving the United States." Although initially intended for defensive purposes during a period between two world wars, the use of the Communications Act now—given the ubiquitous nature and complexity of internet communications—could further our own destruction. For instance, in the case of a relatively constrained cyber-attack, a subsequent "internet shutdown" could potentially increase damage (in intensity and scope) by halting life-sustaining services and encouraging more devastating types of attacks, while diminishing the public's ability to obtain information— in other words, increasing a prepared attacker's capabilities and facilitating access to other targets for kinetic operations. Alternatively, its use as a form of domestic control could ultimately cost lives, as the emotional base of a public that has grown accustomed to—even dependent on—freedom of movement in cyberspace, shifts from a period of relative calm to confusion, fear and anger.

Even if an Internet kill-switch was used purely as a defensive measure (as opposed to a domestic political weapon), a self-imposed communications shutdown could provide an aggressor an unexpected advantage, or otherwise be enacted as a result of a manipulative tactic in an enemy's calculations for their own success. In this context, the Russian strategy of "reflexive control" comes to mind.

Reflexive control is described by LTC (Retired) Timothy L. Thomas (Foreign Military Studies Office, U.S. Army, Ft. Leavenworth, KS) by formulating the question: "How do I make you do something for yourself that you are really doing for me?" For example, such a defensive measure (taking control of or killing the internet within a large region) could be taken because of adversarial cyber manipulation performed with the intention of getting their enemy (in this case the U.S.) to do something for their own sake (stop the malware from spreading), which is in reality part of and highly beneficial to the aggressor's strategic plan (loss of communications). Reflexive control can be used with incredible efficacy to encourage an enemy to act first (even if the act is a defensive measure), offering sufficient provocation (e.g. acts suggestive of an intent to initiate conflict), and provide the aggressor with enough domestic or international political cover to launch a "preemptive" strike, as well as the distraction necessary to carry out further attacks. The detonation of one or more strategically placed high-altitude nuclear weapons for HEMP could easily be the next (and perhaps the final) operation in this Blackout War.

Cyberspace is now essential to the existence of governments and those governed, yet dangerous in its relative anonymity and connectivity to virtually all corners of the world. It is a place for economics and civil discourse while simultaneously a battleground for war waged by nation-states, adversarial groups, and autonomous actors. Ultimately, the use of a kill-switch against the population of the United States as a first strike weapon in a Blackout War, whether by warriors of an adversarial nation, or presented as a means of control by a government that has bought in, sold out, or succumbed to hostile intent, could mean the end of our sovereignty.

In any case, timing is critical. In cyberwarfare, as with any type of conventional war, not all participants play by the same rules. Regulations developed for reasons of adhering to ethical norms and cultural traditions tend to slow response and, even with the best defense, give attackers who lack similar restrictions the distinct—and crucial—advantage of time. Time, in cyberspace, can be measured in nanoseconds. Decisive action may be crucial.

Testimony before a House Armed Services Subcommittee by incoming USCYBERCOM Commander Admiral Michael Rogers (March 5, 2015), revealed that U.S. cyber forces "have had the equivalent of a close-in fight with an adversary, which taught us how to maneuver and gain the initiative that means the difference between victory and defeat." Still, he conceded: "Neither the U.S. Government, the states, nor the private sector can defend their information systems on their own against the most powerful cyber forces. The public and private sectors need one another's help." As to exactly what that "help" could be remains in question.

While the private sector might be of assistance in the cyber defense realm, their active resistance in the form of counterattack is, to this point, illegal. For those living and working within the sovereign geographical boundaries of the United States, cyber response (a.k.a. retaliation) is a highly debated and regulated option reserved for federal entities authorized to defend the nation against adversaries operating in cyberspace. This is largely due to the fact that a cyberattack performed in retaliation by one or more private entities could easily be misconstrued as an attack sponsored by the sovereign nation of the United States. Yet the desire by private entities to respond in defense of their own networks is understandable, as a lack of quick response by authorities is most often seen as political quiescence.

Currently, national cyber protection relies on mitigation using passive defense (e.g. information assurance, cybersecurity, and defense-in-depth); but reliance on a blanket of protection is no longer sufficient. The sophistication and sheer numbers of attacks on all sectors of society are daunting. Attacks spread quickly and have already been successful at taking businesses, large companies, and even regional sectors offline for lengthy periods of time, to include critical infrastructure.

U.S. national sovereignty depends on a functional military, and the military is heavily reliant upon civilian-sector critical infrastructure for their daily deployment and operational needs; thus, the nation's critical infrastructure could easily be considered its "strategic center of gravity" (the "head of the snake" or main point at which to aim in order to take a target down). If critical infrastructure – and most importantly, the electric/energy sector—is the most likely first-strike target of the next war, and if at least part of that warfare is waged in cyberspace against systems that are not necessarily under the control of a military command structure, it would appear that existential vulnerabilities of the United States rest within the private sector. The complexities involved with cyber responsibilities and authorities could cause dangerous, and potentially deadly delays.

Two decades ago, when cyberattacks against businesses began in earnest (e.g. identity theft and/or a rerouting of funds), private sector entities quickly became reticent to call anyone—especially the government—for help, as public knowledge often resulted in lawsuits and business closures. The impulse to withdraw, retreat, and conceal events has changed, however, through recent regulation, legislation, and support provided by government cyber centers; but the steps taken to request and receive assistance can take valuable time. Cyber intrusions can go unnoticed for days or months, and attacks can be instantaneous; thus, although extremely valuable for after-the-fact support, the deployment of real-time reinforcements for extensive cyber defense and countermeasures can be challenging, at best.

Additionally, while private sector entities have long been conditioned to think of threat in terms of natural disasters, and therefore problems they must plan for, they still do not necessarily view threats from adversaries as "their problem." This "stove-piping" of responsibility, even if only conceptual, illustrates the fragile nature of U.S. sovereignty as the probability of Blackout War strategies against what might be seen by potential assailants as a loosely guarded center-of-gravity has increased exponentially with enemy capabilities.

The idea of critical infrastructure as a cyber center-of-gravity and first-strike target is not novel. One only has to research recent history to find major "trial runs" such as the BlackEnergy malware-enabled attacks of 2015, and the use of a sophisticated malware framework known as CRASHOVERRIDE (a.k.a. "Industroyer") in 2016. Would a kill-switch be advantageous as a stop-gap in cases such as these? Maybe, but decisive and timely action would be necessary for successful implementation; and the likelihood of effective use of such within a scenario that would probably have to go through various levels of private leadership, bureaucracy, and federal governance is debatable.

Department of Defense strategic planners look at everything from "worst case" to "most likely" courses of enemy action. Risk assessments identify the most likely scenarios, and resources are applied in accordance with assessments; but regulatory and conceptual issues with regard to authorities and responsibilities, a perennial shortage of resources, decisions that shift with political priorities, and leadership's personal preference to pursue "most likely" scenarios can combine to keep the nation unprepared for worst case. Thus, even if the U.S. center-of-gravity is found to be critical electric infrastructure, it is not necessarily treated as such. Nevertheless, as DoD becomes even more dependent on civilian infrastructure for military operations, is it not safe to assume that a worst-case infrastructure attack scenario should be considered among the "most likely" scenarios? The answer to this question could be an existential one for our survival as a sovereign nation.

Unfortunately, the danger of an internet shutdown does not begin and end with a kill-switch. The successful limitation of any head-of-government's ability to use an Internet kill-switch is only one aspect of a larger problem. Once considered only theoretical, an Internet "takeover" could be caused by many forms of cyberattacks.

Daily occurring ransomware attacks on a variety of critical infrastructure targets are but one example. Payment of increasingly exorbitant amounts of money in order to regain functionality is tantamount to paying terrorists—it is neither advisable, nor wise, and certainly not feasible for either utilities or governments to continue to do so. Ever increasing numbers of simultaneous attacks as well as the broad scope of targeted effects indicate at least a capability to cause wider and more severe damage. The true motives may, in fact, be to break down the ability for businesses, hospitals, utilities, or entire nation states to recover. Thus, ransomware can not only simulate a "kill-switch" but also provide distraction, as aggressors use their victim's tendency to focus on whatever crisis-of-the-moment that the ransomware may have caused to launch a more comprehensive and destructive onslaught—potentially resulting in a Blackout War.

An adversarial use of "KillDisk" malware variants are yet another example. KillDisk malware has been applied in targeting industrial control systems and is known to either wipe hard drives clean (making them inoperable) or encrypt files (usually employed within ransomware). This form of cyber-sabotage was used against Ukraine in 2015 and 2016.

Space-based cyber conflict is also no longer theoretical, as space weapons with close maneuverability (e.g. "killer satellites," Russia's "inspector satellites," or "shadow satellites") now pose a credible threat of space-based destruction of early warning, navigation, weapons guidance, and intelligence collection assets, thus facilitating the onset of a Blackout War.

Regardless of how it is accomplished, a kill-switch or Internet shutdown is essentially sabotage. The naïve use of such as a defensive measure is tantamount to an open invitation to enemy aggression. Its use against the population of the United States as a first strike weapon in a Blackout War, whether by warriors of an adversarial nation, or presented as a means of control by a government that has bought into or sold out to adversarial intent, could mean the end of our sovereignty. A U.S. concession to retain the option of a Presidential kill-switch is national suicide.

American lives are at stake. Our national sovereignty is at stake. Defense of the United States against a "grid-down" scenario, and ultimately a Blackout War, must include action taken to kill the ability of any President to commit sabotage via the use an Internet kill-switch.

CONGRESSMAN CURT WELDON
(Former Vice Chairman House Armed Services Committee)

For the first time in my life, I am concerned about the future of our nation and the world. As the youngest of nine children born into a poor blue-collar family, all of us were ingrained with the notion that America was the beacon for the world and the stabilizer against oppression and dominance of tyrants, dictators and rogue regimes. Each of us understood the examples of our parents to serve!

My 6 brothers and 2 brothers-in-law all proudly served with honor in our military at home and abroad. My high school dream to attend the US Air Force Academy was short-circuited, in spite of receiving a formal nomination, because of eye problems which I could not resolve. Instead, I devoted my life to serving as a Domestic Defender - Firefighter/Fire Chief eventually rising to lead America's 1.2 million First Responders in the US Congress.

On the back cover of my book *Awakening the Sleeping Giant – Political Empowerment of America's Heroes* President GHW Bush's quotation was lifted from a 2007 ten-minute speech that he gave in my honor at the National Fire/EMS/Disaster Dinner before 2,000 leaders in Washington, DC -

"You often heard Curt (Weldon) speak of the Fire Service as the Sleeping Giant. When I was President, if it appeared that I wasn't giving proper attention to your issues, I could always be assured of a phone call from Curt, and I'm sure the other Presidents would all say the same."

"To his credit, the Fire Service was never a partisan issue. It was a personal issue, based on his own experience as a volunteer firefighter. He's the reason why both ends of Pennsylvania Avenue have heard the fire service's voice and answered so many of your calls. He's the reason why you, the Fire

and Emergency Services, was awakened twenty years ago, and has become such a political force in our nation's Capital."

"It's the goal of every political leader, who is blessed with the opportunity to serve the public, to leave behind a legacy – a legacy that in some way makes our nation stronger, better and safer. Curt, you've done just that through your dedication and your commitment to our nation's 1 million First Responders. So, on behalf of Barbara and myself, thank you for your 20 years of incredible service to this great nation, and best wishes as you begin a new chapter in your life."
—President GHW Bush

My goal was to challenge America's Firefighters and First Responders to organize and demand action from our national leaders in the White House and Congress – and we did – with amazing success!

Co-Chairs who worked with me on behalf of our Domestic Defenders included Senators Joe Biden, John McCain, Al Gore and House Members Steny Hoyer, Bill Pascrell, Sherry Boehlert, Peter King and hundreds more. Our work was always bi-partisan, and our success is easily measured in the successes that we achieved.

We forced Administrations of both Political Parties to 'do the right thing' and support measures to enhance our nation's preparedness and security against domestic disasters. There were no gaps between Members of the House and Senate in forcing reluctant or unfocused government agencies to come together in support of our nation's disaster response leaders.

At the same time, to my dismay, coherent collaboration against 21st Century military threats did not achieve the same clarity and success. Spending my 20-year career on the Armed Services and Homeland Security Committees, support for our troops and their families was always bi-partisan and strong.

Yet understanding the emerging Asymmetric Threats that we knew we would face in the 21st Century was unclear, unfocused and improperly explained and outlined by our intelligence and threat assessment agencies. Primarily focused on new weapons systems including aircraft, ships and traditional platforms took center stage each year as Defense Budgets were submitted and debated.

Dedicated Members in both political parties supported the big traditional military platforms, but a small group of us focused on the non-sexy threats that we knew would become the 'Achilles Heel' of America's 21st Century national security–as well as our economic stability. As Vice Chair of both the Armed Services and Homeland Security Committees, I was always eager to understand that which was emerging–especially what we referred to as Asymmetric Threats.

It was natural that prime Defense Contractors would rather have us focus on ships, planes and tanks as opposed to systems to protect and defend against cyber-attacks, EMP, chemical/biological warfare and threats not easily understood but demonstrating the power and capability to bring our nation "to our knees" in ways never imagined.

Arrogance, stupidity and financial greed in the US military/industrial/intelligence complex helped empower our adversaries to understand and deploy these Asymmetric Threats while we focused on the big profit platforms each one of which can be neutralized by much less complex asymmetric threats. I remember well verbalizing our adversaries like Iran and North Korea understanding that they could neutralize our superior and majestic platforms that they could never afford by understanding and deploying cyber and electronic measures that would "level the playing field" against our superior and well-equipped military.

As Chair of the Oversight Sub-Committees for Research & Development, Procurement and Emerging Threats with Dr. Peter Pry at my side, we organized and convened the first Congressional Hearings on Cyber Threats, EMP, loose Suitcase Nukes, pandemics and other WMD. As an educator by profession, I visualized threats for my colleagues as much as possible by having the Army set up a SCUD Missile Launcher next to the US Capital Building, build and showcase a briefcase nuclear weapon as well as a suitcase chem/bio emitting device and we brought in witnesses from our allies and adversaries who testified undercover and under protection.

Our pleas and messaging twenty years ago was not loud or forceful enough, as the mainstream media and our embarrassed agencies downplayed and trivialized threats that were not easily understood or verified. Unfortunately, those threats were understood and perfected by our enemies and adversaries–and now the threats to our sovereignty and security are real and staring us in the face.

BLACKOUT WARFARE is not an overexaggerated threat conceived by paranoid doomsday forecasters. Blackout Warfare is real–and it is now upon us in dimensions and scenarios never imagined twenty years ago. Now is not the time for casting blame or embarrassment. Now is the time for the White House, the Pentagon and the Congress to focus and act!

And ultimately, as it was with our First Responders, we as Americans must demand immediate action and solutions. We must awaken our fellow citizens to the immediate threat from Blackout Warfare. To do less is unacceptable!

DR. JOHN M. POINDEXTER
(Former National Security Advisor, President Ronald Reagan)

The risk and consequence of Blackout Warfare as described by Dr. Pry far outweigh those of climate change models. The US Government must immediately address the recommendations of the EMP Commission. As a start, the electrical grid must be hardened to protect against kinetic, cyber and EMP attacks. There are solutions available, but government must take the lead working with private industry to accomplish this. It will be expensive, but we dare not afford not to do it. The risk and consequence are too great.

ABOUT THE AUTHORS

Professor Cynthia E. Ayers

Ms. Ayers is Deputy Director of the EMP Task Force on National and Homeland Security, a nonprofit Congressional Advisory Board. She is a national security threat analyst and consultant, having retired from the National Security Agency (NSA) in 2011 with over 38 years of military and civil service (combined). Her intelligence community career included a position as NSA Representative to the DCI's Counterterrorism Center at CIA headquarters, where she worked throughout the attack on the USS *Cole* and the 9/11 crisis (2000-2002). Her government service culminated in an eight-year assignment as the National Security Agency's Visiting Professor to the U.S. Army War College (US-AWC), where she taught electives on contemporary threats to national security from an intelligence perspective (cyber warfare, terrorism, etc.) as well as military applications of artificial intelligence. She advised students on research concerning strategic intelligence, counterterrorism, information operations/warfare, cyber warfare, critical infrastructure protection and community resilience.

Post-retirement, Ms. Ayers was employed as Vice President of EMPact America, a bipartisan, not-for-profit group working in support of electric grid vulnerability mitigation and community education. More recently, she worked as a temporary, part-time research assistant and consultant with George Mason University's Learning Agent Center on a grant concerning artificial intelligence-based systems, and as an independent cyberwarfare consultant within the Strategic Concepts and Doctrine Division of the Center for Strategic Leadership, U.S. Army War College. She also spent two years as a Senior Advisor to the Executive Director of the Patuxent Partnership.

Ms. Ayers has provided a plethora of briefings and presentations on critical infrastructure issues at organizational gatherings, conferences, and workshops to members of the non-profit sector, government entities, and interested groups within academic institutions. She has testified before the Canadian Standing Senate Committee on National Security and Defence; the Joint Standing Committee on Energy, Utilities, and Technology of the Maine State Legislature; the Energy Policy Committee of the Michigan State Legislature; members of Indiana's State Legislature, and the reestablished Congressional EMP Commission.

Ms. Ayers has written several published articles on critical infrastructure and national security issues, a monograph on cyber sovereignty (*Rethinking Sovereignty in the Context of Cyberspace*), and co-authored academic papers on the development of cognitive agents for intelligence analysis. She also assisted with the development and prosecution of a program used for the cognitive assessment of U.S. Army candidates for General Officer.

Ambassador Henry F. Cooper

Henry F. (Hank) Cooper was raised on a South Carolina farm and worked summers at the Savannah River Plant and Savannah River National Laboratory, while studying Mechanical Engineering at Clemson College (now Clemson University). He earned his BS in 1958 and MS in 1960, while also serving as an Assistant Professor of Engineering Mechanics, until he became a Member of the Technical Staff of Bell Telephone Laboratories (BTL) where he conducted independent research in a number of areas—including development of Telstar, our first telecommunications satellite that was lost following the 1962 Starfish Prime high-altitude nuclear test in the South Pacific. It was one of several important satellite systems lost due to EMP and associated radiation effects—consequently responding to this threat became highly classified and was largely ignored by those who built, operate and oversee our critical civil infrastructure today, an existential threat to all we hold dear today.

After being commissioned as a lieutenant in the US Air Force in 1958, he had received an educational delay to pursue advanced degrees in Mechanical Engineering, culminating in a PhD from New York University in 1964, while also conducting research at BTL. He then reported for duty at the Air Force Weapons Laboratory (AWL), leading studies of nuclear weapons effects and developing simulation tools to support design and assessment of our strategic systems and their supporting command, control and communications systems. After completing his active duty commitment, he remained as Scientific Advisor responsible for developing theoretical methods to predict nuclear weapons effects and simulators to test operational strategic systems and develop new ones.

In 1970, he joined R&D Associates (RDA)—formed from the Physics Division of the RAND Cooperation, where he became a senior advisor to the Defense Nuclear Agency, particularly in developing theoretical and experimental simulation ways to assure survival of our Minuteman ICBMs. He also served on several Air Force Scientific Advisory Board and Defense Science Board Task Forces supporting development of new strategic systems and their command, control and communications systems. In 1979, he became Deputy Assistant Secretary of the Air Force with oversight responsibilities for all Air Force Strategic and Space Systems—most of which became key elements of the Reagan Revolution that modernized all our military systems. After briefly returning to RDA, he was appointed and confirmed by the U.S. Senate in 1983 as Assistant Director of the Arms Control and Disarmament Agency (ACDA), where he led development of President Reagan's space arms control policy and engaged in numerous interagency activities, including backstopping our negotiations with the Soviet Union and development of associated verification methods. During this period, he was invited by the Commander Strategic Air Command (SAC) to join the JSTPS Scientific Advisory Group where he served for the next 20 years, including during SAC's transformation to U.S. Strategic Command.

In 1985, he became President Reagan's Ambassador and Deputy Defense and Space Negotiator with the Soviet Union—where his primary responsibility was to assure that President Reagan's Strategic Defense Initiative (SDI) was not inhibited by Soviet negotiating strategy—as was its objective. When Ambassador Max Kampelman became Counselor to Secretary of State George Shultz, he became Chief Negotiator, served for the remainder of the Reagan Administration and initiated the follow-on talks in the George H.W. Bush administration. In 1992, he became a JAYCOR Senior Vice President, and was invited by Defense Secretary Dick Cheney, as Russia was emerging in the wake of the Soviet breakup, to lead a Presidentially mandated study to recommend how the SDI program should be redirected and associated arms control policy. Following President Bush's approval of Cooper's recommended Global Protection Against Limited Strikes (GPALS) approach, Secretary Cheney invited him to become SDI Director and "make it happen." During his SDI watch, he led the initiation of Navy's Aegis BMD system, the Army's Ground Based BMD systems, the Israeli Arrow Program, and the Brilliant Pebbles space-based interceptor system, which he still considers to be the most important SDI initiative, regrettably abandoned by the Clinton administration and not yet revived.

Following his service as SDI Director, he returned to the private sector and after a couple of years of consulting became Chairman of Applied Research Associates (ARA), which has grown to be the largest high technology corporation in New Mexico. During this period he also became a member of the Board of Directors of High Frontier, and upon the death of its founder Retired US Army Lieutenant General Daniel O. Graham its Chairman. After retiring from ARA in 2015, he has extended his advocacy for building the most cost-effective missile defense systems—those based in space—to urging the "powers that be" to address the existential threat to the nation's electric power grid—especially from EMP.

Colonel Robert P.J. Lindseth (Retired)

Robert P.J. Lindseth (a.k.a." Uncle Bob") is the publisher and executive editor of the *Morning Nuke*, a family of publications focused on American Nuclear Deterrence, and on the Nation's nuclear armed adversaries, their weapons, and combat systems to include Information Operations, Electronic Warfare and supporting intelligence and information systems. Colonel Lindseth as a retired Intelligence officer spent his entire career in the dark arts, science and tradecraft of intelligence operations. As the Deputy Director for Intelligence on Joint Staff he supported the Chairman and Secretary of Defense on critical classified operations in the Middle East, Latin America, Vietnam, Korea and Russia. Upon retirement Professor Lindseth instructed classified topics at the National Intelligence University (NIU) sitting as First Chair on numerous prize winning Theses, observing many to be implemented into Air Force Doctrine and in one case a systems development for major aircraft upgrade. He is a Member and past President of the Board of Directors, Association of Old Crows, Elected term, 2004 to Present (Information Operations and Electronic Warfare Association). His awards include: Member Omicron Delta Epsilon, Economics Honorary Society, Legion of Merit Medal, Meritorious Service Medal, among others.

Michael Mabee, CSM USA (Retired)

Michael Mabee is author of *The Civil Defense Book: Emergency Preparedness for a Rural or Suburban Community* (ISBN-13: 978-19744320943, first edition 4 July 2013, second edition 17 October 2017). He works with the Secure the Grid Coalition to hold the government and electric power industry accountable to protect the U.S. electric grid. Michael works with communities and governments to build a culture of preparedness—and to ready the nation for catastrophic disasters. He is affiliated with the Secure the Grid Coalition and Infraguard's National Disaster Resilience Council.

Michael Mabee has worked as an urban emergency medical technician and paramedic, a suburban police officer, and in the federal civil service. Michael received his B.A. in English from Southern Connecticut State University in 1994 and is a graduate of the United States Army Sergeants Major Academy, Fort Bliss, Texas.

Michael has a great deal of experience—both overseas and in the U.S.—working in worlds where things went wrong. He is a veteran of both Persian Gulf wars, serving with the U.S. Army as a Platoon Sergeant in Operations Desert Shield, Desert Storm, and Provide Comfort. In his most recent deployment, Michael served as a brigade level Command Sergeant Major in Iraq. He also participated in two humanitarian missions to Guatemala. He retired from the U.S. Army Reserve in 2006 at the rank of Command Sergeant Major (CSM). Michael was decorated by both the U.S. Army and the federal government for his actions on 9/11/2001 at the World Trade Center in New York City. (In sum, quite like Forrest Gump, he is generally at the right place at the wrong time.)

For over a decade, Michael has conducted public interest research on the security of the electric grid because of the absolutely vital role of this infrastructure in powering every one of the nation's 16 critical infrastructures and in undergirding not just the well-being but the very survival of our country. Michael maintains one of the world's most comprehensive grid security databases as an unpaid volunteer grid security researcher. He has been quoted by the Wall Street Journal, the Washington Post and many other publications on grid security and has intervened and submitted testimony in over 200 federal dockets on electric grid security issues. He has participated in federal rulemaking related to grid security and has written two books about how communities can prepare for and survive a long-term power outage. He continues to write and speak about emergency preparedness for a long-term blackout. Visit Michael's website HERE or write to CivilDefenseBook@gmail.com.

Dr. John M. Poindexter, Vice Admiral USN (Retired)

Poindexter served in the administration of President Ronald Reagan as Military Assistant from 1981 to 1983, as Deputy National Security Advisor from 1983 to 1985, and as National Security Advisor from 1985 to 1986. From 1983 to 1985, Poindexter was responsible for leading and managing the National Security Council staff as chairman of the Crisis Pre-planning Group. As National Security Advisor, he provided recommendations to the President on all matters pertaining to national security, foreign policy and defense policy. Major events in which he played a significant role while at the White House included the Strategic Defense Initiative, Operation Urgent Fury, the Achille Lauro incident, Operation El Dorado Canyon (launched in response to Libyan terrorist attacks), the Reykjavik Summit with the Soviet Union that marked the beginning of the end of the Cold War, and the Iran-Contra Affair.

John Poindexter graduated from the United States Naval Academy in 1958, where he was first in his class. From 1961 to 1964, Poindexter studied as a graduate student at the California Institute of Technology, where he conducted laboratory research to further develop a model for understanding the Mossbauer effect with Nobel Laureate Rudolph Mossbauer. He earned both his M.S. and Ph.D. in Physics from Caltech.

While commander of a destroyer squadron, he was Surface Warfare and Anti-submarine warfare Commander of battle groups in the Western Pacific Ocean and Indian Ocean, and he developed new tactics and battle management procedures under the Composite Warfare Commander concept. As the commanding officer of USS England (CG-22), he served in the Gulf of Tonkin protecting aircraft carriers and pioneered the shipboard use of computers to manage the ship's force portion of yard overhauls. He was also an executive officer and a chief engineer of destroyers.

As Deputy Commander of the Naval Education and Training Command, his duties included commanding the US Navy's extensive education and training programs, for which he initiated a project to develop a distributed data management system for more efficient management of training pipelines. His significant staff assignments included: Executive Assistant to the Chief of Naval Operations, Administrative Assistant to the Secretary of the Navy and Special Assistant for Systems Analysis to the Secretary of Defense. He served to the rank of Vice Admiral.

After leaving government service for the first time, Poindexter from 1988 to 1989 was senior scientist at Presearch, Inc. From 1990 to 1996, Poindexter served as co-founder of TP Systems, Inc., a software development firm. From 1993 to 1996, he was a consultant to Elkins Group. Then from 1996 through 2001 Poindexter served as senior vice president for SYNTEK Technologies, a high technology firm with contracts in domestic and international defense and commercial business. His duties at SYNYEK included his personal oversight of a contract with the Defense Advanced Research Project Agency(DARPA) known as Project Genoa, which focused on providing advanced decision-support and collaboration tools to rapidly deal with and adjust to dynamic crisis management and allow for inter-agency collaboration in real-time.

After 911 Poindexter came back into government. Starting in January 2002, he established a new office in DARPA and served as the Director of the Information Awareness Office (IAO). The mission of the IAO was to imagine, develop, apply, integrate, demonstrate and transition information technologies, components, and prototype closed-loop information systems that will counter asymmetric threats by achieving total information awareness. The goal of this effort was to enable preemption, advance national security warnings, and the facilitation of national security decision making. Poindexter retired from DARPA on 29 August 2003.

Poindexter is now a private consultant.

David T. Pyne, M.A., J.D.

David received a M.A. in National Security Studies from Georgetown University's prestigious School of Foreign Service and a J.D. from Southwestern University School of Law. He currently serves as Deputy Director of National Operations for the EMP Task Force on National and Homeland Security, as a Vice President for the Association of the United States Army's Utah chapter and a West Valley Police Honorary Colonel. David is a former U.S. Army Headquarters staff officer who previously served as Director of the Utah EMP Task Force, as a Consultant for the U.S. Missile Defense Agency and as an International Analyst for both the Office of the Secretary of Defense and for the Department of the Navy. Mr. Pyne served as National Security Policy Director for U.S. Sen. Mike Lee (R-UT), as the founder of Sen. Lee's Military Advisory Committee and as 2nd Vice President of the Salt Lake Total Force Chapter of the Military Officers Association of America. He also served as Chairman/Vice Chairman of the Utah State Legislative Compensation Commission from 2009-2017. David holds a MA degree in National Security Studies from Georgetown University's prestigious School of Foreign Service. He has been interviewed on television, on several talk radio shows and has been quoted in a number of newspapers, magazine articles and books. Mr. Pyne has had his op-eds published in The National Interest, RealClearHistory, Deseret News, Salt Lake Tribune, the Provo Daily Herald, WorldNetDaily.com and Military.com. He is available to speak to national or state policymakers and staffers, emergency management professionals or to civic and political groups on the EMP threat and other existential threats facing our great nation. David lives in West Jordan, UT and may be reached at emptaskforce.ut@gmail.com.

Dr. William A. Radasky

Dr. Radasky's work has been foundational to advancing Department of Defense scientific and technical understanding of HEMP phenomenology and the vulnerability of military and civilian critical infrastructures.   Dr. Radasky served on the Congressional EMP Commission as a member of the senior scientific and technical staff.

He has worked in the field of high power electromagnetic (HPEM) applications for more than 53 years including studies of electromagnetic pulse (EMP) and intentional electromagnetic interference (IEMI). In 1984 he founded Metatech Corporation where he is President and Managing Engineer. He has published over 560 reports, papers and articles dealing with high power electromagnetic transient environments, effects, protection and standards.

He has participated actively with the IEEE EMC and PES Societies, CIGRE Study Committee C4 and IEC Subcommittee 77C to prepare reports and standards dealing with high power electromagnetic transient phenomena and protection, and has worked with more than 15 power companies worldwide to assess and protect their power delivery systems.

He served as the Chairman of IEC SC 77C from 1992 to 2016 and was the Chairman of the IEC Advisory Committee on EMC (ACEC) for 12 years. He received the IEC Lord Kelvin Award in 2004 for his work dealing with the protection of equipment from high power EM threats, the Dr. Carl E. Baum Memorial Award in 2017, the Richard R. Stoddard IEEE EMC Award in 2018, and is an EMP Fellow (1988) and an IEEE Life Fellow (2012). He was elected to the National Academy of Engineering in 2021 for leadership in the development and application of electromagnetic transient disturbance and protection standards for national security and commercial systems.

He received his B.S. in Electrical Engineering and Engineering Science from the U.S. Air Force Academy in 1968; his M.S. in Electrical Engineering from the University of New Mexico in 1971; and his Ph.D. in Electrical Engineering from the University of California at Santa Barbara in 1981.

Colonel Kevin Riedler (Retired)

Colonel Riedler is a graduate of West Point, BYU, the Army Command and General Staff College, the Army War College, Harvard's Kennedy School of Government, and the Naval Postgraduate School's Center for Homeland Defense and Security. He began his career as a missile officer. During his first deployment to Haiti he was assigned as the "J-6 Automation Officer," managing all computer support for the 20,000 member Joint Task Force–the first such force to face what are now classified as cyber-attacks. Following his Harvard Fellowship, the Army designated "Strategic Planner" as one of his officer skill identifiers. In his follow-on assignment on the Joint Staff, he contributed to the Operational Availability Studies, part of the bi-annual assessment that apportions the services' command units against wartime contingency plans. He deployed to Iraq, tasked with developing that nation's electrical infrastructure security plan. In his second assignment teaching at the Army War College, he contributed to several studies/wargames at the Center for Strategic Leadership (CSL). His final assignment was back on the Joint Staff as the Chief of the J5 Homeland Division, where he and his staff developed plans and policies for the President and Chairman of the Joint Chiefs of Staff on use of the military in defending the homeland. One of the key issues he worked in that job with his OSD counterpart during their bi-weekly White House national security meetings, was the EMP threat. Retiring after 30 years of service, he now resides in North Carolina and contributes to Dr. Pry's national efforts on national preparedness for Blackout Warfare.

Dr. Edward M. Roche Ph.D., J.D.

Ed received an M.Phil and Ph.D. in Political Science from Columbia University with a concentration in Diplomatic History, International Law, and African Political Economy. He earned an M.A. in International Relations from the Johns Hopkins School of Advanced International Studies (SAIS) in Washington, D.C., and has a Certificate with Distinction in European Law from the University of Leiden, a Certificate with Distinction in Management of International Organizations from the University of Geneva, and a Certificate in Molecular Neuropharmacology from the California Institute of Technology. He is certified in Russian and Chinese. Ed is a member of the California Bar Association, the American Society of International Law, the FBI InfraGard partnership cybersecurity group, and Affiliate Researcher for the Columbia Institute for Tele-Information at Columbia Business School. He has served with the United Nations as a Program Evaluator and Expert on e-Government and Internet Governance as well as Expert Advisor for national ICT innovation strategies in Central Asia and Africa. Prior to his work at the UN, he served as Chief Research Officer of the Research Board (Gartner) where he led multi-client research for Chief Information Officers on international technology management and cyber security. He is a member of the Association of Former Intelligence Officers (AFIO) and has consulted on Virtual Worlds and Virtual Reality for the Intelligence Advanced Research Projects Activity (IARPA) and Office of Disruptive Technologies. He wrote the chapter on Industrial Espionage for the AFIO publication *Guide to the Study of Intelligence* and also published *Snake Fish: The Chi Mak Spy Ring and Chinese Industrial Espionage* and *Corporate Spy: Industrial Espionage and Counterintelligence in the Multinational Enterprise*. He also published the seminal book *Managing Information Technology in Multinational Corporations*, "International Convention for the Peaceful Use of Cyberspace" (*Orbis*, 2014) and "La course au cyber armament" (*Netcom*, 2019). Ed taught at the Grenoble Ecole de Management from 2009-2016. He did research for Edward Luttwak for the appendix to the book *Coup d'Etat* and consults on wireless broadband and 5G network strategies for telecommunications providers. He monitors the Cyber Stability work of the UN First Committee on Disarmament, and does analysis of cyber weapons, the cyber arms race, and national strategies for a new arms control convention to manage cyber conflicts. He has published on development of an International Cyber Peacekeeping Force. Ed lives in New York City and can be reached at emr96@columbia.edu

Professor Zhanna Malekos Smith, Esquire

Zhanna Malekos Smith, J.D., is an assistant professor in the Department of Systems Engineering at the U.S. Military Academy at West Point and a senior associate with the Strategic Technologies Program at the Center for Strategic and International Studies in Washington DC. Prior to joining West Point, Malekos Smith was a professor of cyber warfare studies with the U.S. Air War College. A former captain and attorney in the U.S. Air Force's Judge Advocate General's Corps, she received her commission from the Reserve Officers' Training Corps program at the Massachusetts Institute of Technology, where she was a cross-registered student and participated in the Undergraduate Research Opportunities Program. She has held fellowships with the Madeleine Korbel Albright Institute for Global Affairs, the Belfer Center's Cyber Security Project at the Harvard Kennedy School, Duke University Law School as the Reuben Everett cyber scholar, and Stanford University's U.S.-Russia Forum. Malekos Smith writes in the areas of space, cybersecurity, science and technology, and international law and security. She has authored op-eds in Lawfare, The Hill, and Defense One, and has presented her scholarship to various audiences including DEF CON, RSA Conference, and Shmoo-

Con. She received a BA in Russian and international relations from Wellesley College, an MA and Associateship of King's College (AKC) from King's College London, Department of War Studies, and a JD from the University of California, Davis, where she pursued a self-concentration in cyber-law. She serves as a volunteer consultant for Hostage US, a nonprofit that supports the families of Americans taken hostage abroad and hostages when they return home.

Admiral William O. Studeman, USN (Retired)

Admiral Studeman served as Director of the National Security Agency (NSA), Director of U.S. Navy Intelligence, Acting Director of Central Intelligence and the CIA (with two extended periods as Acting Director of Central Intelligence and the CIA), Deputy Director of Central Intelligence (DDCI) and the CIA. As DDCI, he served in both the Bush I and Clinton Administrations under Directors of Central Intelligence Bob Gates, Jim Woolsey, and John Deutch.

Bill Studeman retired from Northrop Grumman Corporation (NGC) in 2005 as Vice President and Deputy General Manager of the Mission Systems Sector dealing with System Integration/ System Engineering of large complex systems. In this position, he focused on strategies, programs, business development, marketing, as well as corporate cross-Sector integration, and on managing Defense and Intelligence technology partnerships and concepts related to Net Centricity/Cyber matters, ISR, IO/IW, Aerospace and Advanced Command Environments. He served in this position for almost 10 years, and continued until recently as an Independent Consultant to NGC and other companies, as well as to the government. Most of his semi-retired time today is spent on Intelligence, Cyber/Information Operations and Defense/Naval Strategy matters.

Admiral Studeman was born in Brownsville, Texas, in 1940, and was raised in Coral Gables, Florida. He holds a BA in History from the University of the South, Sewanee, Tennessee, and an MA in Public and International Affairs from George Washington University and several honorary doctorates. He is a Distinguished Graduate of the Naval and National War Colleges and the National Intelligence University. As a restricted line Naval Intelligence Officer (now Information Warfare Officer), Admiral Studeman served in the Pacific, Atlantic and Mediterranean. Admiral Studeman retired from the Navy in 1995, after 34 years of service.

Admiral Studeman has served on Corporate, University and National Lab boards. He also lectures at Universities on Intelligence and Cyber/Information Warfare matters, and appears in periodic forums/ discussions related to Cyber and Intelligence. He was a Commissioner on the Presidential Commission on WMD, and just departed after 14 years serving as a Congressional and Emeritus member of the Public Interest Declassification Board (PIDB) of the National Archives where he chaired their Technology Working Group. He is a past member of the Defense Science Board, the DNI Senior Advisory Group, the now defunct DNI Intelligence Community Strategic Studies Group (ICSSG), the NGA Independent Advisory Group, NRO Gold Team, the National Intelligence University Board of Visitors, the recent Nuclear Comprehensive Review, and the JIEDDO Senior Advisory Council, and the DNI Advisory Board. He recently chaired the Secretary of the Navy's Advisory Panel (SNAP), the Sandia National Lab Intelligence/Strategy Advisory Group, and was also a Draper Lab Emeritus Corporation Member, member of a Task Force supporting Director DIA on the standup of the DIA DDO/Defense Clandestine Service, member of the Intelligence and National Security Alliance (INSA) Board Emeritus and member of INSA Board of Advisors and Cyber Council, Asia-Pacific and Acquisition Councils, as well as recent member of the STRATCOM Strategic Advisory Group

TF on National C2, the Defense Science Board Cyber Resilience TF and a National Academy of Sciences Naval Studies Board TF on a Cyber topic. He is currently an Advisor to the Advanced Research Lab for Intelligence and Security (ARLIS), a University of Maryland UARC. ADM Studeman is also the Chairman Emeritus of the Board of the Naval Intelligence Foundation (NIF) and senior advisor to the Naval Intelligence Professionals (NIP) association. He also recently served on his University Board of Regents and Board of Advisors. Admiral Studeman is the recipient of the 2007 INSA "William Oliver Baker Award" and the AFCEA 2007 Distinguished Service Award for Intelligence Community support. He is currently an Advisor to the Pan Am Museum Foundation Board, and a former member of the National Cryptologic Museum Foundation Board. He is also the President of the Board and on many Committees of Ginger Cove/Annapolis Life Care, Inc.

Congressman Curt Weldon

Congressman Curt Weldon served for 20 years in the United States Congress retiring as both Vice Chair of the House Armed Services Committee as well as Vice Chair of the House Homeland Security Committee. He also served on the Energy Committee of the House Science Committee. Weldon led the first U.S. Delegation into Libya to meet with Moammar Gadhaffi, led the second and third U.S. Delegations into Libya with Senator Joe Biden as his guest, again meeting with Gadhaffi, and is the only US Official invited to address the entire Libyan nation in 2004. During the height of the Libyan War Weldon, in early April 2011, traveled again to Tripoli to confront Qadaffi and advise him to step down as suggested by the U.S. and Allied Coalition. Weldon also led the first two Delegations into North Korea, met with top North Korean Officials and authored the two part 10 Point Peace Plan. Weldon organized over one dozen formal Inter-Parliamentary Relationships with the US Congress and other countries. Weldon's work in Russia is well documented – he authored the 48-page 'New Time-New Beginning" strategy endorsed by over 150 Members of Congress and was the Keynote Speaker at the 100th Anniversary of Kurchatov Institute along with Japanese Prime Minister Koizumi and Russian Foreign Minister Primakov. While in Congress he organized and Co-Chaired the US/ FSU Energy Caucus, the Oceans Security Initiative and the International Energy Advisory Council, working with Oil & Gas CEO's worldwide. Weldon has led over 60 bipartisan Delegations to over 100 nations. He has taught and lectured at Universities around the world including the Technical University of Budapest, Cambridge University (London), Chinese National Defense University (twice), Fudan University, MGMO University (Moscow), Karic University (Belgrade), Al Fateh University (Tripoli) as well as numerous Universities in the US. He has been awarded 5 Honorary Doctorate Degrees and is an Academician/Member of the Russian Federation Academy of Social Sciences. He has received over 100 National and International Awards and Commendations for his public service. Congressman Weldon held the first unclassified hearings on the EMP threat before the U.S. Congress from 1995-2000 and played a major role in establishing the Congressional EMP Commission.

Jeffrey R. Yago, P.E.

Jeffrey Yago is a licensed Professional Engineer with more than 50 years experience working in the field of energy and emergency power. He is the author of three books, including most recently *Lights On!* and *The ABC's of EMP*. After graduating in both mechanical engineering and industrial management, plus some graduate work in computer science after graduation, Jeff Yago worked 10 years as department head then later rising to Vice President of a mid-sized professional engineering firm before starting his own consulting engineering firm in 1990. His firm specializes in facility condition assessments of large universities, hospitals, government facilities, and our military bases, both in the states and in Europe, including several "3-letter" agency facilities. This field work has included HVAC systems, electrical systems, emergency generator and battery backup systems, and campus-wide central automation systems. Jeff Yago has learned firsthand about the lack of backup power system readiness in the United States today, especially related to critical military and government facilities. In 2005 Mr. Yago started writing freelance articles for multiple national publications before becoming a regular feature writer for Self-Reliance Magazine. He has been a speaker at many self-reliant expos throughout the country each year, and has discussed his concerns about EMP and our country's lack of emergency preparedness on multiple national radio talk shows. In 2016 he published his second book titled "Lights On", with sales ranked highest in its category on Amazon, followed in 2020 by his current book, "the ABC's of EMP." He is known for taking complex subjects and turning them into easy-to-understand reading using his unique writing style. This has served him well when dealing with the very difficult subject of EMP. Other interests—Mr. Yago was awarded five United States patents for his design work, is a substitute organist for his church, and holds a commercial helicopter pilot license. Mr. Yago has been inducted into the "Order of the Engineer" by the National Society of Professional Engineers, which recognizes those professional engineers who have demonstrated the highest level of professional ethics throughout their professional engineering career. Mr. Yago grew up in Texas but now resides in Virginia.

Dr. Peter Vincent Pry

Dr. Peter Vincent Pry is Executive Director of the EMP Task Force on National and Homeland Security, a Congressional Advisory Board dedicated to achieving protection of the United States from electromagnetic pulse (EMP), cyber-attack, mass destruction terrorism and other threats to civilian critical infrastructures on an accelerated basis. Dr. Pry served as Chief of Staff of the congressional Commission to Assess the Threat to the United States from Electromagnetic Pulse (EMP) Attack (2001-2017); as Director of the United States Nuclear Strategy Forum, an advisory board to Congress on policies to counter Weapons of Mass Destruction; and on the staffs of the Congressional Commission on the Strategic Posture of the United States (2008-2009); the Commission on the New Strategic Posture of the United States (2006-2008); the House Armed Services Committee (1995-2001); and the CIA (1985-1995).

Dr. Pry served as Professional Staff on the House Armed Services Committee (HASC) of the U.S. Congress, with portfolios in nuclear strategy, WMD, Russia, China, NATO, the Middle East, Intelligence, and Terrorism. While serving on the HASC, Dr. Pry was chief advisor to the Vice Chairman of the House Armed Services Committee and the Vice Chairman of the House Homeland Security Committee, and to the Chairman of the Terrorism Panel. Dr. Pry played a key role: running hearings in Congress that warned terrorists and rogue states could pose an EMP threat, establishing the Congressional EMP Commission, helping the Commission develop plans to protect the United States from EMP, and working closely with senior scientists who first discovered the nuclear EMP phenomenon.

Dr. Pry was an Intelligence Officer with the Central Intelligence Agency responsible for analyzing Soviet and Russian nuclear strategy, operational plans, military doctrine, threat perceptions, and developing U.S. paradigms for strategic warning. He also served as a Verification Analyst at the U.S. Arms Control and Disarmament Agency responsible for assessing Soviet compliance with strategic and military arms control treaties.

Dr. Pry has written numerous books on national security issues, including: *Will America Be Protected? (Volumes I and II)*; *The Power And The Light: The Congressional EMP Commission's War To Save America*; *POSEIDON: Russia's New Doomsday Machine*; *The Long Sunday: Nuclear EMP Attack Scenarios*; *Blackout Wars*; *Apocalypse Unknown: The Struggle To Protect America From An Electromagnetic Pulse Catastrophe*; *Electric Armageddon: Civil-Military Preparedness For An Electromagnetic Pulse Catastrophe*; *War Scare: Russia and America on the Nuclear Brink*; *Nuclear Wars: Exchanges and Outcomes*; *The Strategic Nuclear Balance: And Why It Matters*; and *Israel's Nuclear Arsenal*. Dr. Pry often appears on TV and radio as an expert on national security issues. The BBC made his book *War Scare* into a two-hour TV documentary *Soviet War Scare 1983* and his book *Electric Armageddon* was the basis for another TV documentary *Electronic Armageddon* made by the National Geographic.

DR. PETER PRY

This recognizes Dr. Peter Pry *for his outstanding accomplishments during his 10 years of service at the Central Intelligence Agency. A noted expert in his field, Dr. Pry conducted groundbreaking research that illuminated one of the most important issues of our time—the US-Soviet nuclear competition. On the vanguard of strategic intelligence analysis during the Cold War, he developed much of what the US Government knows about Soviet planning for nuclear war, including Soviet views of the character of war, perceptions of US intentions, assessment of the nuclear balance, and operational plans. In the post-Cold War period, his work has been central to the US Government's understanding of evolving Russian threat perceptions and military doctrine and the construction of new paradigms for strategic warning and stability assessments.*

Dr. Pry can take pride in knowing that his work has contributed significantly to the security of the United States. He has been a pillar of the Intelligence Community and will be sorely missed. Without a doubt, his continued public service on Capitol Hill will reflect the same expertise, professionalism, and dedication that have characterized his exemplary career at the CIA.

We wish him much success in his new endeavor.

Lawrence K. Gershwin	Charles E. Allen	John E. McLaughlin

Made in the USA
Monee, IL
24 January 2022